Mathematics Around Us skills and applications

L. Carey Bolster

Gloria Felix Cox

E. Glenadine Gibb

Viggo P. Hansen

Joan E. Kirkpatrick

David F. Robitaille

Harold C. Trimble

Irvin E. Vance

Ray Walch

Robert J. Wisner

Scott, Foresman and Company

Glenview, Illinois; Dallas, Texas;
Oakland, New Jersey; Tucker, Georgia;
Palo Alto, California; and Brighton, England

Authors

L. Carey Bolster
Supervisor of Mathematics
Baltimore County Public Schools
Towson, Maryland

Gloria Felix Cox
Principal
Los Angeles Unified School District
Los Angeles, California

E. Glenadine Gibb
Professor of Mathematics Education
The University of Texas at Austin
Austin, Texas

Viggo P. Hansen
Professor, Mathematics Education
California State University
Northridge, California

Joan E. Kirkpatrick
Associate Professor,
Elementary Education
University of Alberta
Edmonton, Alberta, Canada

David F. Robitaille
Assistant Professor
of Mathematics Education
University of British Columbia
Vancouver, British Columbia, Canada

Harold C. Trimble
Professor of Education
Ohio State University
Columbus, Ohio

Irvin E. Vance
Director, School/Community Outreach
Math. TV Project
Education Development Center
Newton, Massachusetts

Ray Walch
Former Teacher of Mathematics
Public Schools
Westport, Connecticut

Robert J. Wisner
Professor of Mathematics
New Mexico State University
Las Cruces, New Mexico

Consultant

Sidney Sharron
Coordinator,
Educational Communications
and Media Branch
Los Angeles Unified School District
Los Angeles, California

Acknowledgments

For permission to reproduce the photographs on the pages indicated, acknowledgment is made to the following:

The Oriental Institute, The University of Chicago: 16–17; Gjon Mili: 22–23; National Audubon Society photo by Robert J. Ashworth: 30; United States Steel Corporation: 43; Scott, Foresman and Company, *Health and Growth Book Five* © 1971, photos by Ray Komorski: 52, 54; L. J. Fineman/F.P.G.: 56; Amtrak: 57 (*left*); McNeely/Van Cleve: 57 (*right*); SPORTS ILLUSTRATED photo by Jerry Cooke © Time Inc.: 92; SPORTS ILLUSTRATED photo by Neil Leifer © Time Inc.: 95; Dan Morrill: 100–101; Loyola Medical Center, Loyola University: 119; Hayward R. Blake: 165; Colgate-Palmolive Company: 219 (*top*); Volkswagen: 219 (*center*); General Mills: 219 (*bottom*); National Audubon Society photo by Leonard Lee Rue III: 264–265; The Sea Library/R. Lang: 268; NASA: 288–289; Photograph by Dennis & Diane Cassia and Judy Cassia: 294; Thomas Medcalf: 304–305; Scott, Foresman and Company, *Health and Growth Book Eight* © 1972, adaptation of illustrations: 307; Robert F. Arteaga: 308; Barbara Van Cleve/Van Cleve: 343; U.S. Bureau of Engraving and Printing: 354; U.S. National Park Service photo by Cecil Stoughton: 363 (*left*); Mount Everest Foundation: 363 (*right*).

ISBN: 0-673-04235-9

Regional offices of Scott, Foresman and Company are located in Dallas, Texas; Glenview, Illinois; Oakland, New Jersey; Palo Alto, California; Tucker, Georgia; and Brighton, England.

Unit 1 Number Patterns

Unit 2 Metric System and Decimals

Unit 3   Geometry and Measurement

Unit 4 Number Theory, Fractions, and Mixed Numbers

Unit 5 Ratio, Proportion, and Percent

Unit 6 Probability, Statistics, and Integers

Unit 1

Number Patterns

$$2614 + r = 5808$$

r

2614 meters

5808 meters

Evaluating Expressions: Addition and Subtraction

Here are two mathematical *expressions*.

$$n + 1$$

$$t - 3$$

In these expressions, n and t are *variables*. A variable is used to represent a number.

The tables below show values of $n + 1$ and $t - 3$ when n and t are replaced by different numbers.

n	$n + 1$	
0	1	$0 + 1$
2	3	$2 + 1$
5	6	$5 + 1$
8	9	$8 + 1$
9	10	$9 + 1$

t	$t - 3$	
4	1	$4 - 3$
5	2	$5 - 3$
7	4	$7 - 3$
10	7	$10 - 3$
12	9	$12 - 3$

Complete each table.

1.

w	$w + 2$
1	3
2	4
3	
7	
9	

2.

d	$d - 4$
4	0
6	2
10	
11	
13	

3.

m	$13 - m$
4	9
5	
7	
8	
9	

4.

z	$7 + z$
0	
4	
5	
7	
8	

5.

b	$b - 5$
6	
9	
11	
12	
14	

6.

x	$12 - x$
3	
4	
6	
8	
9	

7.

k	$6 + k$
0	
2	
3	
6	
9	

8.

g	$g + 9$
1	
3	
4	
6	
8	

The Expressions Game

This is a game for two or more players. Make ten expression cards like these.

$n + 4$	$n - 3$	$9 - n$	$n - 1$	$3 + n$
$12 - n$	$6 + n$	$n - 2$	$n + 1$	$10 - n$

Shuffle the cards and place them face down in a pile.

To begin each round, each player writes one of the following numbers on a piece of paper: 3, 4, 5, 6, 7, 8, or 9. Then the top expression card is turned over. Each player finds the value of that expression when n is replaced with the number that the player chose.

Example
Linda wrote down 7.
The expression card said $n - 3$.
The value of the expression was $7 - 3$, or 4.

Number chosen for n	Value of expression on card	Points
7	4	

The player whose result is closest to 6 wins a point. If two or more players are equally close to 6, they each win a point.

For the next round, each player writes down another number and the next expression card is turned over.

The winner is the player with the most points when all ten expression cards are used up. If two or more players tie, they have a play-off for five rounds.

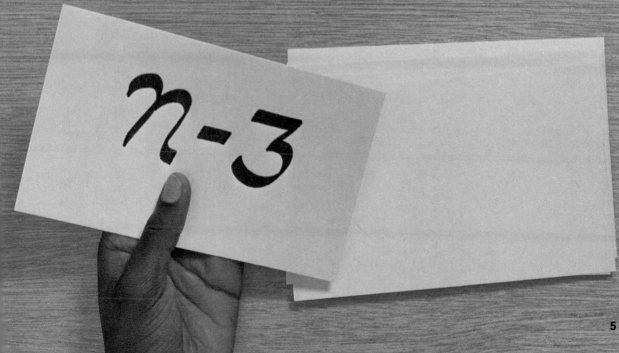

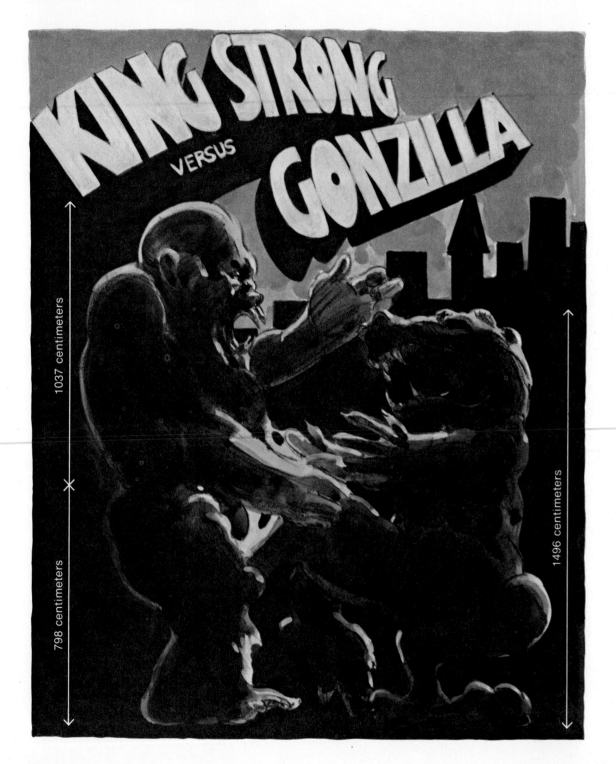

Here are some data about the characters in the movie *King Strong Versus Gonzilla*.

A. How tall is King Strong?

Find 1037 + 798.

$$\begin{array}{r} 1037 \\ + \ 798 \\ \hline 1835 \end{array}$$

King Strong is 1835 centimeters tall.

B. King Strong is how much taller than Gonzilla?

Find 1835 − 1496.

$$\begin{array}{r} 1835 \\ - 1496 \\ \hline 339 \end{array}$$

King Strong is 339 centimeters taller than Gonzilla.

Add.

1. $\begin{array}{r} 327 \\ + 415 \end{array}$ **4.** $\begin{array}{r} 214 \\ + 586 \end{array}$

2. $\begin{array}{r} 627 \\ + 593 \end{array}$ **5.** $\begin{array}{r} 831 \\ + 275 \end{array}$

3. $\begin{array}{r} 885 \\ + 926 \end{array}$ **6.** $\begin{array}{r} 909 \\ + 153 \end{array}$

7. 46 + 83 + 21 + 35

8. 317 + 92 + 753

9. 4127 + 8095 + 73

10. 35,247 + 63,928

11. 2741 + 6839 + 4217

Subtract.

12. $\begin{array}{r} 576 \\ - 429 \end{array}$ **15.** $\begin{array}{r} 830 \\ - 541 \end{array}$

13. $\begin{array}{r} 352 \\ - 187 \end{array}$ **16.** $\begin{array}{r} 804 \\ - 76 \end{array}$

14. $\begin{array}{r} 912 \\ - 364 \end{array}$ **17.** $\begin{array}{r} 302 \\ - 109 \end{array}$

18. 4371 − 2635

19. 5808 − 3219

20. 3004 − 956

21. 72,030 − 24,561

22. 63,005 − 47,218

Add or subtract to find each answer.

23. Gonzilla weighs 98,826 kilograms. King Strong weighs 90,738 kilograms.

  a. How much heavier is Gonzilla?

  b. How much do the monsters weigh together?

24. King Strong's teeth are 27 centimeters long. Gonzilla's teeth are 15 centimeters longer. How long are Gonzilla's teeth?

25. One monster destroyed 27 cars. The other destroyed 38 cars. How many cars did they destroy in all?

26. King Strong threw a 2143-kilogram boulder at Gonzilla, who threw back a 1783-kilogram boulder. How much heavier was King Strong's boulder?

**More practice
Sets A and B, page 62**

Rounding Numbers

A. Sometimes it is possible to use exact numbers.

The building is 23 stories tall.
There are 435 windows.
There are 318 telephones.

B. Sometimes numbers are so large, or data change so fast, that we know the numbers are not exact.

The population is 1,694,352.
There were 13,258 robberies.
There are 48,714 cars in the city.

Often data like these are reported in *rounded numbers*.

The population is 1,700,000.
There were 13,000 robberies.
There are 50,000 cars in the city.

Each day 73,850 people commute to and from the downtown area.

C. Round 73,850 to the nearest ten thousand.

Is 73,850 nearer 70,000 or 80,000?
Round down to 70,000.

D. Round 73,850 to the nearest thousand.

Is 73,850 nearer 73,000 or 74,000?
Round up to 74,000.

E. Round 73,850 to the nearest hundred.

Is 73,850 nearer 73,800 or 73,900?
It is halfway. Round up to 73,900.

Complete the table.

| City | Population | Population rounded to the | | |
		nearest ten thousand	nearest thousand	nearest hundred
Oakland, California	361,561	360,000	362,000	361,600
1. Montreal, Canada	1,222,255			
2. Abilene, Texas	89,653			
3. Mexico City, Mexico	3,483,649			
4. Saginaw, Michigan	91,849			
5. Glasgow, Scotland	956,195			
6. Buffalo, New York	462,768			

Tell whether you think each number is exact or is rounded.

7. 12,000 people at the free concert.

8. 41 people on the city council.

9. 2500 traffic accidents last year.

10. 133 parks owned by the city.

11. 21,000 food stamps used in stores.

12. 750,000 newspapers sold on Sunday.

laboratory activity

Fill a measuring cup with paper clips. Have six people guess the number of clips in the cup. Round each guess to the nearest ten and the nearest hundred.

	Column 1	Column 2	Column 3
	Guess	Guess rounded to nearest ten	Guess rounded to nearest hundred
1.			
2.			
3.			
4.			
5.			
6.			

7. Count the clips. What is the actual number of clips in the cup?

8. Round the actual number of clips to the nearest ten.

9. Which of the numbers in column 2 of your table match your answer to exercise 8?

10. How many guesses were correct to the nearest ten?

11. Round the actual number of clips to the nearest hundred.

12. Which of the numbers in column 3 match your answer to exercise 11?

13. How many guesses were correct to the nearest hundred?

Repeat this experiment with one cup of uncooked macaroni.

Using Rounded Numbers to Estimate Sums

You can use rounded numbers to estimate sums.

The Riverdale Drill Team sold taffy apples to raise money for uniforms. They sold 692 apples on Thursday and 517 apples on Friday. Estimate 692 + 517.

692 + 517
↓ ↓
700 + 500 = 1200

692 + 517 ≈ 1200

The symbol ≈ means "is approximately equal to."

The data below are for Thursday and Friday. In each exercise, use rounded numbers to estimate the total.

1. $173 collected
   $129 collected

2. 34 trays of apples
   29 trays of apples

3. 29 bags of sticks
   21 bags of sticks

4. 523 customers
   391 customers

5. 48 bags of apples
   33 bags of apples

Use rounded numbers to estimate each sum.

6. 41 + 38

7. 36 + 57

8. 42 + 23

9. 83 + 91

10. 68 + 77 + 22

11. 18 + 53 + 31

12. 695 + 827

13. 905 + 617

14. 713 + 815

15. 203 + 422 + 279

16. 713 + 508 + 894

Radio Station Manager

The manager of a radio station helps prepare a programming log that the announcers follow. In the log below, 8:03:30 means 30 seconds after 8:03.

Radio Programming Log	
8:00:00	News and sports
8:03:00	Citizen's Bank (30 sec.)
8:03:30	Weather
8:04:00	Public service announcement
8:05:00	The Bonnie Scott Show O'Brien's Used Cars (1 min.) Pizza Palace (30 sec.) Frán's Fashions (30 sec.) The Record Hop (1 min.) Miller Jewelers (20 sec.) Pizza Palace (1 min.) The Record Hop (10 sec.) Fran's Fashions (30 sec.) Miller Jewelers (15 sec.) O'Brien's Used Cars (15 sec.)
8:30:00	Station identification

1. How many minutes are listed for commercials between 8:00 and 8:30?

2. The station played these songs from 8:05 to 8:30. What was the total time for the songs?

Blue Waters	3 min. 10 sec.
Love Daze	2 min. 50 sec.
Tiger Rock	2 min. 15 sec.
Night Watch	3 min. 5 sec.
For Your Heart	3 min. 10 sec.
Apple Boogie	3 min.

3. How much time from 8:05 to 8:30 was not used for commercials or music?

The station's music library has these records and tapes.

Long-playing records	4215
45-rpm records	2540
78-rpm records	314
7-inch reel tapes	84
Cartridge tapes	260

4. How many records in all?

5. How many tapes in all?

6. If the station receives 57 promotional records next month, what will the total number of records and tapes be then?

The station sells radio time to advertisers. A radio commercial is called a spot.

Rate Card		
Spots	Prime time	Non-prime time
10 seconds	$ 7	$ 5
15 seconds	$10	$ 8
20 seconds	$12	$11
30 seconds	$19	$14
1 minute	$35	$26

In prime time, how much does an advertiser pay for

7. a 10-second spot and a 30-second spot?

8. a 15-second spot and a 1-minute spot?

In non-prime time, how much does an advertiser pay for

9. a 20-second spot and a 1-minute spot?

10. two 15-second spots and a 1-minute spot?

How much money does the station collect from advertisers for

11. the half-hour, prime-time show described in the log on page 12?

12. a one-hour, prime-time show with ten 1-minute spots, ten 30-second spots, and two 20-second spots?

Order of Operations: Addition and Subtraction

When parentheses are used with addition and subtraction, start with the computation inside the parentheses.

A. $24 - (9 + 12)$
$24 - 21$
3

B. $(24 - 9) + 12$
$15 + 12$
27

When parentheses are not used with addition and subtraction, compute from left to right.

C. $37 - 15 + 6$
$22 + 6$
28

D. $53 - 19 - 21$
$34 - 21$
13

Compute each answer.

1. $16 - (9 + 4)$
2. $(16 - 9) + 4$
3. $(18 - 6) - 3$
4. $18 - (6 - 3)$
5. $(11 + 5) - 4$
6. $11 + (5 - 4)$
7. $8 + 5 + 10$
8. $15 + 6 - 4$
9. $24 - 10 + 3$
10. $40 - 30 - 6$
11. $35 - (10 + 5)$
12. $(19 - 7) + 4$
13. $16 + (8 + 12)$
14. $(20 - 4) - 5$
15. $14 - 9 + 16$
16. $30 - 5 - 10$
17. $(58 + 47) - 35$
18. $47 - (17 + 15)$
★ 19. $(6 - 4) + (3 + 10)$
★ 20. $(9 + 5) - (7 - 3)$

For each exercise, tell whether the statement is true or false. If it is false, insert parentheses to make it true.

Here's how

$9 - 4 + 3 = 2$
False
$9 - (4 + 3) = 2$

21. $12 - 7 - 3 = 8$
22. $12 - 7 - 3 = 2$
23. $8 - 5 + 2 = 1$
24. $8 - 5 + 2 = 5$
25. $6 + 10 + 3 = 19$
26. $9 + 4 - 5 = 8$
27. $15 - 10 + 4 = 1$
28. $25 - 5 - 6 = 14$
29. $12 + 8 + 7 = 27$
30. $6 + 18 - 11 = 13$
31. $30 - 15 - 5 = 20$
32. $42 - 17 - 8 = 33$
33. $83 + 56 + 35 = 174$
34. $37 - 12 + 56 = 81$
35. $94 - 72 - 29 = 51$

Commutative and Associative Properties of Addition

A. Find these sums.

$24 + 15 = $ ▦
$15 + 24 = $ ▦

$203 + 197 = $ ▦
$197 + 203 = $ ▦

$7100 + 8 = $ ▦
$8 + 7100 = $ ▦

Are the sums equal in each pair of exercises?

■ *The **commutative property of addition** says that you can always change the order of the addends and get the same sum.*

$25 + 13 = 13 + 25$

● **Discuss** Is it true that $9 - 5 = 5 - 9$? Do you think there is a commutative property for subtraction?

B. Find these sums.

$(8 + 6) + 7 = $ ▦
$8 + (6 + 7) = $ ▦

$(910 + 2) + 4 = $ ▦
$910 + (2 + 4) = $ ▦

$(12 + 8) + 16 = $ ▦
$12 + (8 + 16) = $ ▦

Are the sums equal in each pair of exercises?

■ *The **associative property of addition** says that you can always change the grouping of the addends and get the same sum.*

$(4 + 7) + 2 = 4 + (7 + 2)$

● **Discuss** Is it true that $(8 - 4) - 3 = 8 - (4 - 3)$? Do you think there is an associative property for subtraction?

Find each sum. Order and group the addends any way that makes your work easier. You might look for numbers that are easy to add mentally. You might look for sums of 10 or 100.

1. $20 + 15 + 30$
2. $17 + 6 + 4$
3. $8 + 2 + 9 + 1 + 4$
4. $37 + 50 + 50$
5. $150 + 73 + 50$
6. $8 + 5 + 2 + 5$
7. $46 + 70 + 30$
8. $30 + 26 + 40$
9. $153 + 300 + 400$
10. $350 + 67 + 50$
11. $40 + 52 + 60$

12.	32	14.	41
	78		19
	15		64
	93		6
	+ 47		+ 52

13.	20	15.	31
	82		79
	8		20
	15		45
	95		60
	54		5
	+ 56		+ 13

15

Writing Addition and Subtraction Expressions

Writing mathematical expressions for word phrases can help you with problem solving.

Write an expression for each phrase.

A. 5 more than a number n

$n + 5$

B. 8 less than a number w

$w - 8$

C. 14 increased by a number k

$14 + k$

D. 12 subtracted from a number q

$q - 12$

Isis and her brother, Tem, lived in ancient Egypt. Write a mathematical expression for each item described below.

E. The number of sacred cats owned by the family if they had 3 cats and then got c more cats.

$3 + c$

F. Tem's age if he is 2 years younger than Isis and she is y years old.

$y - 2$

G. The depth of the Nile River if it was 12 cubits deep and then rose r cubits.

$12 + r$

Write a mathematical expression for each exercise.

1. 7 more than a number n

2. 4 less than a number b

3. 18 plus a number q

4. 25 subtracted from a number z

5. 9 increased by a number t

6. 2 less than a number d

7. 30 decreased by a number y

8. A number k minus 5

9. 1 more than a number v

10. The total number of writing symbols Tem will know if he knows 575 symbols and must learn s more symbols.

11. The number of blank papyrus rolls Isis has left if she had r rolls and wrote on 4 of them.

12. The number of stones in two pyramids if one pyramid has 2,300,000 stones and the other has s stones.

13. The length of a stone sphinx if the paws are 30 cubits long and the rest of the body is c cubits long.

14. The number of female mummies in a tomb if there are m mummies in the tomb and 6 of them are males.

15. The age of a mummy if it was dried with salt for 70 days and then bandaged and dried for d more days.

Solving Equations by Replacing the Variable

A. This formula gives Jean's weekly pay at Pants Unlimited.

Salary	Commission	Total pay

$$S + C = T$$

Find C when S is $66 and T is $84.

$$66 + C = 84$$

The *solution of the equation* is a value for C that makes a true statement. Find the solution.

Try 20. $66 + 20 = 86$ (too large)
Try 18. $66 + 18 = 84$

C is 18. Jean's commission was $18.

B. This formula gives the store's daily profit.

Income	Expenses	Profit

$$I - E = P$$

Find I when E is $610 and P is $210.

$$I - 610 = 210$$

Try 800. $800 - 610 = 190$ (too small)
Try 810. $810 - 610 = 200$ (too small)
Try 820. $820 - 610 = 210$

I is 820. The store's income was $820.

In each exercise one of the given numbers is the solution of the equation. Find the solution.

1. $n + 5 = 18$
23   13   12

2. $14 + w = 22$
8   7   36

3. $k - 5 = 39$
34   44   42

4. $8 + t = 53$
61   55   45

5. $50 = q + 20$
30   70   40

6. $b - 9 = 25$
16   36   34

7. $60 = d - 15$
75   85   45

8. $61 = x + 42$
93   19   21

9. $42 = 17 + g$
15   25   59

Find the solution of each equation. You can try values for the variable until you find one that makes a true statement.

10. $14 + n = 21$

11. $a + 5 = 48$

12. $g - 10 = 32$

13. $t - 7 = 28$

14. $d + 12 = 20$

15. $w - 25 = 4$

16. $15 = 2 + n$

17. $37 = r + 20$

18. $90 = v - 8$

19. $16 + h = 25$

20. $x + 42 = 59$

21. $m - 21 = 62$

22. $34 = 19 + b$

23. $420 + v = 510$

24. $850 = n - 50$

25. $k + 135 = 160$

Write a ten-digit numeral such that the first digit tells the number of zeros in the numeral, the second digit tells the number of ones, the third digit tells the number of twos, and so on.

For example, the numeral 9000000001 is not correct because there are not nine zeros and there is one 1.

Number of
0's 1's 2's 3's 4's 5's 6's 7's 8's 9's
___ ___ ___ ___ ___ ___ ___ ___ ___ ___

Solving Addition and Subtraction Equations

A. How many coins are in the pile labeled n?

Chris wrote this equation for the problem.

$$n + 14 = 43$$

$$n + 14 - 14 = 43 - 14$$

$$n = 29$$

14 is added to n. To "undo" the addition, and get n by itself, subtract 14 from $n + 14$. To keep the equation in balance, do the same thing to both sides. Subtract 14 from 43.

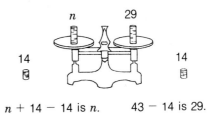

$n + 14 - 14$ is n. $43 - 14$ is 29.

The solution to $n + 14 = 43$ is 29. There are 29 coins in the first pile.

Check: Substitute 29 for n in the original equation. Is $29 + 14 = 43$ a true statement?

Find the solution
of each equation.

B. There are 18 fewer coins in the
shorter stack. How many coins are
in the taller stack?

Pat wrote this equation for the
problem.

$$t - 18 = 75$$

$$t - 18 + 18 = 75 + 18$$

$$t = 93$$

18 is subtracted from t.
To "undo" the subtraction
and get t by itself, add
18 to both sides of the
equation.

$t - 18 + 18$ is t.
$75 + 18$ is 93.

The solution to $t - 18 = 75$ is 93.
There are 93 coins in the taller stack.

Check: Substitute 93 for t in the
original equation.
Is $93 - 18 = 75$ a true
statement?

1. $47 + n = 123$
(Subtract 47
from both
sides.)

2. $t - 56 = 84$
(Add 56 to
both sides.)

3. $q + 24 = 68$

4. $b + 47 = 95$

5. $15 + d = 32$

6. $w - 12 = 47$

7. $y - 56 = 17$

8. $72 = 29 + g$

9. $31 = 8 + s$

10. $54 = r + 31$

11. $9 = z - 32$

12. $k + 45 = 97$

13. $9 + n = 63$

14. $m - 59 = 21$

15. $38 = v - 16$

16. $x + 71 = 112$

17. $86 + d = 349$

18. $c - 94 = 127$

19. $b + 143 = 675$

20. $962 = 507 + n$

Using Equations to Solve Problems

A. In 1844, it took 95 hours by steamboat to go from New Orleans to Memphis to St. Louis. It was 28 hours from Memphis to St. Louis. How many hours was it from New Orleans to Memphis?

Ann wrote this equation.

New Orleans to Memphis	Memphis to St. Louis	New Orleans to St. Louis

28 is added to n. Subtract 28 from both sides of the equation.

$$n + 28 = 95$$
$$n + 28 - 28 = 95 - 28$$
$$n = 67$$

Answer the question.

It was 67 hours from New Orleans to Memphis.

B. After 97 tons of cargo were unloaded, there were 108 tons of cargo left on the boat. How much cargo was on the boat to begin with?

Dolores wrote this equation.

Cargo to begin with	Cargo unloaded	Cargo left

97 is subtracted from c. Add 97 to both sides of the equation.

$$c - 97 = 108$$
$$c - 97 + 97 = 108 + 97$$
$$c = 205$$

Answer the question.

There were 205 tons of cargo on the boat to begin with.

Answer the question in each problem.

1. The total length of the Missouri and Mississippi Rivers is 7503 kilometers. The Missouri is 3725 kilometers long. How long is the Mississippi?

2. After the 180 passengers got off the steamboat *Eclipse*, there were 121 crew members on board. How many people were on board to begin with?

3. The steamboat *Mississippi* was 70 meters longer than the *Clermont*. The *Clermont* was 41 meters long. How long was the *Mississippi*?

4. On one trip, the *Grey Eagle* burned 4000 fuel logs. If the engineers started the trip with 1200 logs, how many more logs did they need?

5. By 1894 on the Missouri River, 294 steamboats had been destroyed. 193 of these were wrecked by hitting dead trees. How many steamboats were destroyed by other things?

This formula gives a steamboat's net speed when traveling downstream.

Engine speed	River speed	Net speed

$$E \; + \; R \; = \; N$$

The numbers in exercises 6–11 refer to meters per minute.

6. Find E when R is 168 and N is 407.

7. Find R when E is 243 and N is 395.

8. Find E when N is 388 and R is 175.

This formula gives a boat's net speed when traveling upstream.

Engine speed	River speed	Net speed

$$E \; - \; R \; = \; N$$

9. Find E when R is 173 and N is 68.

10. Find N when E is 235 and R is 162.

11. Find E when N is 82 and R is 170.

Chapter 1 Test
Addition and Subtraction Patterns, Pages 4-23

Evaluating expressions, pages 4-5

Find the value of each expression when n is 4.

1. $n + 8$

2. $5 + n$

3. $n - 3$

4. $13 - n$

Adding and subtracting, pages 6-14

Add.

5. $\begin{array}{r} 247 \\ + 596 \end{array}$ **6.** $\begin{array}{r} 7245 \\ + 938 \end{array}$

7. $2917 + 634$

8. $427 + 839 + 506$

Subtract.

9. $\begin{array}{r} 843 \\ - 294 \end{array}$ **10.** $\begin{array}{r} 5274 \\ - 637 \end{array}$

11. $4075 - 237$

12. $6003 - 5968$

13. Estimate the sum.

$49 + 32$

14. Compute $21 - (6 + 8)$.

15. Compute $13 - (9 - 7)$.

16. Compute $35 + 15 - 10$.

Problem solving, pages 16-23

Write a mathematical expression.

17. 6 more than a number m.

18. 4 less than a number k.

19. Tom's age if he is 3 years older than Rita and she is y years old.

Find the solution of each equation.

20. $n + 18 = 49$

21. $63 + w = 95$

22. $t - 15 = 62$

Find each answer.

23. Martha had 19 books. Her uncle gave her some more. Then she had 25 books. How many books did her uncle give her?

24. After Isabel spent $15 for a sweater, she had $19 left. How much money did she have to begin with?

$$10 \times 16 = n$$

Exponents and Expanded Notation

A. $4^2 = 4 \times 4 = 16$

The 2 in 4^2 is called an *exponent*. It tells how many times to use 4 as a factor.

Read 4^2 as "four to the second power" or "four squared."

B. $2^3 = 2 \times 2 \times 2 = 8$

"two to the third power" or "two cubed"

C. $10^4 = 10 \times 10 \times 10 \times 10 = 10,000$

"ten to the fourth power"

D. $1^5 = 1 \times 1 \times 1 \times 1 \times 1 = 1$

"one to the fifth power"

E. The underwater mountain range called the Atlantic Ridge is 16,090 meters long.

In this place-value chart, each place corresponds to a power of 10. You can use powers of 10 to write 16,090 in *expanded notation*.

billions period			millions period			thousands period			units period		
hundred billions	ten billions	billions	hundred millions	ten millions	millions	hundred thousands	ten thousands	thousands	hundreds	tens	ones
100,000,000,000	10,000,000,000	1,000,000,000	100,000,000	10,000,000	1,000,000	100,000	10,000	1000	100	10	1
10^{11}	10^{10}	10^9	10^8	10^7	10^6	10^5	10^4	10^3	10^2	10^1	10^0
							1	6	0	9	0

16,090

$10,000 + 6000 + 90$

$(1 \times 10,000) + (6 \times 1000) + (9 \times 10)$

$(1 \times 10^4) + (6 \times 10^3) + (9 \times 10^1)$

Find each answer.

1. 2^2 7. 5^2

2. 6^2 8. 10^2

3. 1^7 9. 10^3

4. 0^5 10. 10^5

5. 7^2 11. 10^6

6. 3^3 12. 10^7

Write each number using exponents.

Here's how

$2 \times 2 \times 2 \times 2$ 2^4

13. 6×6

14. $8 \times 8 \times 8$

15. $2 \times 2 \times 2 \times 2 \times 2$

16. $9 \times 9 \times 9 \times 9$

17. $10 \times 10 \times 10 \times 10$

Give the missing exponent.

18. $81 = 9^{\blacksquare}$

19. $8 = 2^{\blacksquare}$

20. $64 = 8^{\blacksquare}$

21. $100 = 10^{\blacksquare}$

22. $1000 = 10^{\blacksquare}$

23. $10,000 = 10^{\blacksquare}$

Write each number in expanded notation without using exponents.

Here's how

3908

$3000 + 900 + 8$

24. The greatest depth of the Atlantic Ocean is 8381 meters.

25. The greatest depth of the Pacific Ocean is 11,033 meters.

26. The record descent in the Pacific is 10,912 meters.

27. The area of Lake Superior is about 82,068 square kilometers.

28. The area of the Pacific Ocean is about 165,200,000 square kilometers.

Write each number in expanded notation using exponents.

Here's how

20,500

$(2 \times 10^4) + (5 \times 10^2)$

29. There are about 5000 oceanographers in the United States.

30. There are about 20,000 kinds of fish in the oceans.

31. The average depth of the Atlantic Ocean is 4270 meters.

32. There are about 27,200,000 cubic kilometers of water in glaciers and icecaps.

33. There are about 1,360,000,000 cubic kilometers of water on the earth.

Multiplying Multiples of 10

The students at Stevenson School had a walkathon to help raise money for a neighborhood clinic.

Study these examples.

Minutes		Meters per minute		Total meters walked
8	×	70	=	560
10	×	60	=	600
40	×	80	=	3200
90	×	70	=	6300
100	×	80	=	8000
200	×	60	=	12,000

What is a quick way to find 60 × 700?

Find each product.

1. 3 × 70
2. 3 × 700
3. 3 × 7000
4. 10 × 100
5. 100 × 100
6. 10 × 1000
7. 1000 × 1000
8. 40 × 90
9. 400 × 9
10. 400 × 900
11. 4 × 9000
12. 400 × 9000
13. 80 × 100
14. 2 × 1000
15. 10 × 6000
16. 10,000 × 70
17. 50 × 60
18. 800 × 500
19. 10,000 × 10
20. 700 × 100
21. 30,000 × 40
22. 50 × 6000
23. 900 × 9000
24. 5000 × 40,000

Sheila's sponsors agreed to pay her $3 per kilometer. How much money did she collect if she walked

25. 8 kilometers?

26. 10 kilometers?

27. 20 kilometers?

28. 30 kilometers?

Pat got tired and started walking only 20 meters per minute. At this speed, how far did Pat walk in

29. 10 minutes?

30. 40 minutes?

31. 60 minutes?

32. 100 minutes?

There were 200 students in the walkathon. What was the total number of kilometers, if the average distance walked per student was

33. 7 kilometers?

34. 9 kilometers?

35. 10 kilometers?

36. 20 kilometers?

A company agreed to contribute $20 for each student who completed the walkathon route. How much did the company contribute if the route was completed by

37. 70 students?

38. 90 students?

39. 100 students?

40. 200 students?

Multiplying Whole Numbers

Tigers are the largest cats in the world. They can
be up to three meters long. Most tigers are found
in Asia. The total tiger population is so small that
there is danger the tiger will become extinct.

A. A tiger eats about 6 kilograms of meat per day. How much meat does it eat in a year (365 days)?

Find 365×6.

$$\begin{array}{r} 365 \\ \times 6 \\ \hline 2190 \end{array}$$

A tiger eats about 2190 kilograms of meat in a year.

B. A tiger ran 975 meters per minute for 15 minutes. How far did it run?

Find 15×975.

$$\begin{array}{r} 975 \\ \times 15 \\ \hline 4875 \\ 9750 \\ \hline 14625 \end{array}$$
  5 × 975
  10 × 975
  4875 + 9750

The tiger ran 14,625 meters.

Multiply.

1. $\begin{array}{r} 81 \\ \times 4 \\ \hline \end{array}$ 9. $\begin{array}{r} 94 \\ \times 6 \\ \hline \end{array}$

2. $\begin{array}{r} 72 \\ \times 8 \\ \hline \end{array}$ 10. $\begin{array}{r} 62 \\ \times 9 \\ \hline \end{array}$

3. $\begin{array}{r} 927 \\ \times 4 \\ \hline \end{array}$ 11. $\begin{array}{r} 305 \\ \times 7 \\ \hline \end{array}$

4. $\begin{array}{r} 27 \\ \times 80 \\ \hline \end{array}$ 12. $\begin{array}{r} 27 \\ \times 86 \\ \hline \end{array}$

5. $\begin{array}{r} 58 \\ \times 65 \\ \hline \end{array}$ 13. $\begin{array}{r} 352 \\ \times 90 \\ \hline \end{array}$

6. $\begin{array}{r} 352 \\ \times 94 \\ \hline \end{array}$ 14. $\begin{array}{r} 706 \\ \times 38 \\ \hline \end{array}$

7. $\begin{array}{r} 427 \\ \times 500 \\ \hline \end{array}$ 15. $\begin{array}{r} 427 \\ \times 503 \\ \hline \end{array}$

8. $\begin{array}{r} 427 \\ \times 523 \\ \hline \end{array}$ 16. $\begin{array}{r} 891 \\ \times 665 \\ \hline \end{array}$

17. 6×452

18. 9×8714

19. $3 \times 47{,}825$

20. 38×72

21. 41×706

22. 63×5081

23. 875×219

24. 924×6273

**More practice
Sets C, D, and E, pages 62, 63**

Find each answer.

25. If a tiger drinks 22 liters of water per week, how much water does it drink in a year (52 weeks)?

26. A hungry tiger hunted for food for 11 days. How many hours did the tiger go without food? (There are 24 hours in a day.)

27. One tiger scraped the ground every 2 kilometers to mark the edge of its territory. It scraped the ground 85 times. How long is the edge of its territory?

28. A Maharajah of Nepal killed about 98 tigers per year for 4 years. How many tigers did he kill in all?

29. A tigress had 3 cubs. The cubs' average weight was 1457 grams. What was the total weight of the cubs?

30. A zoo had 5 tigers. Their average weight was 148 kilograms. What was the total weight of the tigers?

31

Using Rounded Numbers to Estimate Products

A. Yolanda and Dave used rounded numbers to estimate the number of bricks on the side of a building.

88 rows of bricks
51 bricks per row

88 × 51
↓ ↓
90 × 50 = 4500

88 × 51 ≈ 4500

There were about 4500 bricks.

B. They also estimated the number of apartments in their building.

15 floors in the building
45 apartments per floor

Both numbers end in 5. Yolanda rounded one number up and the other number down. Dave rounded both numbers up.

Yolanda

15 × 45
↓ ↓
20 × 40 = 800

15 × 45 ≈ 800

Dave

15 × 45
↓ ↓
20 × 50 = 1000

15 × 45 ≈ 1000

The exact value of 15 × 45 is 675. Which estimate was closer to the exact value?

Estimate the answers.

1. 18 rows of cars in the parking lot.
   42 cars in each row.
   How many cars?

2. 15 floors in the building.
   95 children on each floor.
   How many children?

3. 21 trash cans per block.
   12 blocks scheduled for pickup.
   How many trash cans?

4. 45 families on one floor.
   $45 weekly rent per family.
   How much weekly rent?

5. 22 blocks in the neighborhood.
   58 sidewalk squares per block.
   How many sidewalk squares?

Estimate each product. Round three-digit numbers to the nearest hundred.

6. 42×71
7. 29×68
8. 52×19
9. 35×85
10. 45×75
11. 89×58
12. 24×76
13. 53×49
14. 17×90
15. 25×25

16. 21×43
17. 39×52
18. 78×41
19. 307×606
20. 892×495
21. 572×444
22. 650×450
23. 328×682
24. 499×715
25. 550×350

laboratory activity

1. Measure the length of your shoe to the nearest centimeter.

2. Use heel-to-toe steps to measure the width of your classroom.

3. Multiply the number of steps by the length of each step to find the width of the room in centimeters.

4. Use this same technique to find the width of a room in your home.

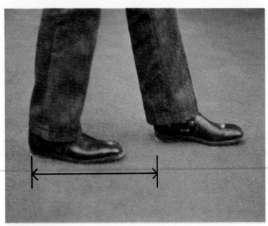

5. Measure the length of your pace to the nearest centimeter.

6. Use paces to measure the length of a hallway in your school.

7. Multiply the number of paces by the length of each pace to find the length of the hallway in centimeters.

8. Use this same technique to find the length of a sidewalk.

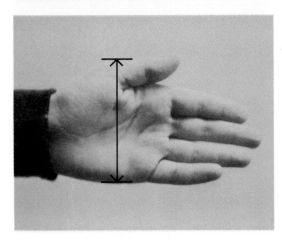

9. Measure the width of your hand to the nearest centimeter.

10. Use your hand to measure the width of your desk.

11. Multiply the number of hands by the width of your hand to find the width of your desk in centimeters.

12. Use this same technique to find the length of a table in your home.

Commutative and Associative Properties of Multiplication

A. Find each product.

$8 \times 12 =$ ▦
$12 \times 8 =$ ▦

$10 \times 24 =$ ▦
$24 \times 10 =$ ▦

$32 \times 17 =$ ▦
$17 \times 32 =$ ▦

Are the products equal in each pair of exercises?

■ *The **commutative property** of multiplication says that you can always change the order of the factors and get the same product.*

$58 \times 21 = 21 \times 58$

B. Find each product. Start with the computation inside the parentheses.

$(7 \times 3) \times 2 =$ ▦
$7 \times (3 \times 2) =$ ▦

$(40 \times 20) \times 10 =$ ▦
$40 \times (20 \times 10) =$ ▦

$(36 \times 51) \times 4 =$ ▦
$36 \times (51 \times 4) =$ ▦

Are the products equal in each pair of exercises?

■ *The **associative property** of multiplication says that you can always change the grouping of the factors and get the same product.*

$(8 \times 9) \times 4 = 8 \times (9 \times 4)$

Find each product. Order and group the factors any way that makes your work easier.

1. $4 \times 73 \times 5$
2. $56 \times 2 \times 3$
3. $2 \times 2 \times 67$
4. $531 \times 20 \times 4$
5. $30 \times 10 \times 725$
6. $20 \times 30 \times 24$
7. $50 \times 80 \times 20$
8. $25 \times 17 \times 4$
9. $6 \times 7 \times 18$
10. $5 \times 36 \times 20$
11. $462 \times 10 \times 10$
12. $8 \times 2 \times 300$
13. $20 \times 6 \times 5$
14. $9 \times 61 \times 8$
15. $2 \times 6 \times 5 \times 5$
16. $6 \times 7 \times 5 \times 2$
17. $5 \times 2 \times 10 \times 7$
18. $4 \times 3 \times 5 \times 3$
19. $8 \times 4 \times 6 \times 25$
20. $16 \times 2 \times 37 \times 10$

Evaluating Expressions: Multiplication

A. Parentheses can be used to show multiplication.

3(4) means "3 times 4."

(5)12 means "5 times 12."

B. When multiplication occurs in an expression with a variable, parentheses are not necessary.

$3n$ means "3 times n."

$8w$ means "8 times w."

This table lists values of $7m$ for different values of m.

m	$7m$	
2	14	7(2)
3	21	7(3)
9	63	7(9)
10	70	7(10)
12	84	7(12)
50	350	7(50)

Find each product.

1. 8(2)

2. (5)6

3. 9(8)

4. 18(2)

5. 4(25)

6. (106)5

7. 9(14)

8. 63(3)

9. 24(0)

10. 0(43)

11. (1)56

12. 72(1)

13. 4(2)(3)

14. 7(5)(2)

15. 2(8)(3)

16. 9(5)(7)

17. 2(4)(5)(3)

18. 8(7)(2)(10)

Complete each table.

19.

k	$8k$
2	
9	
12	
56	

20.

v	$4v$
8	
10	
15	
70	

21.

q	$25q$
2	
10	
15	
80	

22. Find the value of ab when a is 8 and b is 14.

23. Find the value of gh when g is 40 and h is 12.

24. Find the value of $5rs$ when r is 6 and s is 4.

Order of Operations:
Addition, Subtraction, and Multiplication

When you work with addition, subtraction, and multiplication, follow these rules.

■ *First do all computations inside parentheses.*

Then do all remaining multiplications.

Then do all remaining additions and subtractions.

A. **4(7 − 1)**   Do the computation inside parentheses.

    4(6)   Then multiply.

    24

B. **4(7) − 1**   Multiply.

    28 − 1   Then subtract.

    27

C. **13 + 5(2)**   Multiply.

    13 + 10   Then add.

    23

D. **24 − 2(6 + 3)**   Do the computation inside parentheses.

    24 − 2(9)   Then multiply.

    24 − 18   Then subtract.

    6

Compute each answer.

1. $7(3 + 1)$
2. $7(3) + 1$
3. $6(5 - 2)$
4. $6(5) - 2$
5. $2 + 3(7)$
6. $(2 + 3)7$
7. $9 - 4(2)$
8. $(9 - 4)2$
9. $3(6 - 4)$
10. $8(5 - 2)$
11. $(6 + 5)7$
12. $(8 - 8)12$
13. $2 + 4(5)$
14. $22 - 4(3)$
15. $9 + 2(7)$
16. $2(8 + 5)$
17. $23 - 7(2)$
18. $(6 + 4)3$
19. $8(7) - 2$
20. $3 + 3(6)$

21. $3(2) + 4(5)$
22. $7(3) + 7(4)$
23. $8(5) - 6(3)$
24. $6(7) - 6(4)$
25. $2 + 3(5) + 1$
26. $8 + 9(2) + 4$
27. $12 + 7 - 3(2)$
28. $4 + 9 + 6(5)$
29. $2(4 + 1 + 3)$
30. $5(7 + 6 + 8)$
31. $2(8 + 3 - 4)$
32. $5(4)(3) + 6$
33. $7(2)(4) - 9$
34. $50 - 2(3)(4)$
35. $9 + 4(3 + 2)$
36. $12 - 2(1 + 3)$
37. $25 - (2 + 4)3$
38. $30 - (8 - 2)4$
39. $7(5) - (2 + 9)$
40. $4(8) - (6 - 5)$

Evaluating Expressions:
Addition, Subtraction, and Multiplication

Complete each table.

1.

k	5k + 2
3	17
4	
7	
10	

5(3) + 2

5(4) + 2

2.

k	5(k + 2)
3	25
4	
7	
10	

5(3 + 2)

5(4 + 2)

3.

b	3(7 + b)
4	33
5	
10	
21	

3(7 + 4)

3(7 + 5)

4.

t	54 − 3t
2	48
5	
12	
15	

54 − 3(2)

54 − 3(5)

5.

g	(9 + g)6
4	78
7	
12	
30	

(9 + 4)6

(9 + 7)6

Find the value when
n is 4.

6. $n + 8$

7. $12 - n$

8. $15n$

9. $2n + 6$

10. $19 - 3n$

11. $7 + 3n$

12. $(6 + n)2$

13. $(n - 1)5$

14. $4n - 5$

15. $7(n + 6)$

16. $3(n - 2)$

17. $9(8 - n)$

18. $6(2 + n)$

19. $(12 - n)3$

20. $8n - 15$

Find the value when
w is 2 and y is 3.

21. $5wy$

22. $8wy + 1$

23. $2(w + y)$

24. $3w + y$

25. $7w - 4y$

time out

Copy the diagram.
Arrange the numbers
from 1 through 8 in the
squares in such a way
that no two consecutive
numbers are next to each
other horizontally,
vertically, or diagonally.
For example, none of the
following is allowed.

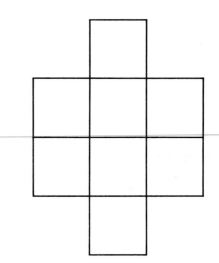

Distributive Property

A. $5(3 + 4)$ $\quad\quad$ $5(3) + 5(4)$
$$5(7) \quad\quad\quad 15 + 20$$
$$35 \quad\quad\quad\quad 35$$

B. $6(8 + 1)$ $\quad\quad$ $6(8) + 6(1)$
$$6(9) \quad\quad\quad 48 + 6$$
$$54 \quad\quad\quad\quad 54$$

The examples above show that
$5(3 + 4) = 5(3) + 5(4)$ and
$6(8 + 1) = 6(8) + 6(1)$.

Is $7(4 + 2) = 7(4) + 7(2)$?

■ *When you write 7(4 + 2) as 7(4) + 7(2),
you are using the **distributive property**.*

c. In this example, Dorothy used the
distributive property to help her
compute the answer mentally.

$5(60 + 8)$
340

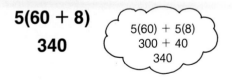

5(60) + 5(8)
300 + 40
340

D. In this example, it was easier for
her to add 7 and 3 and then multiply.

$29(7 + 3)$
290

29(10)
290

Give each missing number without
computing.

1. $3(7 + 2) = 3(7) + 3(\text{▨})$

2. $9(4 + 6) = 9(\text{▨}) + 9(6)$

3. $8(7 + 5) = 8(7) + \text{▨}(5)$

4. $6(3 + 9) = \text{▨}(3) + 6(9)$

5. $30(70 + 55) = 30(70) + 30(\text{▨})$

6. $15(6 + 2) = 15(\text{▨}) + 15(2)$

7. $12(10 + 4) = 12(10) + \text{▨}(4)$

8. $4(16 + 10) = 4(\text{▨}) + 4(10)$

Find each answer. Use the distributive
property whenever it makes your work
easier.

9. $20(9 + 5)$ 17. $5(60 + 8)$

10. $50(10 + 3)$ 18. $7(100 + 30)$

11. $17(6 + 4)$ 19. $75(40 + 60)$

12. $25(10 + 2)$ 20. $8(6 + 3)$

13. $26(30 + 70)$ 21. $7(20 + 5)$

14. $4(20 + 4)$ 22. $39(2 + 8)$

15. $43(5 + 5)$ 23. $12(100 + 3)$

16. $3(40 + 2)$ 24. $56(75 + 25)$

Carpenter

A carpenter buys wood for a project. Wood is often sold in board feet.

Diagram A

12 in.   12 in.   1 in.

one board foot

Diagram B

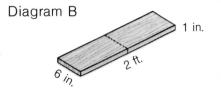

6 in.   2 ft.   1 in.

Diagram B shows the same amount of wood as diagram A. Both pictures show one board foot.

Diagram C

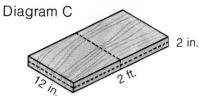

12 in.   2 ft.   2 in.

four board feet

Diagram D

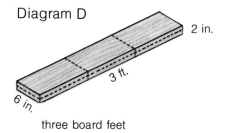

6 in.   3 ft.   2 in.

three board feet

How many board feet are there in a piece of wood that measures

1. 12 inches by 1 inch by 8 feet?

2. 6 inches by 1 inch by 8 feet?

3. 12 inches by 2 inches by 8 feet?

How many board feet are there in a pile of wood that contains

4. 34 of the boards in diagram B?

5. 280 of the boards in diagram C?

6. 500 of the boards in diagram C?

7. 875 of the boards in diagram D?

8. 1500 of the boards in diagram D?

At $350 per 1000 board feet, what is the cost of

9. 5000 board feet?

10. 9000 board feet?

11. 21,000 board feet?

One piece of pine measures 12 inches by 1 inch by 14 feet.

12. How many board feet are there in one piece of pine?

13. How many board feet are there in 500 pieces of pine?

14. What is the cost of 500 pieces at $540 per 1000 board feet?

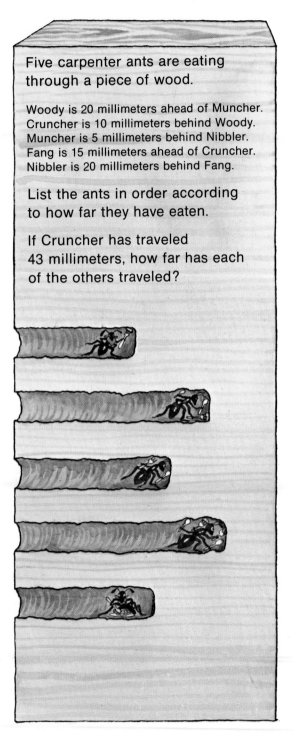

Five carpenter ants are eating through a piece of wood.

Woody is 20 millimeters ahead of Muncher. Cruncher is 10 millimeters behind Woody. Muncher is 5 millimeters behind Nibbler. Fang is 15 millimeters ahead of Cruncher. Nibbler is 20 millimeters behind Fang.

List the ants in order according to how far they have eaten.

If Cruncher has traveled 43 millimeters, how far has each of the others traveled?

Chapter 2 Test
Multiplication Patterns, Pages 26–41

Exponents and expanded notation, pages 26–27

Find each answer.

1. 5^2 **2.** 10^3 **3.** 2^4

Give the missing exponent.

4. $9500 = (9 \times 10^3) + (5 \times 10^{\blacksquare})$

Multiplying, pages 28–33, 35

Multiply.

5. 100×1000

6. 4×800

7. 30×900

8. $\begin{array}{r} 423 \\ \times\ \ \ 6 \\ \hline \end{array}$ **10.** $\begin{array}{r} 26 \\ \times\ 82 \\ \hline \end{array}$

9. $\begin{array}{r} 57 \\ \times\ 30 \\ \hline \end{array}$ **11.** $\begin{array}{r} 435 \\ \times\ 122 \\ \hline \end{array}$

12. 3×214

13. 41×208

14. 210×837

Use rounded numbers to give an estimate of each product.

15. 39×82

16. 61×21

Evaluating expressions, pages 36–39

Compute each answer.

17. $4(15)$

18. $3(6)(2)$

19. $8(6 - 1)$

20. $12 - 5(2)$

21. $3(4) + 3(2)$

Find the value of each expression when n is 3.

22. $7n$

23. $5n + 2$

24. $6(n + 1)$

25. $20 - 2n$

26. $15 - 2(n + 1)$

Problem solving, pages 28–33

27. 9 shelves of books.
12 books on each shelf.
How many books in all?

28. If a cat eats 120 grams of food per day, how many grams of food does the cat eat in 7 days?

Chapter 3 Division Patterns

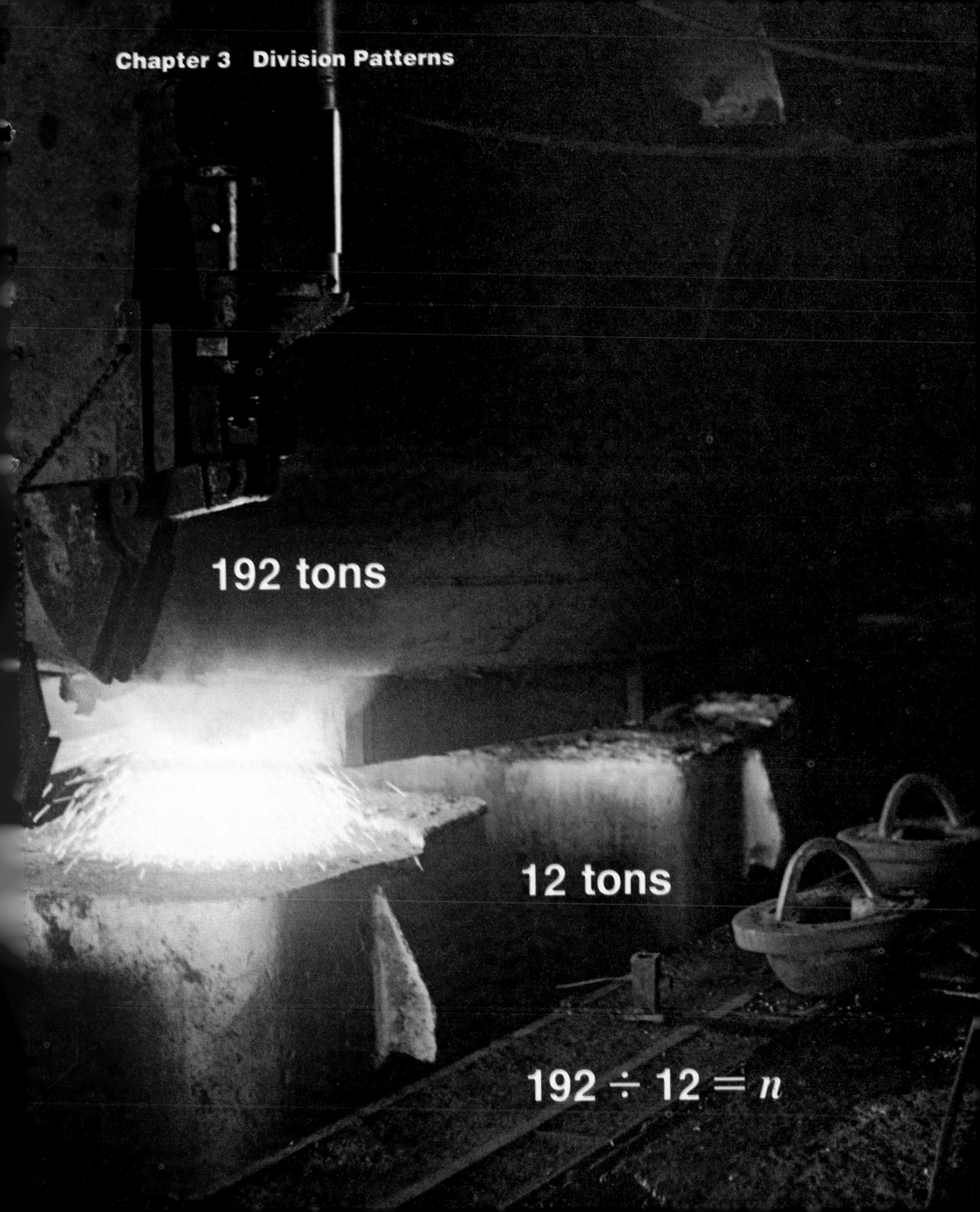
192 tons
12 tons
192 ÷ 12 = n

A store called The High Sign sells posters. The owner is sorting 148 posters into piles of 6. How many piles? How many posters left over?

Find 148 ÷ 6.

```
   24 R4              Check
6)148                    24
 -12                   ×  6
   28                   144
  -24                 +   4
    4                   148
```

There are 24 piles.
There are 4 posters left over.

Divide. You can multiply and add to check your answers.

1. 7)53

2. 6)49

3. 5)78

4. 2)94

5. 7)82

6. 4)953

7. 5)815

8. 3)247

9. 6)145

10. 8)590

11. 3)4272

12. 6)2515

13. 4)3798

14. 8)9040

15. 2)1003

16. 9)2763

17. 8)95662

18. 9)91243

19. 4)28163

20. 2)61007

21. 8)214000

22. 5)367422

23. 6)245108

24. 3)15090

25. 4)70006

**More practice
Set F, page 63**

26. The store received $156 for posters at $2 per poster. How many posters were sold?

27. Four identical posters side by side measured 164 centimeters. How wide was each poster?

28. 1596 posters came off a printing press at the rate of 4 posters per second. How long did the press run?

29. A customer has $92 to spend on display lights costing $7 each. How many lights can she buy? How much money will be left over?

★ 30. 215 posters were shipped in boxes of 6. How many boxes were needed?

45

Dividing: Two-digit Divisors

A. Margaret's hair grew 312 millimeters in 24 months. It grew about how many millimeters per month?

Find 312 ÷ 24.

```
      13
  24)312
    −24
     72
    −72
      0
```

Her hair grew about 13 millimeters per month.

B. On the top of Ron's head, there are about 10,350 hairs in 75 square centimeters of scalp. This is about how many hairs per square centimeter?

Find 10,350 ÷ 75.

```
       138
  75)10350
    −75
     285
    −225
     600
    −600
       0
```

There are about 138 hairs per square centimeter.

46

Divide.

1. 23⟌97
2. 31⟌84
3. 51⟌472
4. 34⟌136
5. 93⟌1209
6. 82⟌2992
7. 28⟌79
8. 19⟌72
9. 27⟌914
10. 78⟌564

11. 47⟌1632
12. 23⟌4860
13. 83⟌4917
14. 56⟌2142
15. 67⟌1273
16. 72⟌7915
17. 51⟌43825
18. 68⟌62104

**More practice
Set G, page 63**

Complete the table.

	Color of hair	Hairs in 64 square centimeters	Hairs per square centimeter
19.	Blonde	11,136	
20.	Brown	8704	
21.	Black	8576	
22.	Red	7168	

23. One hair on Angie's head grew 1296 millimeters in 72 months before it fell out and was replaced. The hair grew about how many millimeters per month?

24. One year, $72 million was spent on hair-coloring products in the United States. This was about how much money per month?

Dividing: Three-digit Divisors

A builder spent $24,475 for 275 office doors. How much did each door cost?

Find 24,475 ÷ 275.

```
        89
275)24475
   -2200
    2475
   -2475
       0
```

Each door cost $89.

Divide.

1. 692)758

2. 413)895

3. 507)4263

4. 765)9180

5. 473)21357

6. 827)14263

7. 127)183007

8. 650)405142

Find each answer.

9. In 120 days, 582,000 people entered the lobby of the building. This was how many people per day?

10. A company budgeted $92,000 for desks. How many $215.desks could be bought? How much money was left?

★ 11. There were 19,400 papers to be put in files that would hold 920 papers. How many files were needed?

More practice Set H, page 63

Evaluating Expressions: Division

A. A bar can be used to indicate division.

$\dfrac{30}{2}$ means "30 divided by 2."

$\dfrac{n}{4}$ means "n divided by 4."

$\dfrac{12}{w}$ means "12 divided by w."

Compute.

1. $\dfrac{15}{3}$ 4. $\dfrac{80}{8}$ 7. $\dfrac{225}{5}$ 10. $\dfrac{258}{43}$

2. $\dfrac{63}{9}$ 5. $\dfrac{120}{40}$ 8. $\dfrac{500}{4}$ 11. $\dfrac{174}{29}$

3. $\dfrac{100}{20}$ 6. $\dfrac{91}{7}$ 9. $\dfrac{84}{21}$ 12. $\dfrac{609}{203}$

B. These tables list values for $\dfrac{m}{3}$ and $\dfrac{210}{t}$ when m and t are replaced by different numbers.

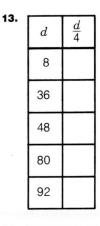

m	$\dfrac{m}{3}$	
12	4	$\dfrac{12}{3}$
60	20	$\dfrac{60}{3}$
84	28	$\dfrac{84}{3}$
150	50	$\dfrac{150}{3}$

t	$\dfrac{210}{t}$	
2	105	$\dfrac{210}{2}$
5	42	$\dfrac{210}{5}$
10	21	$\dfrac{210}{10}$
30	7	$\dfrac{210}{30}$

Complete each table.

13.

d	$\dfrac{d}{4}$
8	
36	
48	
80	
92	

14.

g	$\dfrac{420}{g}$
2	
3	
4	
10	
60	

15.

y	$\dfrac{y}{5}$
20	
65	
110	
200	
230	

★ 16.

a	b	$\dfrac{a}{b}$
15	3	5
63	9	
24	6	
138	3	
175	7	

49

Order of Operations

When you are working with more than one operation, follow these rules.

■ *First do all operations inside parentheses; also, any operations above and below division bars.*

Then do all remaining multiplications and divisions.

Then do all remaining additions and subtractions.

A. $\dfrac{10 + 8}{2} = \dfrac{18}{2} = 9$

Do the operation above the division bar. Then divide.

B. $\dfrac{6(7 - 3)}{8} = \dfrac{6(4)}{8} = \dfrac{24}{8} = 3$

Do the operation inside the parentheses. Then do the operation above the division bar. Then divide.

C. $9 - \dfrac{6 + 4}{2} = 9 - \dfrac{10}{2} = 9 - 5 = 4$

Do the operation above the division bar. Then divide. Then subtract.

Compute each answer.

1. $\dfrac{6(3)}{2}$

2. $\dfrac{20}{2(5)}$

3. $\dfrac{9(4)}{2(3)}$

4. $\dfrac{6}{3}(5)$

5. $\dfrac{8 + 6}{2}$

6. $\dfrac{12}{4 + 2}$

7. $\dfrac{8 + 7}{4 - 1}$

8. $\dfrac{6}{2} + 5$

9. $\dfrac{20}{4} - 3$

10. $8 + \dfrac{12}{3}$

11. $\dfrac{28}{4} - \dfrac{10}{2}$

12. $\dfrac{4(7 + 3)}{5}$

13. $\dfrac{9(2 + 2)}{6}$

14. $\dfrac{20}{2(6 - 4)}$

15. $\dfrac{2(8 + 4)}{3(7 - 5)}$

16. $\dfrac{5(4)}{10} + 1$

17. $\dfrac{40}{2(4)} - 3$

18. $12 - \dfrac{6(5)}{3}$

19. $\dfrac{8(2)}{4} + \dfrac{7(4)}{2}$

20. $6 + \dfrac{21 - 6}{3}$

21. $\dfrac{32}{8} - (11 - 9)$

22. $\dfrac{6(5)}{3} - (5 + 2)$

23. $\dfrac{3(8)}{6(2)} + \dfrac{10(3)}{5(2)}$

24. $\dfrac{20}{4} - \dfrac{2(1 + 4)}{5}$

Evaluating Expressions

Complete each table.

1.

k	$\dfrac{k+4}{3}$
8	
14	
23	
59	

$\dfrac{8+4}{3}$

2.

h	$\dfrac{3h}{2}$
6	
8	
10	
24	

$\dfrac{3(6)}{2}$

3.

w	$\dfrac{5(w-1)}{4}$
9	
13	
21	
41	

$\dfrac{5(9-1)}{4}$

4.

d	$9-\dfrac{d}{7}$
14	
28	
35	
56	

$9-\dfrac{14}{7}$

Find the value of each expression when n is 4.

5. $\dfrac{6n}{8}$

6. $\dfrac{10(n-2)}{4}$

7. $\dfrac{n+8}{3}$

8. $9+\dfrac{n}{2}$

9. $\dfrac{6n}{3}-1$

10. $\dfrac{140}{2(n+3)}$

Find the value of each expression when a is 2 and b is 3.

11. $\dfrac{9a}{b}$

12. $\dfrac{5(b+7)}{a}$

13. $\dfrac{a+b}{5}$

★ **14.** $\dfrac{8a}{4}-\dfrac{6(b+2)}{10}$

Paula and Ricardo are serving cupcakes at a school party. If they arrange the cupcakes in groups of 2, 3, 4, 5, or 6, they always have exactly one cupcake left over. What is the smallest number of cupcakes they could have?

Writing Multiplication and Division Expressions

This picture shows the
network of blood vessels
in a human heart.

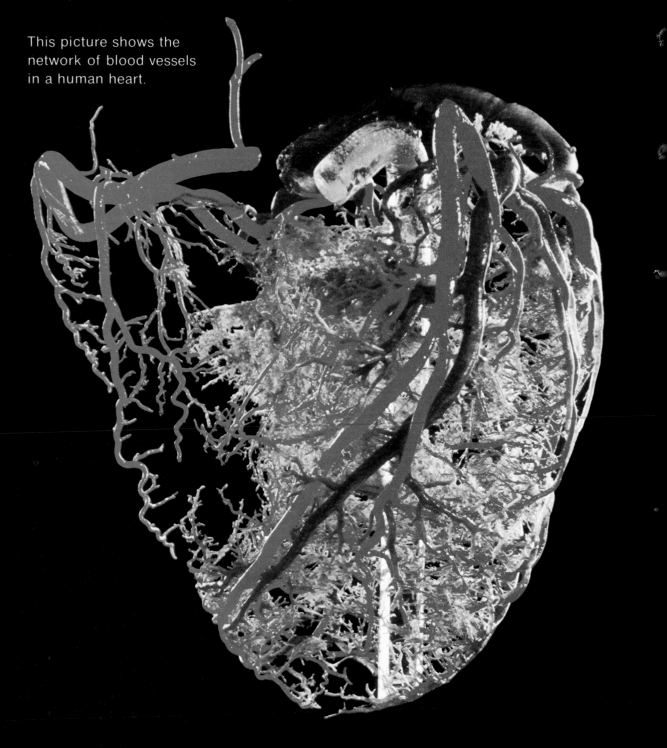

Write a mathematical expression for each word phrase.

A. 8 times a number n

8n

B. A number y times 4

$y(4)$, or $4y$

C. A number h divided by 25

$$\dfrac{h}{25}$$

Write a mathematical expression for each description.

D. The weight of an adult's heart if a child's heart weighs c grams and the adult's heart is 5 times as heavy.

$5c$

E. The number of minutes it takes the heart to pump b liters of blood at a rate of 4 liters per minute.

$$\dfrac{b}{4}$$

Write a mathematical expression for each exercise.

1. 7 times a number d

2. A number v divided by 4

3. 24 divided by a number r

4. A number t multiplied by 15

5. A number w times 6

6. 250 divided by a number x

7. 12 multiplied by a number g

8. A number k divided by 20

9. The number of heartbeats in m minutes for an adult whose heart beats 78 times per minute.

10. The amount of blood in each pulmonary vein if r liters of blood travels from the lungs to the heart through 4 pulmonary veins.

11. The number of grams per liter of blood if 5 liters of blood weighs g grams.

12. The number of red blood cells in w milliliters of blood if there are 5,000,000 red blood cells per milliliter.

13. The number of days it takes the body to use up n milliliters of blood at the rate of 60 milliliters per day.

14. The thickness of a human hair if it is 15 times as thick as a capillary that is d millimeters thick.

15. The number of days it takes the heart to pump t tons of blood at the rate of 8 tons of blood per day.

16. The number of blood cells manufactured in s seconds at a rate of 2,000,000 blood cells per second.

Solving Multiplication and Division Equations

When you breathe air into your lungs,
oxygen enters the blood vessels of the
lungs and then is carried to all the
body cells.

A. Here is an expression for the total number of breaths a person takes in 8 minutes at the rate of b breaths per minute.

$$8b$$

Find b when the total number of breaths is 128.

$8b = 128$ — b is multiplied by 8. To "undo" the multiplication and get b by itself, divide $8b$ by 8. You must also divide 128 by 8.

$$\frac{8b}{8} = \frac{128}{8}$$

$b = 16$ — $\frac{8b}{8}$ is b. $\frac{128}{8}$ is 16.

The rate is 16 breaths per minute.

B. Here is an expression for the number of breaths required to breathe in n liters of air at the rate of 2 liters per breath.

$$\frac{n}{2}$$

Find n when the number of breaths is 48.

$\dfrac{n}{2} = 48$ — n is divided by 2. To "undo" the division and get n by itself, multiply both sides of the equation by 2.

$(2)\dfrac{n}{2} = (2)48$

$(2)\frac{n}{2}$ is n. (2)48 is 96.

$n = 96$

The amount of air is 96 liters.

Find the solution of each equation.

1. $6a = 150$

2. $\dfrac{d}{7} = 90$

3. $\dfrac{m}{45} = 2$

4. $12n = 132$

5. $126 = 3q$

6. $20 = \dfrac{s}{4}$

7. $207 = 23t$

8. $12 = \dfrac{g}{36}$

9. $25e = 25$

10. $0 = 71y$

11. $\dfrac{v}{7} = 31$

12. $\dfrac{b}{31} = 7$

13. $40 = \dfrac{p}{5}$

14. $51 = 17u$

15. $752 = 8w$

16. $7 = \dfrac{t}{14}$

17. $\dfrac{n}{15} = 5$

18. $24c = 120$

19. $4g = 340$

20. $\dfrac{k}{12} = 9$

21. $98 = 14h$

22. $9 = \dfrac{y}{200}$

23. $7b = 126$

24. $35v = 140$

25. $\dfrac{w}{12} = 150$

26. $20 = \dfrac{a}{21}$

27. $\dfrac{x}{13} = 13$

28. $891 = 33n$

Using Equations to Solve Problems

A. This formula is for computing distance traveled.

Rate   Time   Distance

$$rt = d$$

How long does it take a jet airplane to travel 495 kilometers at 9 kilometers per minute?

Substitute values for r and d in the formula.
$$9t = 495$$

Find t. Since t is multiplied by 9, divide both sides of the equation by 9.
$$\frac{9t}{9} = \frac{495}{9}$$

$$t = 55$$

Answer the question.   It takes 55 minutes.

B. This formula is for computing fuel-consumption rate.

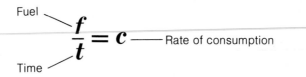

Fuel

$$\frac{f}{t} = c$$ — Rate of consumption

Time

How much fuel is burned in 4 hours by a power boat that consumes 26 liters of fuel per hour?

Substitute values for t and c in the formula.
$$\frac{f}{4} = 26$$

Find f. Since f is divided by 4, multiply both sides of the equation by 4.
$$(4)\frac{f}{4} = (4)26$$

$$f = 104$$

Answer the question.   104 liters of fuel is burned.

Use the distance formula for problems 1, 2, and 3.

1. How long does it take a train to travel 640 kilometers at a rate of 128 kilometers per hour?

2. How fast is a submarine traveling if it travels 192 kilometers in 6 hours?

3. How long does it take a truck to travel 595 kilometers at a rate of 85 kilometers per hour?

Use the fuel-consumption formula for problems 4, 5, and 6.

4. How much fuel is burned in 2 hours by a jet plane that consumes 3500 liters of fuel per hour?

5. How much fuel is burned in 8 hours by a car that consumes 11 liters of fuel per hour?

6. How much fuel is burned in 12 hours by a motorcycle that consumes 7 liters of fuel per hour?

Use this cost formula for problems 7, 8, and 9.

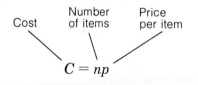

Cost   Number of items   Price per item

$$C = np$$

7. What is the price per tire if 4 tires cost $92?

8. Outboard motors cost $140 each. How many motors can be bought for $840?

9. What is the price per helmet if 3 motorcycle helmets cost $126?

How big is ten thousand? These activities may help you get a good idea. Divide to find each answer. Ignore all remainders.

1. Count the number of pennies in a stack that is about one centimeter tall. About how many centimeters tall would a stack of 10,000 pennies be?

2. Count the number of pencils in a handful. About how many handfuls of pencils would there be in 10,000 pencils?

3. Place paper clips end to end to make a row about one meter long. Count the clips. About how many meters long would a row of 10,000 paper clips be?

4. Count the number of new staples in a row about one centimeter long. About how many centimeters long would a row of 10,000 staples be?

5. Count the number of sheets of paper in a stack about one centimeter tall. About how many centimeters tall would a stack of 10,000 sheets of paper be?

side trip

Short Division

When you work with one-digit divisors, it saves time to use short division.

A. Find 2983 ÷ 7. For each step, multiply and subtract mentally and then write the remainder in front of the next digit in the dividend.

Think
```
      4
7)2983
 −28
  18
```

Write
$$7 \overline{)2\,9'8\,3}^{\,4}$$

```
     42
7)2983
 −28
  18
 −14
  43
```

$$7 \overline{)2\,9'8\,^4 3}^{\,42}$$

```
    426 R1
7)2983
 −28
  18
 −14
  43
 −42
   1
```

$$7 \overline{)2\,9'8\,^4 3}^{\,426\ R1}$$

B. Find 37,698 ÷ 8.

$$8 \overline{)37\,^5 6\,9'8}^{\,4712\ R2}$$

Divide. Use short division.

1. 2)79

2. 6)91

3. 5)802

4. 7)430

5. 3)147

6. 5)218

7. 4)7023

8. 6)9511

9. 2)1435

10. 3)8802

11. 9)28404

12. 6)17352

13. 8)61665

14. 2)42380

15. 4)813207

16. 6)900215

17. 3)67015584

18. 7)120371185

Dividing, pages 44–48

Divide. Give the quotient and the remainder.

1. $4\overline{)39}$

2. $5\overline{)82}$

3. $7\overline{)256}$

4. $2\overline{)9104}$

5. $32\overline{)85}$

6. $57\overline{)454}$

7. $63\overline{)8194}$

8. $76\overline{)5225}$

9. $218\overline{)754}$

10. $574\overline{)7608}$

Evaluating expressions, pages 49–51

Compute each answer.

11. $\dfrac{35}{7}$

12. $\dfrac{8(3)}{6}$

13. $\dfrac{27}{10-1}$

14. $\dfrac{2(3+7)}{4}$

Find the value of each expression when n is 3.

15. $\dfrac{24}{n}$

16. $\dfrac{13-n}{5}$

17. $\dfrac{2(n+6)}{3}$

18. $17 - \dfrac{6n}{9}$

Problem solving, pages 52–57

Write a mathematical expression.

19. 5 times a number n

20. A number w divided by 7

21. 36 divided by a number k

22. Mr. Manetti's age if he is 3 times as old as Pamela and she is y years old.

Find the solution of each equation.

23. $\dfrac{d}{3} = 12$

24. $4b = 72$

Use this formula for problem 25.

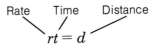

$$\underset{\text{Rate}}{} \underset{\text{Time}}{} \underset{\text{Distance}}{} \quad rt = d$$

25. How long does it take a boat to travel 126 kilometers at a rate of 21 kilometers per hour?

Use this formula for problem 26.

$$\underset{\text{Fuel}}{} \; \dfrac{f}{t} = c \; \text{— Rate of consumption}$$

Time

26. How much fuel is burned in 6 hours by an airplane that consumes 3000 liters of fuel per hour?

Unit 1 Test

Addition and subtraction patterns, pages 4–23

Add.

1. $\begin{array}{r} 314 \\ + 258 \\ \hline \end{array}$ 2. $\begin{array}{r} 558 \\ + 739 \\ \hline \end{array}$

3. $2904 + 8276$

4. $792 + 485 + 608$

Subtract.

5. $\begin{array}{r} 471 \\ - 398 \\ \hline \end{array}$ 6. $\begin{array}{r} 512 \\ - 244 \\ \hline \end{array}$

7. $3075 - 1886$

8. $9002 - 3575$

9. Compute $32 - (7 + 8)$.

10. Write a mathematical expression for "7 more than a number n."

11. Find the solution of $k + 28 = 45$.

12. Find the solution of $w - 7 = 31$.

13. José had 17 records. Lea gave him some more. Then José had 23 records. How many records did Lea give José?

Multiplication patterns, pages 26–41

Find each answer.

14. 6^2

15. 10^4

Multiply.

16. $\begin{array}{r} 732 \\ \times \quad 6 \\ \hline \end{array}$ 17. $\begin{array}{r} 28 \\ \times 53 \\ \hline \end{array}$

18. 40×800

19. 351×609

20. Compute $7(8 - 2)$.

21. Find the value of $28 - 6b$ when b is 3.

22. If Kazuko drinks 450 milliliters of milk each day, how many milliliters of milk does she drink in 6 days?

Division patterns, pages 43–59

Divide.

23. $7\overline{)2536}$

24. $52\overline{)839}$

25. $37\overline{)1315}$

26. $412\overline{)6717}$

27. Compute $47 - \dfrac{30}{3(2)}$.

28. Find the value of $\dfrac{2(t + 4)}{8}$ when t is 8.

29. Write a mathematical expression for "9 times a number y."

30. Find the solution of $6r = 78$.

31. Find the solution of $\dfrac{g}{4} = 56$.

32. Use this formula to find how many $4 books can be bought for $68.

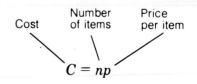

$$C = np$$

Cost — Number of items — Price per item

61

More Practice

Set A	Set B	Set C	Set D
1. 316 + 671	**1.** 597 − 23	**1.** 3 × 7659	**1.** 34 × 4711
2. 618 + 480	**2.** 569 − 489	**2.** 6 × 321	**2.** 82 × 365
3. 854 + 7841	**3.** 5260 − 267	**3.** 4 × 6534	**3.** 14 × 46,168
4. 1260 + 667	**4.** 5580 − 3665	**4.** 8 × 49	**4.** 66 × 86
5. 8715 + 5953	**5.** 122 − 69	**5.** 1 × 574	**5.** 78 × 1836
6. 2818 + 42,680	**6.** 30,074 − 563	**6.** 7 × 479	**6.** 23 × 118
7. 64,320 + 7651	**7.** 357 − 145	**7.** 3 × 78,325	**7.** 46 × 65,786
8. 57 + 71 + 43	**8.** 71,487 − 3889	**8.** 7 × 78	**8.** 46 × 679
9. 11 + 25 + 86	**9.** 7839 − 409	**9.** 4 × 86,926	**9.** 71 × 218
10. 4603 + 8752	**10.** 11,778 − 545	**10.** 9 × 1039	**10.** 24 × 1275
11. 493 + 8638	**11.** 139 − 74	**11.** 5 × 212	**11.** 55 × 25
12. 50,575 + 6026	**12.** 9549 − 7667	**12.** 8 × 234	**12.** 87 × 78,083
13. 842 + 286	**13.** 46,830 − 4504	**13.** 2 × 743	**13.** 63 × 803
14. 8756 + 804	**14.** 607 − 169	**14.** 9 × 226	**14.** 36 × 5329
15. 46 + 72 + 33	**15.** 88,303 − 835	**15.** 5 × 9778	**15.** 77 × 162
16. 8649 + 8736	**16.** 773 − 85	**16.** 3 × 466	**16.** 41 × 298
17. 2095 + 80,290	**17.** 3593 − 673	**17.** 9 × 92	**17.** 95 × 40,246
18. 198 + 2196	**18.** 6946 − 5321	**18.** 6 × 5671	**18.** 69 × 97
19. 93 + 34 + 22	**19.** 90,929 − 3382	**19.** 4 × 697	**19.** 38 × 5394
20. 474 + 174	**20.** 741 − 314	**20.** 7 × 7809	**20.** 53 × 445
21. 56,161 + 9071	**21.** 8999 − 103	**21.** 2 × 7925	**21.** 96 × 72,181
22. 7733 + 7455	**22.** 28,252 − 683	**22.** 6 × 53	**22.** 57 × 614
23. 488 + 424	**23.** 5663 − 4339	**23.** 8 × 5237	**23.** 92 × 401
24. 5085 + 630	**24.** 544 − 348	**24.** 5 × 94,617	**24.** 85 × 1977

More Practice

Set E

1. 617 × 255
2. 246 × 4457
3. 370 × 627
4. 819 × 10,468
5. 178 × 4685
6. 943 × 710
7. 527 × 579
8. 460 × 4618
9. 897 × 455
10. 235 × 150
11. 550 × 50,549
12. 189 × 5733
13. 325 × 864
14. 763 × 3267
15. 651 × 792
16. 730 × 135
17. 673 × 7851
18. 392 × 17,325
19. 235 × 686
20. 459 × 7746
21. 572 × 272
22. 448 × 866
23. 987 × 7662
24. 763 × 17,456

Set F

1. 3)304
2. 6)59
3. 7)5222
4. 4)258
5. 7)971
6. 3)6459
7. 5)66643
8. 8)704
9. 6)317
10. 2)462975
11. 7)798
12. 9)84
13. 4)7893
14. 8)331
15. 5)9072
16. 3)96974
17. 8)43
18. 6)342

Set G

1. 46)92
2. 62)895
3. 13)93
4. 32)6106
5. 14)951
6. 27)77
7. 57)1232
8. 99)11284
9. 26)758
10. 18)606
11. 80)26385
12. 55)675
13. 70)1125
14. 62)20491
15. 28)109
16. 93)14186
17. 88)6183
18. 71)95161

Set H

1. 153)880
2. 299)1023
3. 134)723
4. 546)46831
5. 818)5691
6. 124)625
7. 296)18504
8. 534)7342
9. 782)77166
10. 269)822
11. 314)569115
12. 625)3546
13. 504)81818
14. 141)5636
15. 572)299178
16. 506)46353
17. 242)1443
18. 675)835401

Individualized Skills Maintenance

Diagnosis

A. 1406 + 183

    1213 + 695

    89 + 4875

B. 3782 − 1541

    9696 − 7537

    30,000 − 375

C. 8 × 42

    9 × 873

    6 × 6097

D. 100 × 96

    1000 × 431

    10,000 × 700

E. 26 × 33

    73 × 406

    55 × 827

F. 912 × 406

    673 × 915

    213 × 5810

Practice

Set A (pp. 6–7)

1. 1304 + 592
2. 5261 + 327
3. 4153 + 1426
4. 863 + 51
5. 2857 + 124
6. 1904 + 3275
7. 8379 + 47
8. 5276 + 658
9. 2904 + 197
10. 8679 + 3642

Set C (pp. 30–31)

1. 4 × 38
2. 5 × 46
3. 7 × 82
4. 3 × 647
5. 9 × 152
6. 7 × 830
7. 5 × 1742
8. 8 × 9527
9. 4 × 3146
10. 6 × 32,965

Set E (pp. 30–31)

1. 82 × 89
2. 74 × 59
3. 53 × 94
4. 78 × 22
5. 35 × 99
6. 48 × 105
7. 14 × 665
8. 41 × 216
9. 91 × 339
10. 65 × 410

Set B (pp. 6–7)

1. 5847 − 541
2. 6309 − 3107
3. 8794 − 5682
4. 3957 − 648
5. 6435 − 244
6. 8102 − 6082
7. 3251 − 238
8. 6407 − 579
9. 1820 − 938
10. 92,617 − 4728

Set D (pp. 28–29)

1. 10,000 × 878
2. 1000 × 86
3. 100 × 612
4. 10,000 × 4403
5. 1000 × 99
6. 100 × 6183
7. 1000 × 757
8. 100 × 2246
9. 10,000 × 55
10. 100 × 952

Set F (pp. 30–31)

1. 117 × 432
2. 548 × 235
3. 105 × 896
4. 325 × 610
5. 455 × 989
6. 860 × 340
7. 598 × 4401
8. 440 × 6968
9. 672 × 7057
10. 963 × 1395

Unit 2

Metric System and Decimals

Meter, Centimeter, and Millimeter

In the metric system, the base unit of length is the *meter* (m). *Millimeter* (mm) and *centimeter* (cm) are other commonly used units of length.

The length of the golf club is about one meter.

The diameter of the golf tee measures about one centimeter.

100 centimeters = 1 meter

The tip of the ball marker measures about one millimeter.

1000 millimeters = 1 meter

Name some other objects that measure about

1. one meter.

2. one centimeter.

3. one millimeter.

About how many meters is

4. the height of a classroom door?

5. the height of a classroom?

6. the width of a classroom?

7. the length of the chalkboard?

About how many centimeters is

8. the length of your shoe?

9. the length of a ball-point pen?

10. the height of a wastebasket?

11. the width of your desk?

12. the length of your arm?

Choose the best measure.

13. Length of a safety pin

    26 mm   26 cm   26 m

14. Length of a tennis racket

    68 mm   68 cm   68 m

15. Length of a basketball court

    29 mm   29 cm   29 m

16. Length of a new pencil

    192 mm   192 cm   192 m

17. Height of a thirteen-year-old girl

    154 mm   154 cm   154 m

18. Height of the Empire State Building

    381 mm   381 cm   381 m

19. Length of a baseball bat

    91 mm   91 cm   91 m

20. Length of a small paper clip

    31 mm   31 cm   31 m

21. Height of a giant redwood tree

    76 mm   76 cm   76 m

22. Length of a classroom

    10 mm   10 cm   10 m

Kilometer

In the metric system, the *kilometer* (km)
is used to measure long distances.

The length of five city blocks is
about one kilometer.

1000 meters = 1 kilometer

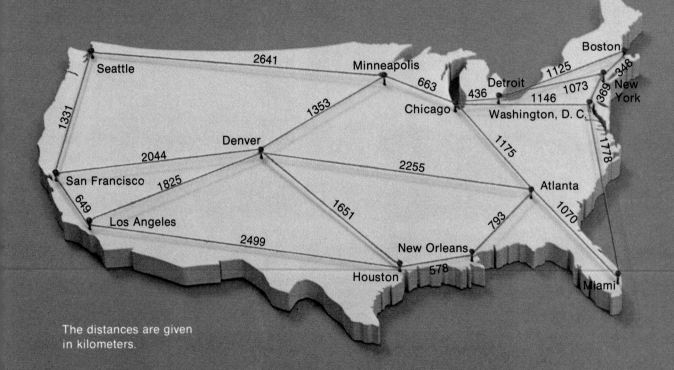

The distances are given
in kilometers.

For exercises 1–12, use the map on page 70.

How many kilometers from

1. Los Angeles to Houston?

2. Chicago to Washington, D.C.?

3. Minneapolis to Seattle?

4. Boston to Detroit?

Find the length of each trip.

5. Los Angeles to Houston through Denver

6. Minneapolis to Atlanta through Chicago

7. Chicago to New York through Washington, D.C.

8. Boston to Detroit through New York

How much farther is it from

9. New York to Washington, D.C., than from New York to Boston?

10. Denver to Atlanta than from Denver to Houston?

11. Detroit to Boston than from Detroit to Chicago?

12. Los Angeles to Houston than from Los Angeles to Denver?

To measure distances, make a trundle wheel. One complete turn of the wheel measures about one meter.

Open a compass to 16 centimeters. Draw a circle on a piece of cardboard. Mark the center point of the circle. Cut out the wheel and make a mark on the edge.

Stick a pencil through the center of the wheel. Attach a stick to the pencil.

Use your trundle wheel to measure the length and width of a room, a hallway, or a driveway.

Estimating and Measuring Length

A. The length of this fly to the nearest centimeter is about four centimeters.

Estimate the length of each insect to the nearest centimeter. Then measure to check your estimate.

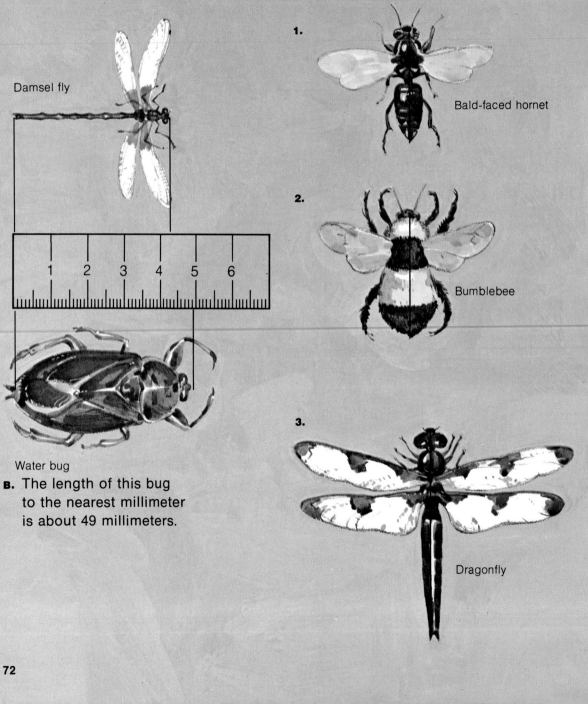

Damsel fly

Water bug

B. The length of this bug to the nearest millimeter is about 49 millimeters.

1. Bald-faced hornet

2. Bumblebee

3. Dragonfly

Estimate the wingspread of each butterfly to the nearest millimeter. Measure to check your estimate.

About how long is each worm? Estimate the length of each worm to the nearest centimeter and to the nearest millimeter. Measure to check your estimates.

4.

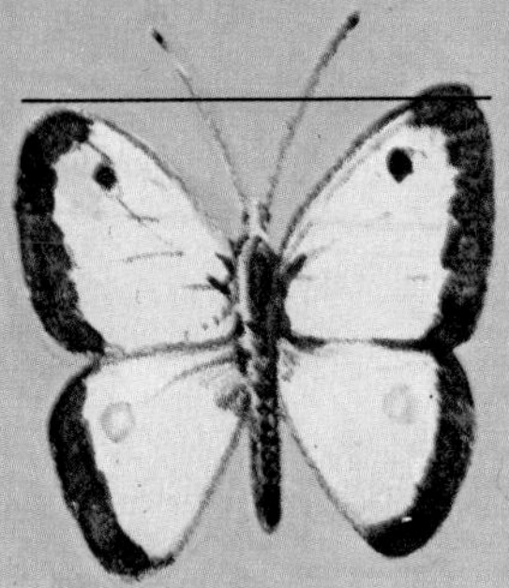

Common Sulphur butterfly

5.

Black Swallowtail butterfly

6.

American Copper butterfly

7. Earthworm

8. Roundworm

9. Sandworm

Roundworm

Earthworm

Sandworm

cm 1 2 3 4 5 6 7 8 9 10 11 12 13 14 15

Equal Metric Units of Length

Equal Metric Units of Length	
1 kilometer (km)	= 1000 meters (m)
1 hectometer (hm)	= 100 meters (m)
1 dekameter (dam)	= 10 meters (m)
10 decimeters (dm)	= 1 meter (m)
100 centimeters (cm)	= 1 meter (m)
1000 millimeters (mm)	= 1 meter (m)

A. $8 \text{ km} = \blacksquare \text{ m}$
$1 \text{ km} = 1000 \text{ m}$
$8 \times 1000 = 8000$
$8 \text{ km} = 8000 \text{ m}$

B. $400 \text{ cm} = \blacksquare \text{ m}$
$100 \text{ cm} = 1 \text{ m}$
$400 \div 100 = 4$
$400 \text{ cm} = 4 \text{ m}$

Find each missing number.

1. 7 km = ▦ m
2. 3 km = ▦ m
3. 5 km = ▦ m
4. 4 hm = ▦ m
5. 6 dam = ▦ m
6. 800 cm = ▦ m
7. 2000 mm = ▦ m
8. 4000 mm = ▦ m
9. 700 cm = ▦ m
10. 60 dm = ▦ m

For each exercise, tell whether or not the measures are equal.

11. 5000 mm   5 m
12. 7 km   700 m
13. 400 cm   4 m
14. 8 km   8000 m
15. 900 mm   9 m
16. 2 km   2000 m
17. 5 dam   50 m
18. 6 hm   60 m

For each exercise, choose an equal measure.

19. 6 m
    6000 cm   600 cm   60 cm
20. 4000 m
    4 km   400 km   40 km
21. 7 m
    70 mm   700 mm   7000 mm

Equal Measures Game

A game for two players.

In this game, you need 24 cards. Twenty of the cards are shown. The other four are labeled 6000 m, 7 m, 7000 mm, and 4000 m.

Deal ten cards to each player. A player lays down pairs of cards that show equal measures.

The winner of a round is the player who lays down more pairs of equal measures. If the players have the same number of pairs, there is no winner in the round.

The first player to win three rounds wins the game.

On the right are David's and Jane's cards for one round.

1. List the pairs of equal measures in each hand.

2. Who won the round?

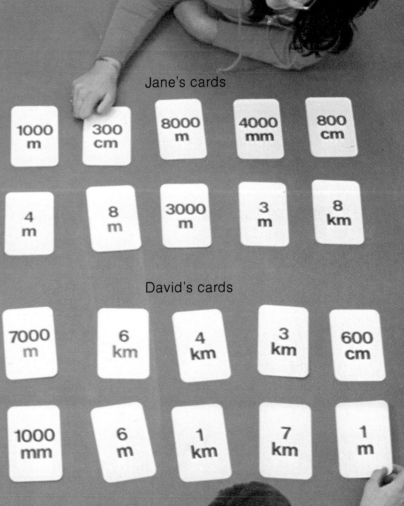

Jane's cards

1000 m	300 cm	8000 m	4000 mm	800 cm
4 m	8 m	3000 m	3 m	8 km

David's cards

7000 m	6 km	4 km	3 km	600 cm
1000 mm	6 m	1 km	7 km	1 m

Metric Units of Area

A. In the metric system, *area* is commonly measured in square meters (m²), square centimeters (cm²), and square millimeters (mm²).

 1 cm²

A square centimeter is a unit of area with sides one centimeter long.

B. You can find the area of a rectangle by counting square units.

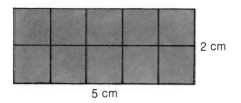

2 cm

5 cm

Area = 10 cm²

You can also find the area of a rectangle by multiplying the length times the width.

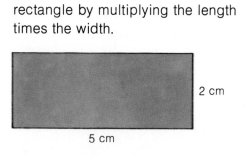

2 cm

5 cm

Area = length × width

Area =   5   ×   2

Area =   10 cm²

Find the area of each rectangle.

1.
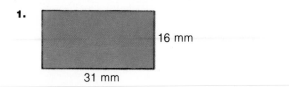
16 mm

31 mm

2.
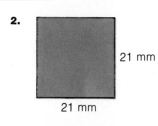
21 mm

21 mm

3.
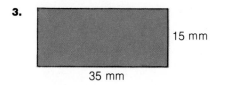
15 mm

35 mm

Complete the table.

	Length of rectangle	Width of rectangle	Area of rectangle
4.	6 m	10 m	
5.	14 cm	26 cm	
6.	32 cm	45 cm	
7.	12 m	5 m	
8.	49 mm	37 mm	
★ **9.**		12 cm	36 cm²
★ **10.**	25 m		525 m²

76

Metric Units of Volume

A. In the metric system, *volume* is commonly measured in cubic meters (m³), cubic decimeters (dm³), and cubic centimeters (cm³).

1 cm³

Each edge of this cube measures one centimeter. The volume of the cube is one cubic centimeter.

B. You can find the volume of a rectangular prism by counting cubic units.

1 cm
4 cm
5 cm

Volume = 20 cm³

You can also find the volume of a rectangular prism by multiplying the length times the width times the height.

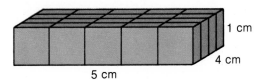

1 cm
4 cm
5 cm

Volume = length × width × height

Volume =   5   ×   4   ×   1

Volume =   20 cm³

Find the volume of each rectangular prism.

1.

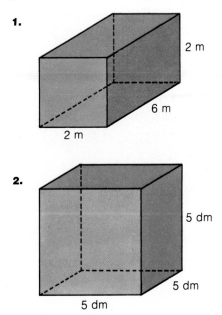

2 m
6 m
2 m

2.

5 dm
5 dm
5 dm

Complete the table.

	Length of prism	Width of prism	Height of prism	Volume of prism
3.	2 dm	3 dm	2 dm	
4.	10 cm	10 cm	12 cm	
5.	4 m	2 m	3 m	
6.	10 dm	8 dm	4 dm	
7.	9 m	8 m	2 m	
8.	26 cm	12 cm	14 cm	
★ **9.**	5 m		8 m	280 m³
★ **10.**		18 dm	4 dm	576 dm³

Liter and Milliliter

Liter (ℓ) and *milliliter* (ml) are also metric units of volume.

A. One cubic decimeter is equal to one liter.

$1 \text{ dm}^3 = 1 \ell$

This pitcher holds about one liter.

B. One cubic centimeter is equal to one milliliter.

$1 \text{ cm}^3 = 1 \text{ ml}$

This eyedropper holds about one milliliter. There are 1000 milliliters in 1 liter.

Choose the more sensible measure.

1. Aquarium

17 ml   17 ℓ

2. Teaspoon

5 ml   5 ℓ

3. Test tube

50 ml   50 ℓ

4. Thermos bottle

900 ml   900 ℓ

5. Saucepan

2 ml   2 ℓ

6. Ginger-ale bottle

500 ml   500 ℓ

7. Pail

10 ml   10 ℓ

8. Coffee cup

20 ml   200 ml

9. Washing machine

4 ℓ 40 ℓ

10. Drinking glass

250 ml   2500 ml

Finding the Volume of Irregular Objects

You can use a graduated cylinder to find the volume of an irregular object.

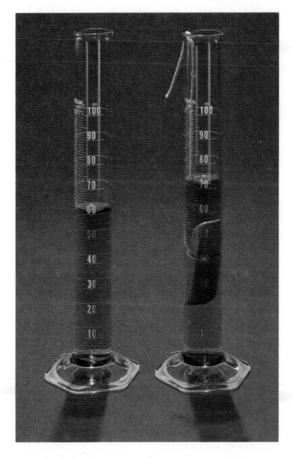

A marble, a crayon, and a bolt were placed in cylinders containing 75 ml of liquid. The readings are shown here.

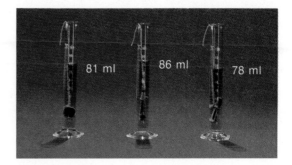

81 ml   86 ml   78 ml

1. Which object has the greatest volume?

2. The volume of the marble is ▦ cm³.

3. The volume of the crayon is ▦ cm³.

4. The volume of the bolt is ▦ cm³.

The cylinder contains about 60 ml of water.

An eraser is submerged. Now the reading is about 72 ml.

The difference is 72 − 60 = 12 ml.

The volume of the eraser is about 12 cm³.

Complete the table.

	Object	Original level (ml)	Level with object (ml)	Volume (cm³)
5.	Candle	36	41	
6.	Rock	14	22	
7.	Pencil	85	93	
8.	Marking pen	62	90	
9.	Key	89	91	
10.	Bead	24	31	

Metric Units of Mass

In the metric system, the base unit of mass is the *kilogram* (kg).

A pair of shoes has a mass of about one kilogram.

A raisin has a mass of about one *gram* (g).

1000 grams = 1 kilogram

Kilogram, gram, and milligram are units of mass.

The mass of an object is the same on the moon as it is on the earth. The gravitational force on an object is less on the moon than it is on the earth.

In common usage, the units of mass are often referred to as units of weight. The term *weight* is also used to mean the gravitational force on an object.

A straight pin has a mass of about 125 *milligrams* (mg).

1000 milligrams = 1 gram

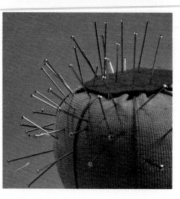

Which unit would you use to describe the mass of each object?

1. Volkswagen

   gram   kilogram

2. Nickel (five-cent piece)

   gram   kilogram

3. Basketball

   milligram   gram

4. Thirteen-year-old boy

   gram   kilogram

5. Pencil

   gram   kilogram

6. Thumbtack

   milligram   kilogram

7. Adult tiger

   gram   kilogram

8. Eyelash

   milligram   gram

Choose the most sensible measure.

9. Station wagon

   2181 mg   2181 g   2181 kg

10. Quarter (25-cent piece)

    6 mg   6 g   6 kg

11. Sewing needle

    380 mg   380 g   380 kg

12. Thirteen-year-old girl

    43 mg   43 g   43 kg

13. Television set

    19 mg   19 g   19 kg

14. Can of tomatoes

    453 mg   453 g   453 kg

15. Small paper clip

    515 mg   515 g   515 kg

16. Lion

    170 mg   170 g   170 kg

PEANUTS

Ten milligrams equals one centigram.

Ten decigrams equals one gram.

Ten grams equals one grampa.

KEEP GOING... I CAN HARDLY WAIT TO SEE WHAT COMES NEXT...

Temperature: Celsius and Kelvin

The base unit for measuring temperature in the metric system is the *kelvin*. Scientists measure temperature in kelvins (K).

Thermometers in most countries measure temperature in degrees *Celsius* (°C).

Tell whether the temperature would be labeled kelvin or degrees Celsius.

1. Average room temperature: 20

2. Air on a winter day: ⁻14

3. Boiling water: 373.15

4. Air on a summer day: 26

5. Body temperature: 310.15

Use the Celsius scale. Choose the more sensible temperature for each activity.

6. Shoveling snow

   14°C   ⁻4°C

7. Sledding

   ⁻10°C   10°C

8. Water skiing

   28°C   10°C

9. Planting a garden

   14°C   0°C

10. Raking leaves

    36°C   16°C

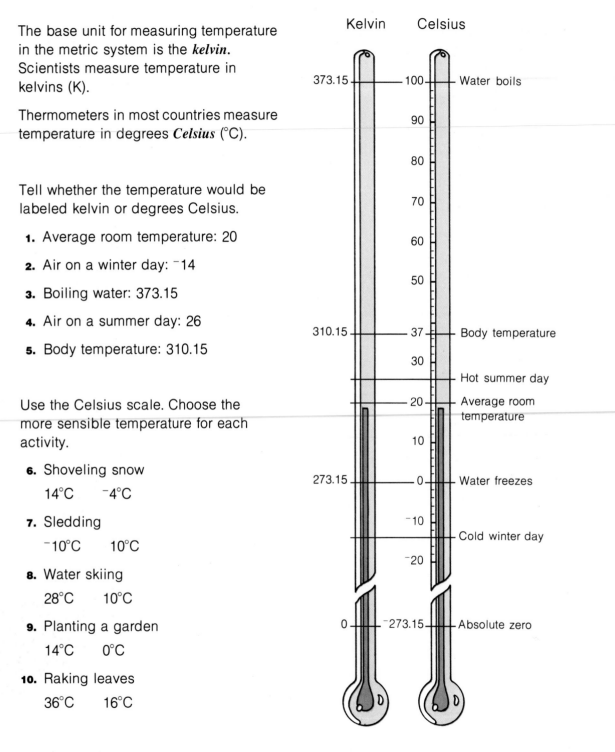

laboratory activity

Marilyn used a balance to find the mass of a stick of gum. Two #1 paper clips have a mass of one gram. Four paper clips balance the stick of gum. The mass of the stick of gum is about two grams.

Follow the directions to make a balance.

Find the mass of a few objects, such as a pencil, a sheet of paper, a dime, a quarter, a button, an earring, and an eraser.

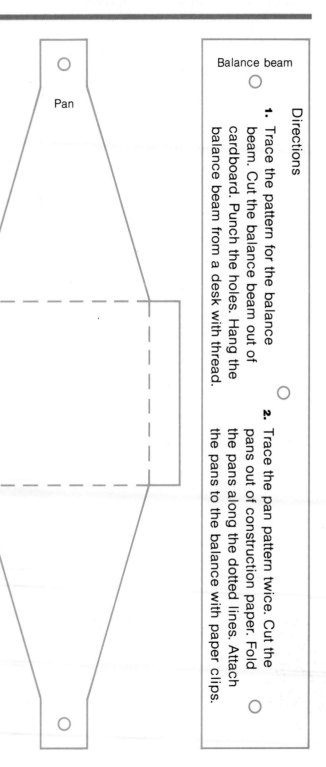

Pan

Directions

1. Trace the pattern for the balance beam. Cut the balance beam out of cardboard. Punch the holes. Hang the balance beam from a desk with thread.

2. Trace the pan pattern twice. Cut the pans out of construction paper. Fold the pans along the dotted lines. Attach the pans to the balance with paper clips.

Balance beam

Relationship Among the Metric Units

A. A container that holds one cubic decimeter of water has a capacity of one liter. The mass of the water is one kilogram.

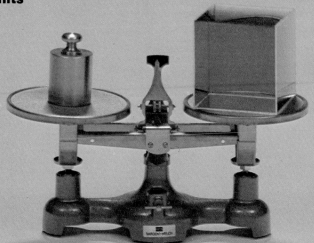

B. A container that holds one cubic centimeter of water has a capacity of one milliliter. The mass of the water is one gram.

The tables on this page show the special relationships among the metric units of volume, capacity, and mass for different amounts of water.

Volume	Capacity	Mass
1 cubic centimeter (1 cm³)	1 milliliter (1 ml)	1 gram (1 g)
1 cubic decimeter (1 dm³)	1 liter (1 ℓ)	1 kilogram (1 kg)

c. Give the missing numbers. Look for a pattern to help you.

Volume	Capacity	Mass
(?) cm³	16 ml	16 g
4 cm³	(?) ml	4 g
(?) dm³	18 ℓ	18 kg
39 dm³	39 ℓ	(?) kg

Give the missing numbers.

	Volume	Capacity	Mass
1.	13 cm³	(?) ml	13 g
2.	(?) dm³	6 ℓ	(?) kg
3.	(?) dm³	(?) ℓ	4 kg
4.	(?) cm³	64 ml	(?) g
5.	(?) cm³	(?) ml	32 g

Give the missing units.

D. Give the missing units. Look for a pattern to help you.

Volume	Capacity	Mass
25 (?)	25 ml	25 g
83 cm³	83 ml	83 (?)
10 dm³	10 ℓ	10 (?)
21 dm³	21 (?)	21 kg

	Volume	Capacity	Mass
6.	14 dm³	14 (?)	14 kg
7.	8 (?)	8 ℓ	8 kg
8.	23 cm³	23 ml	23 (?)
9.	19 dm³	19 (?)	19 kg
10.	32 (?)	32 ml	32 g
11.	25 (?)	25 (?)	25 kg
12.	11 dm³	11 (?)	11 (?)

In each exercise, which measures are the same amount?

13. 26 cm³ of water

26 kg   26 g

14. 26 cm³ of water

26 ml   26 ℓ

15. 3 ℓ of water

3 cm³   3 dm³

16. 3 ℓ of water

3 g   3 kg

17. 85 ml of water

85 kg   85 g

18. 85 ml of water

85 dm³   85 cm³

19. 12 dm³ of water

12 ℓ   12 ml

20. 63 g of water

63 dm³   63 cm³

Chapter 4 Test
Metric System, Pages 68–85

Metric units of length,
pages 68–75

Choose the best measure.

1. Length of a golf club

75 mm 75 cm 75 m

2. Distance between
Omaha, Nebraska, and
Des Moines, Iowa

189 cm   189 m   189 km

3. Give the length of
the paper clip to the
nearest centimeter.

4. Give the length of
the key to the
nearest millimeter.

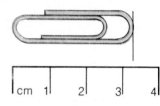

Give the missing numbers
to show equal measures.

5. 500 cm = ▦ m

6. 7 km = ▦ m

Metric units of area and
volume, pages 76–79, 84–85

Give the area of each
rectangle.

7.

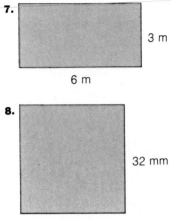

6 m

3 m

8.

32 mm

32 mm

Give the volume of each
prism.

9.

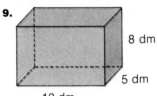

8 dm

5 dm

12 dm

10.

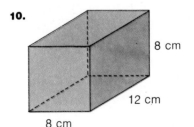

8 cm

12 cm

8 cm

Choose the more sensible
measure.

11. Milk carton

2 ml   2 ℓ

12. Bathtub

400 ml   400 ℓ

Which measures are
the same amount?

13. 18 dm³ of water

18 ml   18 ℓ

14. 4 ml of water

4 cm³   4 dm³

Metric units of mass and
temperature, pages 80–81, 83

Choose the most sensible
measure.

15. Bicycle

11 mg   11 g   11 kg

16. Pencil

5 mg   5 g   5 kg

Choose the more sensible
temperature for each
activity.

17. Snow skiing

30°C   0°C

18. Picnicking

26°C   60°C

CASH

Dollars | Cents

B87 . 42

$53.95
29.13
+ 4.34

Place Value

millions	hundred-thousands	ten-thousands	thousands	hundreds	tens	ones	tenths	hundredths	thousandths	ten-thousandths	hundred-thousandths	millionths
3	7	4	9	1	6	3	5	8	0	7	9	4

3,749,163.580794

Here are the areas of some islands given in square kilometers. Give the place value of the 3 in each number.

Here's how

Ceylon   65.3   **tenths**

1. Singapore   0.543

2. Kangaroo   4.35

3. Vancouver   32.1

4. Greenland   2130

5. Barbados   0.430

6. Simni   0.053

7. Taiwan   35.8

8. Trinidad   4.83

9. Orango   0.300

10. Iceland   103

11. Ramree   2.30

12. Prince Charles   9.43

Write a decimal.

Here's how

seventy-three hundredths   **.73**

13. three hundred forty-seven thousandths

14. six hundred twenty and four tenths

15. sixty-seven thousandths

16. two thousand fourteen ten-thousandths

17. ninety-five and sixty-two thousandths

18. four ten-thousandths

19. thirty-six thousand four hundred thirteen hundred-thousandths

20. twenty and eighty-one thousandths

21. forty thousand and three tenths

22. seventy-six millionths

Writing Equal Decimals

For exercises 1 and 2, give the missing
numbers for A, B, and C.

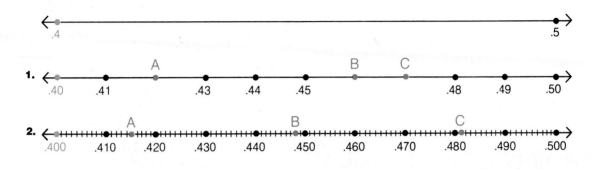

Decimals that name the same number
are equal decimals.

.4 = .40 = .400

Use the number lines. Write an equal
decimal in hundredths.

3. .430   **6.** .450

4. .500   **7.** .4

5. .480   **8.** .5

Complete the table. For each
exercise, show three equal decimals.

	Tenths	Hundredths	Thousandths
9.	.8		.800
10.		.60	
11.			.200
12.	.5		

In each exercise, tell whether the
numbers are equal or not equal.

Here's how

    .80   .080   **not equal**

13. .7   .70

14. 3.080   3.008

15. .630   .63

16. .003   .0030

17. 9.870   9.780

18. 5.6   5.600

19. 913.6   91.36

20. 8.75   8.57

21. 6.07   6.0700

22. .600   .6

Comparing Decimals

A. Compare these numbers.

.46 and .54

.46 < .54

> Forty-six hundredths is less than fifty-four hundredths.

B. Compare these numbers.

.081 and .08

.081 > .080

.081 > .08

> .08 = .080
> Eighty-one thousandths is greater than eighty thousandths.

C. Compare these numbers.

.57 and .570

.570 = .570

.57 = .570

> .57 = .570
> Fifty-seven hundredths is equal to five hundred seventy thousandths.

Replace 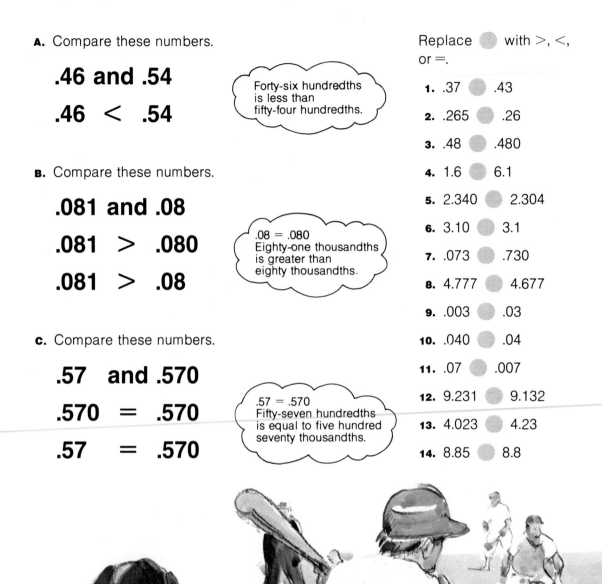 with >, <, or =.

1. .37 ⬤ .43
2. .265 ⬤ .26
3. .48 ⬤ .480
4. 1.6 ⬤ 6.1
5. 2.340 ⬤ 2.304
6. 3.10 ⬤ 3.1
7. .073 ⬤ .730
8. 4.777 ⬤ 4.677
9. .003 ⬤ .03
10. .040 ⬤ .04
11. .07 ⬤ .007
12. 9.231 ⬤ 9.132
13. 4.023 ⬤ 4.23
14. 8.85 ⬤ 8.8

National League Batting Champions

Year	Player	Average
1969	Pete Rose	.348
1970	Rico Carty	.366
1971	Joe Torre	.363
1972	Billy Williams	.333
1973	Pete Rose	.338

American League Batting Champions

Year	Player	Average
1969	Rod Carew	.332
1970	Alex Johnson	.329
1971	Tony Oliva	.337
1972	Rod Carew	.318
1973	Rod Carew	.350

National League Leading Pitchers

Year	Player	Earned run average
1969	Juan Marichal	2.10
1970	Tom Seaver	2.81
1971	Tom Seaver	1.76
1972	Steve Carlton	1.98
1973	Tom Seaver	2.07

American League Leading Pitchers

Year	Player	Earned run average
1969	Dick Bosman	2.19
1970	Diego Segui	2.56
1971	Vida Blue	1.82
1972	Luis Tiant	1.91
1973	Jim Palmer	2.40

Use the batting averages in the tables.

15. List the National League batting champions and their averages from least to greatest.

16. List the American League batting champions and their averages from least to greatest.

Use the earned run averages in the tables.

17. Who had the lower earned run average?

    a. Steve Carlton or Vida Blue

    b. Jim Palmer or Diego Segui

    c. Juan Marichal or Dick Bosman

    d. Luis Tiant or Tom Seaver (1971)

91

Adding Decimals

A. In the 1972 Olympics, Micki King of the United States won the gold medal in the women's three-meter diving event. She scored 289.14 points in the preliminary diving competition and 160.89 points in the final diving competition.

What was her total score?

$$\begin{array}{r} 289.14 \\ +\ 160.89 \\ \hline 450.03 \end{array}$$

Micki King's total score was 450.03 points.

B. Ulrika Knape of Sweden won the gold medal in women's platform diving. The scores for her dives in final competition were 48.3, 56.16, and 67.23 points.

What was her total score in the final diving competition?

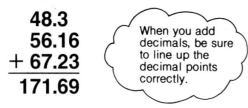

$$\begin{array}{r} 48.3 \\ 56.16 \\ +\ 67.23 \\ \hline 171.69 \end{array}$$

When you add decimals, be sure to line up the decimal points correctly.

Ulrika Knape's total score in the final diving competition was 171.69 points.

Add.

1.   .37
  + .48

2.   2.78
  + .86

3.   7.83
  + .005

4.   32.5
  + .43

5.   18.00
  + 8.72

6.   .65
  + .002

7.   .437
  + 4.794

8.   149
  + 13.78

9.   65.39
  + 7.064

10.   78.1
  + 5

11.   164.346
  +   7.392

12.   3.917
  + 92.4783

13.   .746
  + 12.005

14.   298.5
  + 352.5

15.   1.67
  3.42
  + 18.96

16.   .6
  .9
  + .7

17.   7
  14.27
  + 28.5

18.   .896
  .437
  + .624

19.   19.6
  32.7
  10.5
  + 12.3

20.   14.9
  .72
  3.6
  + .01

21. 8.45 + .65

22. .984 + 2.497

23. 14.56 + .42

24. .06 + .07

25. 13.67 + 3.3 + .448

26. 941.63 + 48 + .06

27. .004 + .02 + .3

28. 14.9 + .72 + 3.6 + .01

29. 26.32 + 8.92 + .673 + 14.3

30. .002 + .012 + .006 + .0083

The scores of final-dive competition
in the 1972 Olympics are given below.
Find the total score for each diver.

31. Craig Lincoln, United States
   46.02   72.24   72.24

32. Klaud DiBiasi, Italy
   57.51   67.86   40.5

33. Richard Rydze, United States
   55.89   58.32   64.38

34. Micki King, United States
   53.82   50.82   56.25

35. Maria Janicke, East Germany
   51.12   50.16   56.16

**More practice
Set A, page 126**

Subtracting Decimals

The scoring in the men's 400-meter relay in the 1972 Olympics is given below.

Medal	Country	Time (seconds)
Gold	U.S.	38.19
Silver	U.S.S.R.	38.5
Bronze	West Germany	38.79

A. The U.S. team finished ▦ seconds ahead of the West German team.

$$\begin{array}{r} 38.79 \\ -\ 38.19 \\ \hline .60 \end{array}$$

The U.S. team finished 0.60 second ahead of the West German team.

B. The U.S. team finished ▦ seconds ahead of the U.S.S.R. team.

$$\begin{array}{r} 38.50 \\ -\ 38.19 \\ \hline .31 \end{array}$$

You can write a zero to show hundredths.

The U.S. team finished 0.31 second ahead of the U.S.S.R. team.

Subtract.

1. $\begin{array}{r} 8.75 \\ -\ 1.43 \\ \hline \end{array}$ **11.** $\begin{array}{r} 16.43 \\ -\ 9.5 \\ \hline \end{array}$

2. $\begin{array}{r} .964 \\ -\ .089 \\ \hline \end{array}$ **12.** $\begin{array}{r} 4.8 \\ -\ 1.075 \\ \hline \end{array}$

3. $\begin{array}{r} 1.00 \\ -\ .25 \\ \hline \end{array}$ **13.** $\begin{array}{r} 173.85 \\ -\ 96.97 \\ \hline \end{array}$

4. $\begin{array}{r} 7.346 \\ -\ 2.568 \\ \hline \end{array}$ **14.** $\begin{array}{r} 4.6304 \\ -\ .8796 \\ \hline \end{array}$

5. $\begin{array}{r} 12.21 \\ -\ 9.99 \\ \hline \end{array}$ **15.** $\begin{array}{r} .847 \\ -\ .5394 \\ \hline \end{array}$

6. $\begin{array}{r} 88.08 \\ -\ 9.09 \\ \hline \end{array}$ **16.** $\begin{array}{r} 200.04 \\ -\ 37.56 \\ \hline \end{array}$

7. $\begin{array}{r} 378.6 \\ -\ 46.8 \\ \hline \end{array}$ **17.** $\begin{array}{r} 3.46 \\ -\ 1.793 \\ \hline \end{array}$

8. $\begin{array}{r} 71.4 \\ -\ 9.8 \\ \hline \end{array}$ **18.** $\begin{array}{r} .004 \\ -\ .002 \\ \hline \end{array}$

9. $\begin{array}{r} .14 \\ -\ .06 \\ \hline \end{array}$ **19.** $\begin{array}{r} .864 \\ -\ .405 \\ \hline \end{array}$

10. $\begin{array}{r} 58.3 \\ -\ 49.9 \\ \hline \end{array}$ **20.** $\begin{array}{r} 2.486 \\ -\ .897 \\ \hline \end{array}$

21. 864.42 − 435.88

22. 39.65 − 4.84

23. .0903 − .086

24. 3.4631 − 1.958

25. 110.06 − 87.98

26. .98 − .432

The scoring in the women's 400-meter dash in the 1972 Olympics is given below.

Medal	Athlete	Country	Time (seconds)
Gold	Monika Zehrt	East Germany	51.08
Silver	Ria Wilden	West Germany	51.21
Bronze	Kathy Hammond	U.S.A.	51.64

27. Monika Zehrt finished ▦ seconds ahead of Ria Wilden and ▦ seconds ahead of Kathy Hammond.

The scoring in the men's 110-meter hurdles in the 1972 Olympics is given below.

Medal	Athlete	Country	Time (seconds)
Gold	Rod Milburn	U.S.A.	13.24
Silver	Guy Drut	France	13.34
Bronze	Thomas Hill	U.S.A.	13.48

28. Rod Milburn finished ▦ seconds ahead of Guy Drut and ▦ seconds ahead of Thomas Hill.

More practice
Set B, page 126

Estimating Costs

Sheila estimated the total cost
of these items to the nearest dollar.

Film	$ 1.20
Flashcubes	2.50
Camera	29.95

A. $1.20 is closer to $1 than to $2.
Round down to $1.

B. $2.50 is halfway between $2 and $3.
Round up to $3.

C. $29.95 is closer to $30 than to $29.
Round up to $30.

$34 Estimated cost

Estimate the total cost of the
purchases on each sales slip.
Then find the actual sum.

1.

Bikes Unlimited

Bicycle lock	$ 5.13
Bicycle radio	14.50
Headlight	3.98
Horn	2.44

2.

Simply Slacks

Blue jeans	$13.75
Corduroys	15.25
Shirt	10.90
Belt	4.19

3.

1st String Sports

Tennis shoes	$ 9.97
Socks	1.25
Tennis Balls	2.79
Sleeping Bag	17.99
Air Mattress	5.62

4.

Discount Drugs

Shampoo	$1.19
Magazine	.75
Vitamins	4.35
Book	1.95

5.

Bigger Burgers

Big Burger	$ .98
Hamburger Deluxe	1.25
Cheeseburger Deluxe	1.40
Malt - chocolate	.60
Hot Fudge Sundae	.75
Root Beer Float	.70

6.

Hobby Hut

Chess game	$ 9.75
Candle	2.95
Necklace	4.59
Poster	2.25

time out

Trace the tangram pieces shown here. Then cut out each piece and number it.

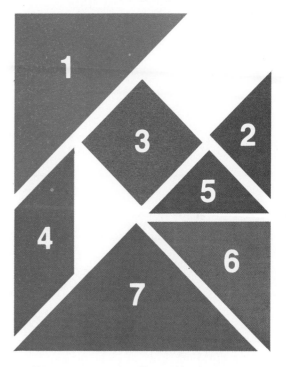

1. Form a square using all seven tangram pieces.

2. Form a square using the tangram pieces numbered 2–6.

3. Form a right triangle by adding tangram pieces 1 and 7 to the square in exercise 2.

Perimeter

To find the *perimeter* of a figure, add the lengths of the sides.

Find the perimeter of each figure. All the lengths are given in centimeters.

The perimeter of each figure is given. Find the missing measure. All the measures are given in centimeters.

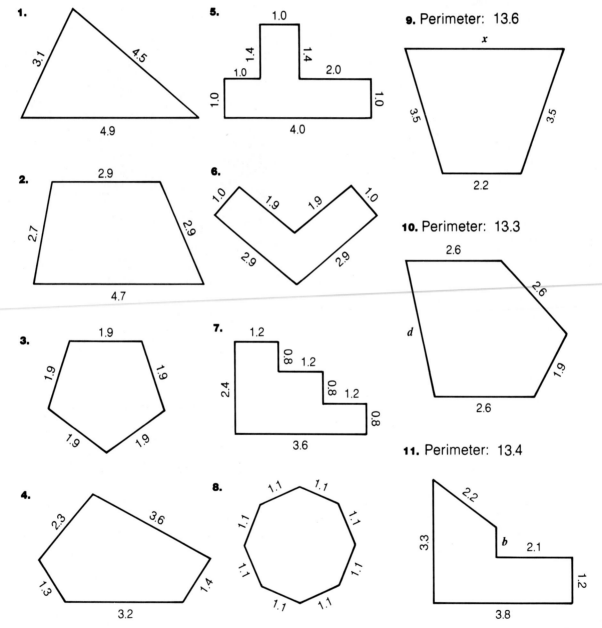

1.
3.1 4.5 4.9

5.
1.0 1.4 1.4 1.0 2.0 1.0 4.0

9. Perimeter: 13.6
x 3.5 3.5 2.2

2.
2.9 2.7 2.9 4.7

6.
1.0 1.9 1.9 1.0 2.9 2.9

10. Perimeter: 13.3
2.6 2.6 d 1.9 2.6

3.
1.9 1.9 1.9 1.9 1.9

7.
1.2 0.8 1.2 0.8 1.2 2.4 0.8 3.6

11. Perimeter: 13.4
2.2 3.3 b 2.1 1.2 3.8

4.
2.3 3.6 1.3 1.4 3.2

8.
1.1 1.1 1.1 1.1 1.1 1.1 1.1 1.1

98

Restaurant Manager

Ms. Krolikowski, manager of a restaurant, shows her employees how to find the total amount of an order.

Lawrence began figuring the total amount of the order shown here. The sales tax is $.05 for every dollar. Complete his work.

Then find how much change the customer would receive if she gave Lawrence $20.00.

Hamburger Haven			
Item	Cost of item	Number of items	Total
Hamburger	$ .30	2	.60
Double hamburger	.50	2	
Cheeseburger	.35		
Double cheeseburger	.60	1	
Fishburger	.50	2	
Fries—small	.30	3	
Fries—large	.45	2	
Malt—choc.	.45	1	
Malt—straw.	.45		
Malt—van.	.45		
Coke—small	.20	2	
Coke—large	.30	2	
Milk	.20	1	
Coffee	.20	2	
Hot chocolate	.20		
		Subtotal	
		Sales tax	
		Total	

Using Equations to Solve Problems

A. In Platte Center, it rained Tuesday morning and afternoon. It rained 0.56 centimeter in the afternoon. The weather bureau recorded 2.32 centimeters of rain Tuesday. How much rain fell in Platte Center Tuesday morning?

Amount of rain (A.M.)	Amount of rain (P.M.)	Total amount of rain

Write an equation.

$$d \quad + \quad .56 = 2.32$$

.56 was added to d.
Subtract .56 from both sides of the equation.

$$d + .56 - .56 = 2.32 - .56$$

$$d = 1.76$$

Answer the question.   In Platte Center, 1.76 centimeters of rain fell Tuesday morning.

B. The temperature at Offutt Air Force Base fell 1.6°C between 8:00 P.M. and 10:00 P.M. The temperature was 20.7°C at 10:00 P.M. What was the temperature at 8:00 P.M.?

Temperature at 8:00 P.M.	Fall in temperature	Temperature at 10:00 P.M.

Write an equation.

$$t \quad - \quad 1.6 = 20.7$$

1.6 was subtracted from t. Add 1.6 to both sides of the equation.

$$t - 1.6 + 1.6 = 20.7 + 1.6$$

$$t = 22.3$$

Answer the question.   The temperature at 8:00 P.M. was 22.3°C.

Solve each equation.

1. $6.2 + m = 13.1$

2. $x - 1.37 = 4.59$

3. $b + .43 = 18.27$

4. $8.00 + n = 13.47$

5. $d - 6.7 = 4.2$

6. $3.71 + s = 9.00$

7. $t + .92 = 7.25$

8. $w - 32.2 = .9$

9. $8.81 + c = 11.35$

10. $e + 9.42 = 24.39$

11. $y - 5.372 = 4.296$

12. $1.222 + a = 15.111$

Find each answer.

13. It rained 1.6 centimeters in Greensboro on Monday. It also rained Wednesday. Greensboro received 4.0 centimeters of rain Monday and Wednesday. How much rain did Greensboro receive Wednesday?

14. The barometric pressure rose 2.71 centimeters between 2:00 P.M. and 6:00 P.M. At 6:00 P.M. the barometric pressure was 75.18 centimeters. What was the barometric pressure at 2:00 P.M.?

15. It snowed 6.8 centimeters in Fargo on Monday. It also snowed in Fargo on Tuesday. It snowed a total of 8.5 centimeters on Monday and Tuesday. How much snow did Fargo receive Tuesday?

16. The barometric pressure fell 0.65 centimeter between 3:00 A.M. and 8:00 A.M. The barometric pressure was 76.6 at 8:00 A.M. What was the barometric pressure at 3:00 A.M.?

Chapter 5 Test
Adding and Subtracting Decimals, Pages 88–101

Writing and comparing decimals,
pages 88–91

Give the place value of the 6
in each number.

1. 33.607

2. .5764

Write a decimal.

3. twenty-nine and thirty-six
hundredths

4. four and sixty-two thousandths

Replace ● with >, <, or =.

5. 3.45 ● 3.450

6. .049 ● .409

7. 6.327 ● 6.237

Adding and subtracting decimals,
pages 92–98

Add.

8. 123.42
  + 97.09

9. .657
  + .348

10. 16.42 + 3.981

Subtract.

11. 81.37
  − 75.09

12. 4.00
  − 3.75

13. 5.74 − 3.585

For each polygon, find the missing
measure. All measures are given
in centimeters.

14. Perimeter: 11.7

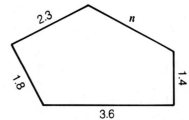

15. Perimeter: 11.8

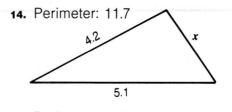

Problem solving, pages 100–101

16. Ms. Jensen drove 36.8 kilometers
to Williamsburg. Then she drove
to Reedsville. She drove
44.1 kilometers in all. How far
is Reedsville from Williamsburg?

17. Iyo bought a radio. She also
bought a battery for $.89. She
spent $16.48 in all. How much
did the radio cost?

18. After Carlos spent $15.89 on
groceries, he had $2.44 left.
How much did he have before he
bought groceries?

$6\overline{)1.14}$

Multiplying Decimals

In each example below, count the number of decimal places in the factors and in the product.

Write each product with the decimal point in the correct position.

Here's how

$$
\begin{array}{r}
8.6 \\
\times \ .6 \\
\hline
516 \quad 5.16
\end{array}
$$

A.
$$
\begin{array}{r}
12.7 \\
\times \quad .4 \\
\hline
5.08
\end{array}
$$
— 1 decimal place
— ▓ decimal place
— ▓ decimal places

B.
$$
\begin{array}{r}
406 \\
\times \ .007 \\
\hline
2.842
\end{array}
$$
— 0 decimal places
— ▓ decimal places
— ▓ decimal places

C.
$$
\begin{array}{r}
6.39 \\
\times \quad .08 \\
\hline
.5112
\end{array}
$$
— ▓ decimal places
— ▓ decimal places
— ▓ decimal places

To multiply decimals, multiply as with whole numbers. The number of decimal places in the product is the sum of the decimal places in the factors.

1.
$$
\begin{array}{r}
34.2 \\
\times \quad 8 \\
\hline
2736
\end{array}
$$

2.
$$
\begin{array}{r}
1.12 \\
\times \quad 9 \\
\hline
1008
\end{array}
$$

3.
$$
\begin{array}{r}
13.8 \\
\times \quad .4 \\
\hline
552
\end{array}
$$

4.
$$
\begin{array}{r}
2.05 \\
\times \ .07 \\
\hline
1435
\end{array}
$$

5.
$$
\begin{array}{r}
.028 \\
\times \quad 9 \\
\hline
252
\end{array}
$$

6.
$$
\begin{array}{r}
.478 \\
\times \quad .8 \\
\hline
3824
\end{array}
$$

7.
$$
\begin{array}{r}
19.1 \\
\times \ .06 \\
\hline
1146
\end{array}
$$

8.
$$
\begin{array}{r}
8.65 \\
\times \ 4.3 \\
\hline
37195
\end{array}
$$

9.
$$
\begin{array}{r}
.394 \\
\times \ 8.2 \\
\hline
32308
\end{array}
$$

10.
$$
\begin{array}{r}
90.1 \\
\times \ .37 \\
\hline
33337
\end{array}
$$

11.
$$
\begin{array}{r}
.458 \\
\times \ .92 \\
\hline
42136
\end{array}
$$

12.
$$
\begin{array}{r}
8.03 \\
\times \ 2.7 \\
\hline
21681
\end{array}
$$

13.
$$
\begin{array}{r}
408 \\
\times \ .39 \\
\hline
15912
\end{array}
$$

14.
$$
\begin{array}{r}
.732 \\
\times \quad 54 \\
\hline
39528
\end{array}
$$

Multiply.

15.
$$\begin{array}{r} 62 \\ \times\ .04 \\ \hline \end{array}$$

16.
$$\begin{array}{r} 3.12 \\ \times\ \ .8 \\ \hline \end{array}$$

17.
$$\begin{array}{r} 96.1 \\ \times\ .04 \\ \hline \end{array}$$

18.
$$\begin{array}{r} 376 \\ \times\ .006 \\ \hline \end{array}$$

19.
$$\begin{array}{r} 7.5 \\ \times\ 2.9 \\ \hline \end{array}$$

20.
$$\begin{array}{r} 3.06 \\ \times\ \ .09 \\ \hline \end{array}$$

21.
$$\begin{array}{r} 8.6 \\ \times\ 4.8 \\ \hline \end{array}$$

22.
$$\begin{array}{r} 9.05 \\ \times\ \ .37 \\ \hline \end{array}$$

23. $.05 \times 4.33$

24. $.008 \times 892$

25. 6.3×7.5

26. $8.9 \times .57$

27. $.92 \times 3.1$

28. $27.5 \times .039$

29. $.83 \times 903$

More practice
Set C, page 126

12.5 grams   6.25 grams   2.5 grams

Find the mass of

30. twenty dimes. (Find 20×2.5.)

31. fifteen half dollars.

32. thirty quarters.

33. nine dimes.

34. twelve half dollars.

35. twenty-five quarters.

36. one hundred dimes.

37. seventy-five half dollars.

38. Gloria had two half dollars, six quarters, and four dimes. Give the total mass of these coins.

39. Juanita had two half dollars and four quarters. Give the total mass of these coins.

Multiplying Decimals: Zeros in the Product

When you multiply decimals, sometimes you need to write one or more zeros in the product.

A.

$$
\begin{array}{r}
.052 \\
\times \quad .6 \\
\hline
.0312
\end{array}
$$

.052 — 3 decimal places
× .6 — 1 decimal place
.0312 — 4 decimal places

B.

$$
\begin{array}{r}
.029 \\
\times \quad .02 \\
\hline
.00058
\end{array}
$$

.029 — 3 decimal places
× .02 — 2 decimal places
.00058 — 5 decimal places

Multiply.

1. $\begin{array}{r} .07 \\ \times \quad 4 \\ \hline \end{array}$

2. $\begin{array}{r} .07 \\ \times \quad .4 \\ \hline \end{array}$

3. $\begin{array}{r} .07 \\ \times \ .04 \\ \hline \end{array}$

4. $\begin{array}{r} .007 \\ \times \ .04 \\ \hline \end{array}$

5. $\begin{array}{r} .9 \\ \times \ .08 \\ \hline \end{array}$

6. $\begin{array}{r} .06 \\ \times \ .07 \\ \hline \end{array}$

7. $\begin{array}{r} .08 \\ \times \quad .6 \\ \hline \end{array}$

8. $\begin{array}{r} .009 \\ \times \quad .09 \\ \hline \end{array}$

9. $\begin{array}{r} .92 \\ \times \ .08 \\ \hline \end{array}$

10. $\begin{array}{r} .76 \\ \times \ .04 \\ \hline \end{array}$

11. $\begin{array}{r} .036 \\ \times \quad .08 \\ \hline \end{array}$

12. $\begin{array}{r} .89 \\ \times \ .05 \\ \hline \end{array}$

13. .08 × .92

14. .004 × .76

15. .008 × 3.6

16. .06 × .89

17. .9 × .094

18. .06 × .38

19. .008 × .96

20. .06 × 1.62

21. .005 × 8.35

22. .008 × .637

23. .07 × .726

24. .9 × .307

25. .03 × 2.76

26. .004 × 3.26

27. .07 × .485

28. .008 × .709

29. .083 × .06

30. 6.49 × .005

31. .485 × .07

32. 1.2 × .0432

33. .0072 × 4.98

34. .062 × .824

35. .279 × .148

**More practice
Set D, page 126**

Using Multiplication of Decimals: Magic Squares

This square is a multiplication magic square. The product for each row, column, and diagonal is the same number.

What is the magic product for this magic square?

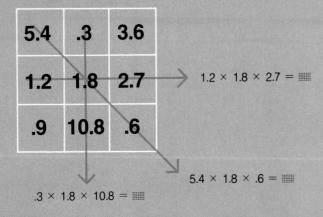

5.4	.3	3.6
1.2	1.8	2.7
.9	10.8	.6

$1.2 \times 1.8 \times 2.7 = $ ▦

$.3 \times 1.8 \times 10.8 = $ ▦

$5.4 \times 1.8 \times .6 = $ ▦

Tell whether each square is a multiplication magic square. If it is, give the magic product.

1.

2.4	.2	3.6
1.8	1.2	.8
.4	7.2	.6

3.

.64	.02	.32
.08	.16	.32
.08	1.32	.04

2.

6.4	.4	12.8
6.5	3.2	1.6
.8	25.6	1.5

4.

28.8	.6	21.6
5.4	7.2	9.6
2.4	86.4	1.8

Multiplying by Powers of 10

A. $10 \times 4.85 = 48.5$
$10^1 \times 4.85 = 48.5$

B. $100 \times 4.85 = 485$
$10^2 \times 4.85 = 485$

C. $1000 \times 4.85 = 4850$
$10^3 \times 4.85 = 4850$

D. $10,000 \times 4.85 = 48,500$
$10^4 \times 4.85 = 48,500$

Notice that, when you multiply by a power of 10, the exponent tells you how many places the decimal point must be moved to the right.

Complete each set of exercises.

1. $10^1 \times .0008 = .008$
$10^2 \times .0008 = $ ▦
$10^3 \times .0008 = $ ▦
$10^4 \times .0008 = $ ▦

2. $10^1 \times 5.6 = 56$
$10^2 \times 5.6 = 560$
$10^3 \times 5.6 = $ ▦
$10^4 \times 5.6 = $ ▦

Multiply.

3. 10×3.846

4. $1000 \times .026$

5. 100×12.47

6. $10,000 \times 8.0203$

7. $100 \times .49$

8. $10 \times .0086$

9. $10,000 \times 12.4$

10. 100×6.25

11. 1000×1.111

12. 1000×8.6

13. $10,000 \times 3.42$

14. $10^3 \times 6.42$

15. $10^2 \times 8.1$

16. $10^1 \times 46.15$

17. $10^2 \times 2.3475$

18. $10^3 \times 26.13$

19. $10^1 \times .006$

20. $10^2 \times 13.406$

21. $10^3 \times 7.7$

22. $10^1 \times .63$

23. $10^4 \times 87.68$

24. $10^4 \times .437$

Complete the table.

	Number	Multiplied by			
		10^1	10^2	10^3	10^4
25.	3.472				
26.	.543				
27.	18.359				
28.	76.24				
29.	1.1				
30.	.67891				

**More practice
Set E, page 126**

Using Multiplication of Decimals: Metric Measures

1 kilometer (km) = 1000 meters (m)
1 meter = 100 centimeters (cm)
1 meter = 1000 millimeters (mm)
1 centimeter = 10 millimeters

1 kilogram (kg) = 1000 grams (g)

1 liter (ℓ) = 1000 milliliters (ml)

The record for the heaviest domestic cat is 19.1 kilograms. Find the mass in grams.

$1000 \times 19.1 = 19{,}100$

The mass of the cat is 19,100 grams.

Here are some world records.
Multiply to find each missing number.

1. Height of tallest man:

   2.65 m = ▦ cm

2. Length of longest human hair:

   7.92 m = ▦ cm

3. Height of shortest woman:

   0.589 m = ▦ mm

4. Length of longest fingernail:

   0.57 m = ▦ mm

5. Measure of smallest waist:

   33.1 cm = ▦ mm

6. Length of longest neck:

   40.1 cm = ▦ mm

7. Height of highest waterfall:

   0.963 km = ▦ m

8. Height of tallest building:

   0.442 km = ▦ m

9. Height of shortest man:

   0.673 m = ▦ mm

10. Mass of heaviest bird egg:

    1.65 kg = ▦ g

11. Volume of smallest bottle:

    0.0015 ℓ = ▦ ml

Dividing a Decimal by a Whole Number

A. Ingrid paid $1.68 for six bottles of cola. Find the cost per bottle.

Find 1.68 ÷ 6.

$$\begin{array}{r} . \\ 6\overline{)1.68} \end{array}$$

Place the decimal point for the quotient directly above the decimal point in the dividend.

$$\begin{array}{r} .28 \\ 6\overline{)1.68} \\ -1\,2 \\ \hline 48 \\ -48 \\ \hline 0 \end{array}$$

Then divide the same way that you divide whole numbers.

The cost per bottle was $.28.

B. Carmen paid $1.84 for 92 ounces of cola. Find the cost per ounce.

Find 1.84 ÷ 92.

$$\begin{array}{r} .0 \\ 92\overline{)1.84} \end{array}$$

Sometimes, when you divide decimals, you need to write one or more zeros in the quotient.

$$\begin{array}{r} .02 \\ 92\overline{)1.84} \\ -1\,84 \\ \hline 0 \end{array}$$

The cost per ounce was $.02.

Divide.

1. $6\overline{)3.72}$
2. $8\overline{)45.6}$
3. $4\overline{)8.64}$
4. $7\overline{)18.2}$
5. $9\overline{).0432}$
6. $8\overline{)10.72}$
7. $5\overline{)2.35}$
8. $6\overline{)4.272}$
9. $9\overline{)864.9}$
10. $12\overline{)1.44}$
11. $16\overline{)1.824}$
12. $18\overline{).216}$
13. $22\overline{)25.52}$
14. $13\overline{)552.5}$
15. $28\overline{).6384}$
16. $61\overline{)9.394}$
17. $92\overline{)3.036}$
18. $39\overline{)235.95}$

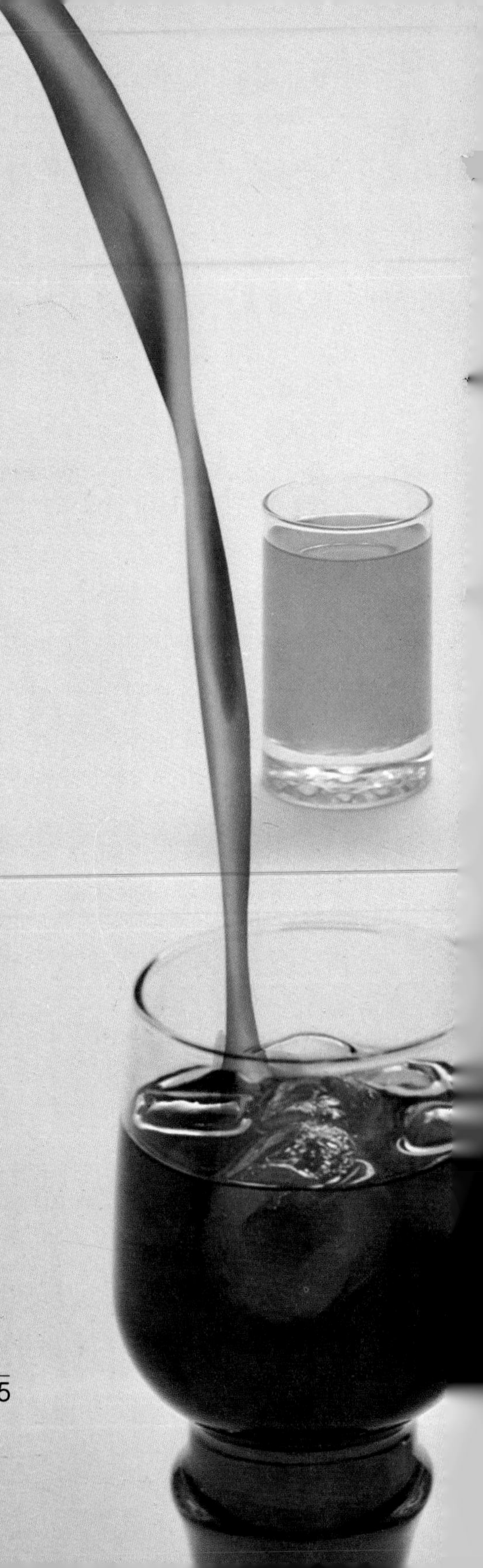

19. $46\overline{)20.608}$

20. $75\overline{)1.8975}$

21. $81\overline{)1725.3}$

22. $53\overline{)5.035}$

23. $62\overline{)65.72}$

24. $49\overline{)1146.6}$

25. $38\overline{)3.6594}$

26. $72\overline{)22.608}$

27. $212\overline{)13.144}$

28. $128\overline{)46.208}$

**More practice
Set F, page 126**

Find the cost per ounce if

29. twelve ounces of root beer sells
for $.36.

30. thirty-two ounces of lemon juice
sells for $.96.

31. forty-eight ounces of cranberry-
apple drink sells for $.96.

32. one hundred forty-four ounces of
cola sells for $2.88.

Find the cost per can if

33. six cans of orange drink sell for
$.84.

34. eight cans of grape soda sell for
$1.68.

35. twelve cans of cola sell for $3.00.

36. twenty-four cans of tomato juice
sell for $3.60.

Dividing Decimals by Decimals

A. Find 2.115 ÷ .05.

$$.05\overline{)2.115}$$

Multiply the dividend and the divisor by 100 to make the divisor a whole number.

$$.05\overline{)2.11\,5}$$

$$5\overline{)211.5}$$

$$\begin{array}{r} 42.3 \\ .05\overline{)2.11\,5} \\ -2\,0 \\ \hline 11 \\ -10 \\ \hline 1\,5 \\ -1\,5 \\ \hline 0 \end{array}$$

Divide.

1. $.5\overline{)185}$

2. $.06\overline{)3.12}$

3. $.003\overline{)1.917}$

4. $.7\overline{)651}$

5. $.08\overline{)1.872}$

6. $.9\overline{)03519}$

7. $.04\overline{)2.632}$

8. $.008\overline{)9464}$

9. $.05\overline{)0085}$

10. $.0009\overline{)2.5650}$

11. $2.6\overline{)120.38}$

12. $.75\overline{)00225}$

13. $.038\overline{)4.94}$

14. $4.2\overline{)2814}$

15. $.23\overline{)9.89}$

16. $.013\overline{)3354}$

17. $6.7\overline{)29.48}$

18. $.85\overline{)2.6605}$

B. Find 42.5 ÷ .125.

$$.125\overline{)42.5}$$

Multiply the dividend and the divisor by 1000.

$$.125\overline{)42.500}$$

$$125\overline{)42500}$$

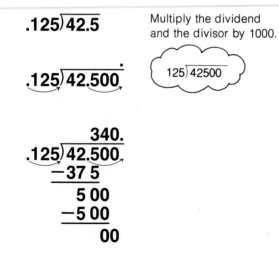

$$\begin{array}{r} 340. \\ .125\overline{)42.500} \\ -37\,5 \\ \hline 5\,00 \\ -5\,00 \\ \hline 00 \end{array}$$

19. $7.2\overline{)6.768}$

20. $.049\overline{).12593}$

21. $.88\overline{)17.248}$

22. $.032\overline{)1.0912}$

23. $.65\overline{)527.8}$

24. $.59\overline{).3245}$

25. $.028\overline{)176.68}$

26. $.91\overline{)873.6}$

27. $.081\overline{).5265}$

28. $6.1\overline{)197.03}$

29. $5.2\overline{)24.96}$

30. $.0035\overline{)2.345}$

31. $1.58\overline{).5056}$

32. $.317\overline{).20605}$

33. $2.03\overline{)12.992}$

34. $5.55\overline{).37185}$

35. $.408\overline{)3.5904}$

36. $8.56\overline{)7.9608}$

More practice
Set G, page 127

Pick the first three horses past the finish line. Here are the clues.

1. The sum of the numbers of the first three horses equals the sum of the numbers of the five also-rans.

2. Of the first three horses, the one with the smallest number wins. The one with the largest number is third.

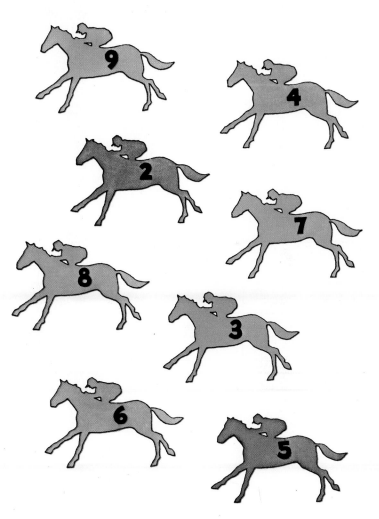

Demographer

A demographer works with statistics about a community. A demographer is interested in population density.

To find the population density of Atlanta, Georgia, a demographer would divide 495,414 (population) by 340 (area in square kilometers).

$$340\overline{)495414.0} \atop 1457.1$$

The population density of Atlanta, Georgia, is 1457.1 people per square kilometer.

Find the population density of each city. Give your answers in tenths.

	City	Population	Area (km²)
1.	Schuyler, Nebr.	3654	4
2.	Kewanee, Ill.	15,785	14
3.	Manchester, N.H.	87,763	86
4.	Salt Lake City, Utah	174,754	145
5.	Milwaukee, Wis.	714,225	250
6.	New York City, N.Y.	7,895,264	832

Rounding Decimals

A. The machine rounded 3.6465 to the nearest tenth.

3.6465 is nearer to 3.6 than to 3.7.

The machine rounded down to 3.6.

B. If the rule were changed to: "Round to the nearest hundredth," what would the output number be?

3.6465 is nearer to 3.65 than to 3.64.

The machine rounded up to 3.65.

C. If the rule were changed to: "Round to the nearest thousandth," what would the output number be?

3.6465 is halfway between 3.646 and 3.647.

The machine rounded up to 3.647.

Rule: *Round to the nearest tenth.*
Find the output number for each given input number.

1. 6.24
2. .85
3. .692
4. 37.821
5. .8904
6. .0652

Rule: *Round to the nearest hundredth.*
Find each output number.

7. 9.132
8. .475
9. 318.589
10. 73.206
11. 2.5634
12. .62517

Rule: *Round to the nearest thousandth.*
Find each output number.

13. .8714
14. .5985
15. 23.1118
16. .82376
17. 79.21043
18. 4.6495

Rounding Quotients

A. In 1973, O. J. Simpson of the Buffalo Bills gained 2003 yards in 332 carries. Find his average number of yards per carry to the nearest tenth of a yard.

Find 2003 ÷ 332.

```
     6.03  ≈ 6.0
332)2003.00
   −1992
     11 00
     −9 96
      1 04
```

Divide until the quotient is in hundredths. Then round to the nearest tenth.

O. J. Simpson's average to the nearest tenth of a yard was 6.0 yards.

B. In 1973, Roger Staubach of the Dallas Cowboys attempted 286 passes. He completed 179 of them. Find his completion average to the nearest thousandth.

Find 179 ÷ 286.

```
      .6258  ≈ .626
286)179.0000
   −171 6
      7 40
     −5 72
     1 680
    −1 430
      2500
     −2288
       212
```

Divide until the quotient is in ten-thousandths. Then round to the nearest thousandth.

Roger Staubach's completion average to the nearest thousandth was .626.

Round each quotient to the nearest tenth.

1. $.08)\overline{60.43}$

2. $.56)\overline{9.104}$

3. $125)\overline{6843}$

4. $38)\overline{14}$

Round each quotient to the nearest hundredth.

5. $.003)\overline{.6832}$

6. $9.2)\overline{182.37}$

7. $46)\overline{7034}$

8. $202)\overline{186}$

Round each quotient to the nearest thousandth.

9. $1.8)\overline{.6327}$

10. $.75)\overline{.92416}$

11. $26)\overline{1804}$

12. $88)\overline{25}$

**More practice
Set H, page 127**

Divide to find the average number of yards per carry for each running back.

	Year	Player	Team	Yards gained	Number of carries	Yards per carry
13.	1972	O. J. Simpson	Buffalo	1251	292	
14.	1971	Floyd Little	Denver	1133	284	
15.	1970	Larry Brown	Washington	1125	237	
16.	1969	Gale Sayers	Chicago	1032	236	
17.	1968	LeRoy Kelly	Cleveland	1239	248	

Divide to find the completion average for each quarterback.

	Year	Player	Team	Passes attempted	Passes completed	Completion average
18.	1972	Norm Snead	New York	325	196	
19.	1971	Roger Staubach	Dallas	211	126	
20.	1970	John Brodie	San Francisco	378	223	
21.	1969	Sonny Jorgensen	Washington	442	274	
22.	1968	Earl Morrall	Baltimore	317	182	

laboratory activity

Throw a football ten times. Measure the length of each throw.

Then add the lengths of the throws. Divide the total length by ten to find your average number of yards per throw. Give your average to the nearest tenth of a yard.

Dividing by Powers of 10

A. $94.36 \div 10 = 9.436$

$94.36 \div 10^1 = 9.436$

B. $94.36 \div 100 = .9436$

$94.36 \div 10^2 = .9436$

C. $94.36 \div 1000 = .09436$

$94.36 \div 10^3 = .09436$

D. $94.36 \div 10,000 = .009436$

$94.36 \div 10^4 = .009436$

Notice that, when you divide by a power of 10, the exponent tells you how many places the decimal point must be moved to the left.

Divide.

3. $34.7 \div 10$

4. $86.13 \div 100$

5. $24.78 \div 1000$

6. $123.4 \div 100$

7. $.6 \div 10$

8. $218.3 \div 1000$

9. $4.9 \div 100$

10. $983.2 \div 10$

11. $3423 \div 10,000$

12. $65.4 \div 100$

13. $582.37 \div 100$

14. $3.25 \div 10,000$

15. $648.62 \div 10^3$

16. $986.4 \div 10^2$

17. $43.527 \div 10^1$

18. $2.374 \div 10^3$

19. $1765 \div 10^4$

20. $.679 \div 10^1$

21. $456.1 \div 10^3$

22. $89.786 \div 10^4$

23. $43.5 \div 10^2$

24. $937.2 \div 10^1$

25. $89.2 \div 10^3$

26. $471.5 \div 10^4$

Complete each set of exercises.

1. $7500 \div 10^1 = 750$
$7500 \div 10^2 = $
$7500 \div 10^3 = $
$7500 \div 10^4 = $

2. $.9 \div 10^1 = .09$
$.9 \div 10^2 = $
$.9 \div 10^3 = $
$.9 \div 10^4 = $

Complete the table.

	Number	Divided by			
		10^1	10^2	10^3	10^4
27.	167.4				
28.	36.437				
29.	6231				
30.	394.95				
31.	3.74				
32.	98				

More practice
Set I, page 127

Using Division of Decimals: Metric Measures

1 kilometer (km) = 1000 meters (m)
1 meter = 100 centimeters (cm)
1 meter = 1000 millimeters (mm)
1 centimeter = 10 millimeters

1 kilogram (kg) = 1000 grams (g)

1 liter (ℓ) = 1000 milliliters (ml)

The length of an average-sized adult's index finger is 76 millimeters. Find the length in centimeters.

76 ÷ 10 = 7.6

The index finger is 7.6 centimeters long.

These data apply to the body of an average adult. Divide to find each missing number.

1. Length of foot:

158 mm = ▦ cm

2. Length of big toe:

42 mm = ▦ cm

3. Length of thighbone:

49.8 cm = ▦ m

4. Length of shinbone:

40.5 cm = ▦ m

5. Length of bone from shoulder to elbow:

362 mm = ▦ m

6. Length of spinal column:

99 mm = ▦ m

7. Length of small intestine:

6 m = ▦ km

8. Length of large intestine:

1.5 m = ▦ km

9. Mass of heart:

3089 g = ▦ kg

10. Mass of brain:

1504 g = ▦ kg

11. Volume of blood:

4750 ml = ▦ ℓ

12. Volume of plasma:

2610 ml = ▦ ℓ

Formulas Involving Decimals

A. Ms. Shim drove 256 kilometers at 48 kilometers per hour. Find her traveling time to the nearest tenth of an hour.

		Rate	Time		Distance
You can use the formula $d = rt$.		r	t	$=$	d
		48	t	$=$	256

t is multiplied by 48. Divide both sides of the equation by 48.

$$\frac{48t}{48} = \frac{256}{48}$$

$$t = 5.3$$

Answer the question.
Her traveling time to the nearest tenth of an hour was 5.3 hours.

B. The density of the rubber in an automobile tire is 2106 kilograms per cubic meter. The volume of the tire is 0.006 cubic meter. Find the mass of the tire to the nearest tenth of a kilogram.

You can use the formula $D = \frac{M}{V}$.

$$\text{Density } D = \frac{M \text{ Mass}}{V \text{ Volume}}$$

M is divided by .006. Multiply both sides of the equation by .006.

$$2106 = \frac{M}{.006}$$

$$(.006)2106 = (.006)\frac{M}{.006}$$

$$12.6 = M$$

Answer the question.
The mass of the tire to the nearest tenth of a kilogram is 12.6 kilograms.

Solve each equation.

1. $4.2s = .21$

2. $6.32b = 8.848$

3. $.07 = \dfrac{x}{.8}$

4. $.013y = .728$

5. $25.1m = 3514$

6. $3.95 = \dfrac{x}{16}$

7. $.62d = 133.3$

8. $.85 = \dfrac{x}{498}$

9. $.8c = 100$

10. $2.5h = 250$

In exercises 11 and 12, use the density formula on page 120. Find the mass to the nearest tenth.

11. D is 1600 and V is .0007.

12. D is 380 and V is .0012.

In exercises 13–16, use the distance formula on page 120.

Find t to the nearest tenth.

13. r is 68 and d is 555.

14. r is 83 and d is 1037.

Find r to the nearest tenth.

15. t is 16.5 and d is 835.

16. t is 15 and d is 1248.

side trip

Base Two

Base two is the numeration system used in the machine language of some computers.

In base-two numeration, only two digits are used, 0 and 1.

This table shows base-ten numerals written in base two.

Base ten	Base two
0	0_{two}
1	1_{two}
2	10_{two}
3	11_{two}
4	100_{two}
5	101_{two}
6	110_{two}
7	111_{two}
8	1000_{two}
9	1001_{two}
10	1010_{two}

The numeral 10_{two} is read "one zero base two."

In a base-two numeral, each place has a value two times as great as the place to its right. Here is a place-value chart for base two.

thirty-two's place	sixteen's place	eight's place	four's place	two's place	one's place
32	16	8	4	2	1
		1	**1**	**0**	**1**

Use the place-value chart to find the value of each digit in the base-two numeral 1101_{two}.

1 eight	1 four	0 twos	1 one

$$(1 \times 8) + (1 \times 4) + (0 \times 2) + (1 \times 1)$$

$$8 \ + \ 4 \ + \ 0 \ + \ 1 \ = 13$$

1101_{two} is 13 in base ten.

Write each base-two numeral in base ten.

1. 1010_{two}

2. 1011_{two}

3. 1111_{two}

4. 10001_{two}

5. 10100_{two}

6. 110110_{two}

7. 101111_{two}

★ 8. 1100011_{two}

You can use the place-value chart on page 122 to help you write a base-ten numeral in base two.

For example, write 58 as a base-two numeral.

Ask these questions.

Are there any 32's in 58?	Yes	1	Subtract 32 from 58. $58 - 32 = 26$
Are there any 16's in 26?	Yes	1	Subtract 16 from 26. $26 - 16 = 10$
Are there any 8's in 10?	Yes	1	Subtract 8 from 10. $10 - 8 = 2$
Are there any 4's in 2?	No	0	
Are there any 2's in 2?	Yes	1	Subtract 2 from 2. $2 - 2 = 0$
Are there any 1's in 0?	No	0	

Write the base-two numeral: 111010_{two}

Write each base-ten numeral in base two.

9. 25

12. 63

10. 18

★ **13.** 127

11. 49

★ **14.** 181

Chapter 6 Test
Multiplying and Dividing Decimals, Pages 104–123

Multiplying decimals,
pages 104–109

Multiply.

1. 4.3×2.8

2. 6.3×89.2

3. 48×3.06

4. 29.7×45.1

5. $.006 \times .04$

6. $6 \times .008$

7. $.58 \times .14$

8. $.86 \times .075$

9. $10^2 \times .074$

10. $10^1 \times .6$

11. $10^4 \times .029$

Dividing decimals,
pages 110–118

Divide.

12. $6\overline{)15.6}$

13. $39\overline{)6.357}$

14. $86\overline{)8.256}$

15. $.04\overline{).648}$

16. $1.6\overline{).1464}$

17. $.75\overline{)652.5}$

18. $630 \div 10^1$

19. $87.9 \div 10^3$

20. $43.8 \div 10^2$

Divide. Round each
quotient to the nearest
hundredth.

21. $62\overline{)84.35}$

22. $.43\overline{)3.291}$

23. $5.8\overline{)4.6}$

Problem solving,
pages 109, 119, 120–121

1 meter (m) =
100 centimeters (cm)

1 centimeter =
10 millimeters (mm)

24. Height of a thirteen-
year-old girl:

1.58 m = ▦ cm

25. Length of a pencil:

18.8 cm = ▦ mm

26. Length of a baseball
bat:

106 cm = ▦ m

27. Length of index
finger:

72 mm = ▦ cm

Solve each equation.

28. $.53c = 35.51$

29. $6.7 = \dfrac{b}{.45}$

30. $.081d = .6723$

Unit 2 Test

Metric system, pages 68–85

Choose the best measure.

1. Length of an eraser

54 mm   54 cm   54 m

2. Nickel (five-cent piece)

5 mg   5 g   5 kg

3. Glass

250 ml   250 ℓ

4. Air on a cold winter day

14°C   ⁻14°C

5. Give the length of the safety pin to the nearest millimeter.

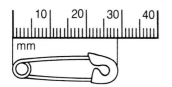

6. Give the area of the rectangle.

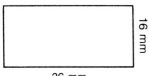

36 mm

16 mm

7. Give the volume of the prism.

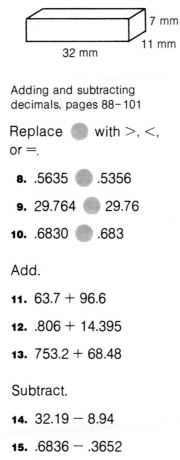

7 mm

11 mm

32 mm

Adding and subtracting decimals, pages 88–101

Replace ⬤ with >, <, or =.

8. .5635 ⬤ .5356

9. 29.764 ⬤ 29.76

10. .6830 ⬤ .683

Add.

11. $63.7 + 96.6$

12. $.806 + 14.395$

13. $753.2 + 68.48$

Subtract.

14. $32.19 - 8.94$

15. $.6836 - .3652$

16. $424.5 - 83.77$

Solve each equation.

17. $4.25 + r = 6.79$

18. $d - .091 = 25.59$

Multiplying and dividing decimals, pages 104–123

Multiply.

19. 3.8×52.9

20. $.006 \times .12$

21. $10^2 \times 6.378$

Divide.

22. $25.2 \div 7$

23. $10.58 \div 2.3$

24. $89.4 \div 10^2$

Divide. Round each quotient to the nearest hundredth.

25. $6\overline{)72.8}$

26. $2.8\overline{)9.63}$

1 kilometer = 1000 meters
1 kilogram = 1000 grams

27. Height of Sears Tower

442 m, or ▦ km

28. Mass of a bowling ball

7.27 kg, or ▦ g

Solve each equation.

29. $3.2c = .768$

30. $7.2 = \dfrac{a}{8.6}$

More Practice

Set A

1. $1.038 + 27.5$
2. $46.1 + 3.5$
3. $841.6 + 56.39$
4. $2.87 + .066$
5. $.93 + .0274$
6. $10.8 + .913$
7. $824.7 + .055$
8. $7.2 + 59.5 + .49$
9. $3.2 + .84 + 7.6$
10. $.09 + .8 + 7 + .46$
11. $.25 + 4.7 + 6 + .38$

Set C

1. $6.18 \times .04$
2. $5.27 \times .6$
3. $.62 \times 913$
4. 4.3×7.5
5. $48 \times .07$
6. $.91 \times 4.5$
7. $9.27 \times .34$
8. $39.1 \times .08$
9. $6.8 \times .75$
10. $256 \times .009$
11. $32.6 \times .098$

Set E

1. 1000×4.287
2. $100 \times .069$
3. 10×31.58
4. $10,000 \times 6.0409$
5. $100 \times .73$
6. $10,000 \times .0015$
7. $10^3 \times 2286.57$
8. $10^1 \times 4.1953$
9. $10^4 \times 36.72$
10. $10^2 \times 419.84$
11. $10^3 \times 70.3$

Set B

1. $185.42 - 97.69$
2. $4.93 - 2.71$
3. $.942 - .5336$
4. $6.3015 - .7196$
5. $847.5 - 26.6$
6. $56.72 - 9.8$
7. $773.18 - 424.99$
8. $8.113 - 4.258$
9. $90.3 - 71.8$
10. $.435 - .067$
11. $.0802 - .054$

Set D

1. $2.18 \times .04$
2. $.006 \times 4.7$
3. $.045 \times .03$
4. $.07 \times .83$
5. $.009 \times .716$
6. $9.23 \times .008$
7. $.005 \times .69$
8. $.674 \times .05$
9. $.8 \times .095$
10. $2.1 \times .0348$
11. $.196 \times .275$

Set F

1. $7 \overline{)26.6}$
2. $4 \overline{)6.88}$
3. $83 \overline{)4639.7}$
4. $46 \overline{)3.404}$
5. $34 \overline{)314.5}$
6. $19 \overline{).06593}$
7. $153 \overline{)12.393}$
8. $27 \overline{)17.874}$
9. $65 \overline{).3965}$

More Practice

Set G

1. $.8\overline{).752}$

2. $.07\overline{).0434}$

3. $.006\overline{).2142}$

4. $5.9\overline{)477.9}$

5. $.43\overline{)401.62}$

6. $.0008\overline{).00536}$

7. $.041\overline{)33.21}$

8. $1.64\overline{).15088}$

9. $.0025\overline{).13425}$

10. $8.02\overline{)48.922}$

11. $.27\overline{).1404}$

12. $.029\overline{).13891}$

13. $3.76\overline{)164.688}$

14. $1.9\overline{).17594}$

15. $.57\overline{).08949}$

16. $.063\overline{)4.851}$

17. $.451\overline{)246.246}$

18. $3.8\overline{)3.154}$

Set H

Round each quotient to the nearest hundredth.

1. $7\overline{)37.37}$

2. $.03\overline{).313}$

3. $98\overline{)5.1}$

4. $8.3\overline{).38}$

5. $505\overline{)87.3}$

6. $36\overline{)8.95}$

7. $.37\overline{)2.8}$

8. $4.4\overline{)59}$

9. $5507\overline{)7389}$

10. $5.59\overline{)62.6}$

11. $.98\overline{).1203}$

12. $11\overline{)5.03}$

13. $8\overline{)55}$

14. $.08\overline{)4.533}$

15. $8.9\overline{)13}$

16. $31\overline{)547}$

Set I

1. $15.8 \div 100$

2. $627.4 \div 10,000$

3. $4934 \div 1000$

4. $7.91 \div 10$

5. $326.58 \div 100$

6. $97.431 \div 1000$

7. $5619.3 \div 10^2$

8. $2.85 \div 10^1$

9. $726 \div 10^4$

10. $81.84 \div 10^3$

11. $2060 \div 10^2$

12. $3.09 \div 10^1$

13. $45.86 \div 10^3$

14. $70394 \div 10^4$

15. $.03 \div 10^2$

Individualized Skills Maintenance

Diagnosis

A. $8\overline{)4632}$

$4\overline{)68000}$

$9\overline{)4341}$

$7\overline{)50489}$

B. $23\overline{)9821}$

$45\overline{)80910}$

$62\overline{)7087}$

$59\overline{)36519}$

C. $307\overline{)8903}$

$418\overline{)48070}$

$621\overline{)3927}$

$572\overline{)67518}$

Practice

Set A (pp. 44–45)

1. $4\overline{)3428}$
2. $6\overline{)1614}$
3. $9\overline{)9846}$
4. $7\overline{)3255}$
5. $9\overline{)9882}$
6. $4\overline{)63552}$
7. $8\overline{)38256}$
8. $5\overline{)96375}$
9. $7\overline{)20895}$
10. $9\overline{)5064}$
11. $5\overline{)4983}$
12. $6\overline{)7049}$
13. $8\overline{)5745}$
14. $5\overline{)28277}$
15. $8\overline{)10868}$
16. $4\overline{)98073}$
17. $7\overline{)30228}$

Set B (pp. 46–47)

1. $93\overline{)6231}$
2. $12\overline{)1104}$
3. $53\overline{)3498}$
4. $33\overline{)3102}$
5. $48\overline{)1728}$
6. $75\overline{)71850}$
7. $69\overline{)37674}$
8. $85\overline{)71145}$
9. $74\overline{)52466}$
10. $14\overline{)5089}$
11. $46\overline{)1349}$
12. $55\overline{)5007}$
13. $24\overline{)4947}$
14. $91\overline{)47155}$
15. $93\overline{)59569}$
16. $58\overline{)83440}$
17. $77\overline{)108814}$

Set C (p. 48)

1. $145\overline{)1015}$
2. $753\overline{)6024}$
3. $699\overline{)6291}$
4. $929\overline{)20438}$
5. $857\overline{)75416}$
6. $407\overline{)39886}$
7. $479\overline{)11496}$
8. $275\overline{)17600}$
9. $141\overline{)13818}$
10. $709\overline{)14967}$
11. $932\overline{)6533}$
12. $803\overline{)5921}$
13. $917\overline{)7361}$
14. $281\overline{)77957}$
15. $753\overline{)57231}$
16. $924\overline{)13414}$
17. $654\overline{)59729}$

Unit 3

Geometry and Measurement

The Circle

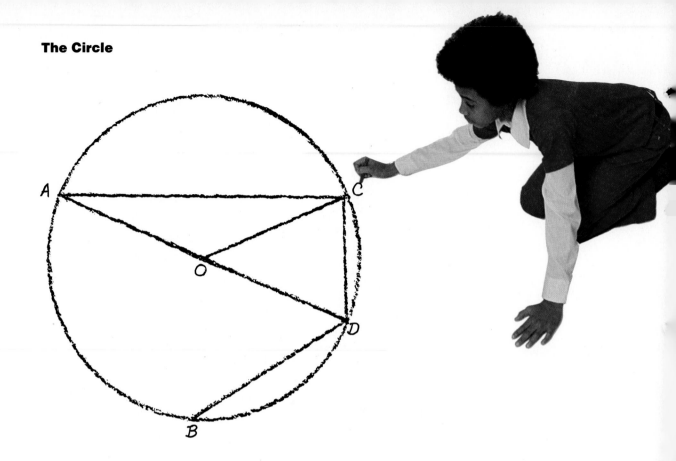

Point O is the *center* of this circle.

The *radius* of circle O is 4.3 cm.

Its *diameter* is 8.6 cm.

1. $\overline{OD}$ ("segment OD") is a radius of circle O. Name another radius.

2. A *chord* is a segment with endpoints on the circle. $\overline{AC}$ is a chord. Name another chord.

3. Diameters are the longest chords in a circle. Name a diameter.

4. An *arc* is part of a circle. Arc ACD is a *semicircle*. Name another semicircle.

5. Draw a circle with a radius of 3 cm. How long is the diameter?

6. Draw a semicircle with a diameter of 15 cm. How long is the radius?

7. Draw $\overline{AB}$ 25 mm long. Draw a circle with a radius of 25 mm and its center at A. Draw a circle with a radius of 25 mm and its center at B.

8. Draw circles with the same center and different radii. These are called *concentric* circles.

9. Draw a circle and two diameters. Connect the endpoints. What figure do you get?

Circle Designs

You can use a compass to divide a circle into six equal parts.

Draw a circle. Select any point on the circle and call it A. Using the same radius, and with A as center, make a small arc that cuts the circle at B. Use B as center and mark off C. Continue the process.

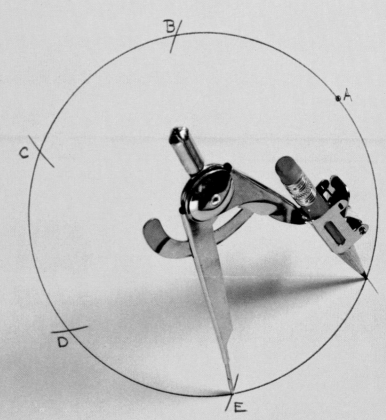

1. Draw a circle. Divide it into six equal parts. Use the six points as centers for drawing the arcs that form the petal design. Keep the same radius.

2. Draw a circle. Divide it into six equal parts. Use the six points as centers for drawing six more circles. Keep the same radius.

3. Invent your own circle designs.

Bisecting a Segment

To *bisect* a segment means to divide it into two segments of the same length. You can do this using only a compass and a straightedge.

Step 1

Draw a segment, $\overline{AB}$. With radius greater than half of $\overline{AB}$ and center A, draw an arc—almost a semicircle.

Step 2

With the same radius and B as center, draw an arc that intersects the first arc in two points.

Step 3

Use a straightedge to find the line passing through C and D. Line CD intersects $\overline{AB}$ at point E.

Point E is the *midpoint* of $\overline{AB}$. $\overline{AB}$ is bisected.

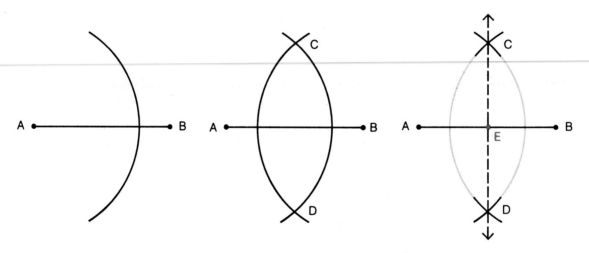

Open your compass to the length of $\overline{AE}$. Use this compass setting to check the length of $\overline{EB}$.

time out

1. **a.** Draw six segments with different lengths.

   b. Bisect each one.

   c. Use your compass to check.

2. **a.** Draw a segment and bisect it.

   b. Bisect each half to get four segments of the same length.

3. **a.** Draw a triangle and bisect any two sides.

   b. Join the midpoints with a segment.

   c. Is this segment half as long as the side that is not bisected?

4. **a.** Draw a triangle and bisect each side.

   b. Draw segments joining the midpoints of the sides.

   c. How many new triangles are formed? Do they seem to be the same size and shape?

5. Do the diagonals of a rectangle bisect each other?

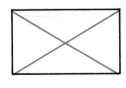 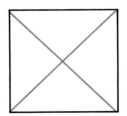

The year 1296 was a square year.
(1296 = 36²)
The year 1936 was a square year.

Is this year a square year?

What is the next square year?

Copying Segments to Construct a Triangle

You can construct
a triangle if you are
given the three sides.

_____ *a* _____

_____ *b* _____

____ *c* ____

Step 1

Draw a segment. Draw
an arc with radius *a*.

Step 2

Draw an arc with radius *b*.

Step 3

Draw an arc with radius *c*.

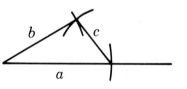

Step 4

Draw the triangle.

1. In an *equilateral* triangle, all three sides are the same length. Construct a triangle each of whose sides is 5 cm long.

2. An *isosceles* triangle has at least two sides of the same length. Construct a triangle whose sides are 6 cm, 6 cm, and 4 cm long.

3. In a *scalene* triangle, no two sides are the same length. Construct a triangle whose sides are 4 cm, 5 cm, and 7 cm long.

★ **4.** Which of the following three segments cannot be used to construct a triangle?

　　a. 17 cm, 8 cm, 1 cm

　　b. 4 cm, 12 cm, 15 cm

A segment joining a midpoint of a side of a triangle and the vertex of the opposite angle is called a *median* of the triangle.

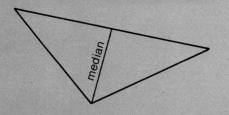

The three medians of a triangle meet at a point. When the triangle is supported at this point, it will balance.

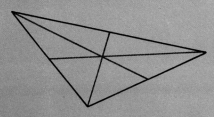

Draw a triangle on a piece of cardboard. Find the midpoint of each side. Draw the medians.

Cut out the triangle. Balance the triangle on the tip of a pencil.

137

Bisecting an Angle

Rays BA and BC form an *angle*.
Their common endpoint, B, is the
vertex of the angle.

This is angle ABC, or ∠ABC. Other
names are ∠CBA and ∠B.

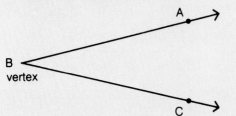

You can use a compass and a
straightedge to bisect ∠ABC—divide
it into two angles of the same size.

Step 1

Draw an arc with B as center.

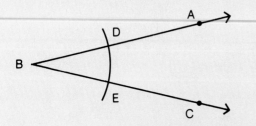

Step 2

Draw an arc with D as center.

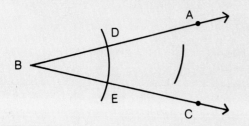

Step 3

Keep the same radius. Draw an arc
with E as center.

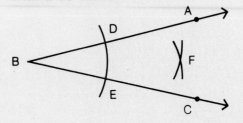

Step 4

Draw ray BF. It bisects ∠ABC
by forming two *adjacent* angles of the
same size, ∠ABF and ∠FBC.

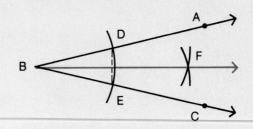

To check this, use your compass
to see whether ray BF bisects $\overline{DE}$.

1. Draw five angles of varying
   sizes. Bisect each one.
   Use your compass to check.

2. Draw a triangle.
   Bisect each angle.

Copying an Angle

Copy ∠PQR.

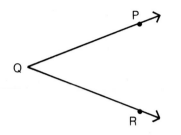

Step 1

Draw one ray of the angle.

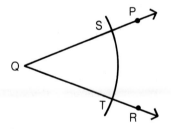

Step 2

Using Q as center, draw an arc through the given angle.

Step 3

Keep the same radius. Draw an arc.

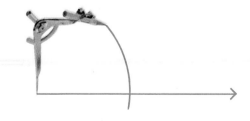

Step 4

Set your compass to the length of $\overline{ST}$.

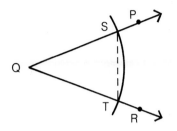

Step 5

Keep this radius. Draw another arc.

Step 6

Draw the second side of the angle.

This angle is the same size as ∠PQR.

1. Draw three different angles and copy each one.

2. Bisect each of your copies.

Constructing Perpendicular Lines

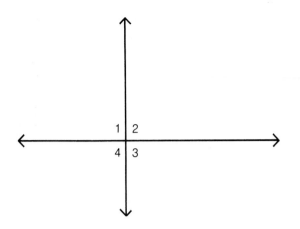

These lines are *perpendicular* to each other. Any two adjacent angles are the same size. Compare angles 1 and 2, 2 and 3, 3 and 4, 4 and 1. Each angle is a *right angle*.

These lines are *not* perpendicular to each other. No two adjacent angles are congruent.

A. Here is a way to construct a line perpendicular to another line and crossing it at a given point.

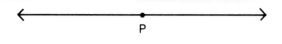

Step 1

With P as center, draw arcs intersecting the line at two points, A and B.

Step 2

Set the points of the compass farther apart. Draw arcs, first using A as center, then B.

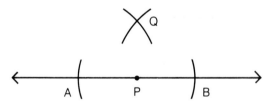

Step 3

Draw a line through Q and P. Line PQ is perpendicular to line AB.

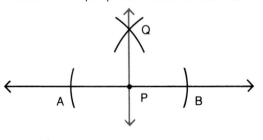

B. You can also construct a perpendicular to a line from a point not on the line.

• P

Step 1

With P as center, draw an arc that intersects the line at two points.

• P

Step 2

Using first A as center, then B, draw intersecting arcs below the line.

• P

Step 3

Draw a line through P and Q. Line PQ is perpendicular to line AB.

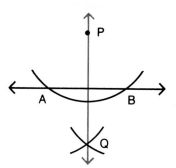

1. Draw a line. Select a point on the line. Construct a perpendicular to the line through that point.

2. Draw a line. Draw a point not on the line. Construct a perpendicular to the line through that point.

3. Draw a circle. Draw two chords that are not diameters. Construct a perpendicular bisector through each chord. Where do they meet?

4. Draw a triangle. Construct a perpendicular bisector through each side.

5. An *altitude* of a triangle is a segment that extends from a vertex to the opposite side and is perpendicular to that side.

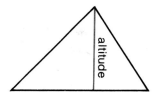

Draw a triangle. Construct an altitude. (You may need to extend the sides of the triangle.)

Constructing Parallel Lines

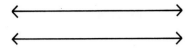

These lines are *parallel.*
No matter how long you
make them, they will
never meet.

These two sets of parallel
lines form a *parallelogram,*
a four-sided figure whose
opposite sides are
parallel.

You can construct parallel
lines with a compass
and a straightedge.

Step 1

Draw a line and a point
not on the line.

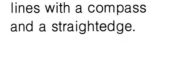

Step 2

Draw line AP.

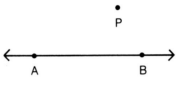

Step 3

Make a copy of ∠PAB
with its vertex at P.

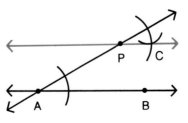

Line PC is parallel
to line AB.

1. Use a compass and
   a straightedge
   to construct a pair
   of parallel lines.

2. **a.** Draw a four-sided
      figure that is
      not a parallelogram.

   b. Find the midpoint
      of each side.

   c. Join the midpoints
      in order.

   d. Describe the
      figure you have
      drawn in part c.

side trip

Triangles and Circles

Kenji drew a triangle and constructed a circle around it.

First, he constructed the perpendicular bisectors of the sides of the triangle.

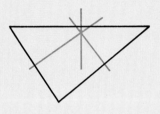

He used the point of intersection as the center of his circle.
He found the radius by setting his compass to the distance between the center and a vertex of the triangle.

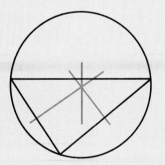

The circle passed through each vertex of the triangle.

1. Draw a triangle and use Kenji's method to construct a circle that passes through the three vertices.

Jeanne drew a triangle and constructed a circle inside it.

First, she constructed the angle bisectors to find the point of intersection.

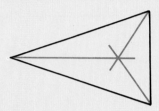

She constructed a perpendicular from that point to one of the sides.

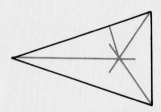

She used the point as the center and the perpendicular distance from the point to the side as the radius.

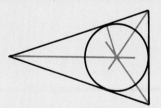

The circle touched each side of the triangle at one point.

2. Try Jeanne's construction using your own triangle.

Using a Protractor

A. Angles are usually measured in degrees, by using a *protractor*. Semicircle protractors are divided into 180 degrees.

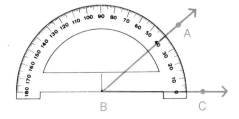

∠ABC measures 40°.

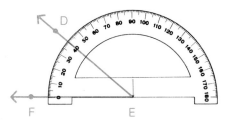

∠DEF measures 40°.

B. Some protractors have two scales. To measure an angle, read the number on the scale that has a zero on one side of the angle.

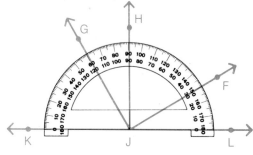

1. Use the protractor in example B. Give the measure of each angle to the nearest degree.

   a. ∠HJL   **c.** ∠GJK   **e.** ∠HJK

   b. ∠FJL   **d.** ∠GJL   **f.** ∠FJK

2. A right angle measures 90°. An *acute* angle is smaller than 90°. An *obtuse* angle is larger than 90°. Tell whether each angle in exercise 1 is right, acute, or obtuse.

3. Draw a semicircle. Label the diameter $\overline{AB}$. Choose a point, P, on the semicircle. Draw a chord from P to A, and a chord from P to B. Measure ∠APB.

4. Measure angles 1, 2, 3, and 4. What is their sum?

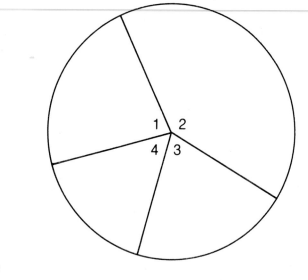

■ *A circle has 360°.*

careers

Pilot

Runway numbers indicate the direction of flight for landings and takeoffs. The numbers refer to points on the magnetic compass. The pilot is landing on runway 24.

The face of the magnetic compass looks like a circle. It is divided into 360 degrees.

If a plane is landing or taking off on runway 24, it has a heading of 240°. That is, it is going southwest.

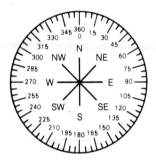

For each heading, give the direction of flight.

1. 180°   4. 225°

2. 270°   5. 315°

3. 90°   6. 135°

This is a map of the runways at Meacham Field, Fort Worth, Texas. A plane landing or taking off on runway 13 (130°) is heading southeast.

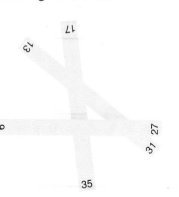

For each runway, give the heading in degrees and use the compass to give the direction of flight.

7. Runway 31

8. Runway 27

9. Runway 17

10. Runway 35

Constructing Polygons

A. A *polygon* is a closed figure made up of segments.

The names of some polygons are shown in the table.

Number of sides	Name of polygon
3	Triangle
4	Quadrilateral
5	Pentagon
6	Hexagon
7	Heptagon
8	Octagon
9	Nonagon
10	Decagon
11	Undecagon
12	Dodecagon

A *regular polygon* has all its sides the same length and all its angles the same size.

What is another name for a regular quadrilateral?

B. You can use a circle to construct a regular hexagon, an equilateral triangle, or a regular dodecagon.

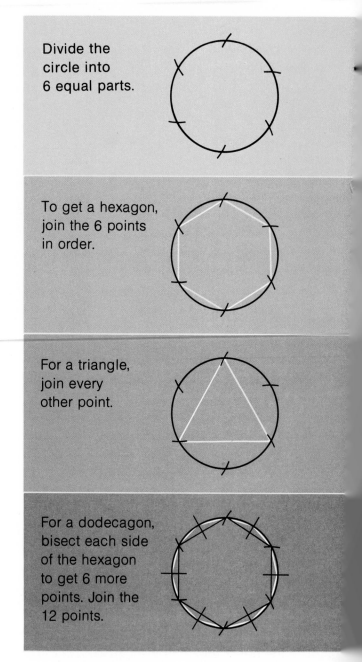

Divide the circle into 6 equal parts.

To get a hexagon, join the 6 points in order.

For a triangle, join every other point.

For a dodecagon, bisect each side of the hexagon to get 6 more points. Join the 12 points.

c. You can also use a circle to construct a square or a regular octagon.

Draw a circle and a diameter.

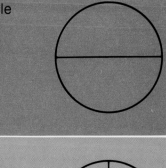

Construct a perpendicular at the center.

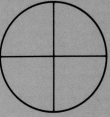

For a square, join the 4 points.

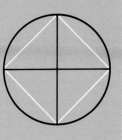

For an octagon, bisect each side of the square to get 4 more points. Join the 8 points.

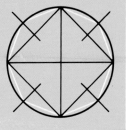

1. Construct these polygons.

   a. Square

   b. Equilateral triangle

   c. Regular hexagon

   d. Regular octagon

   e. Regular dodecagon

2. How many degrees in each *central angle* of a regular hexagon? (Find $360° \div 6$.)

central angle

3. Use your protractor to construct a regular polygon that has $40°$ in each central angle.

4. How many sides in a polygon that has $36°$ in each central angle?

5. There are 24 time zones around the earth. How many degrees in each time zone?

● **Discuss** Why is it difficult to construct regular seven-sided and eleven-sided figures?

Congruent Polygons

Congruent polygons have the same size and shape. These polygons are congruent.

1. There are four pairs of congruent polygons shown below. Name the pairs.

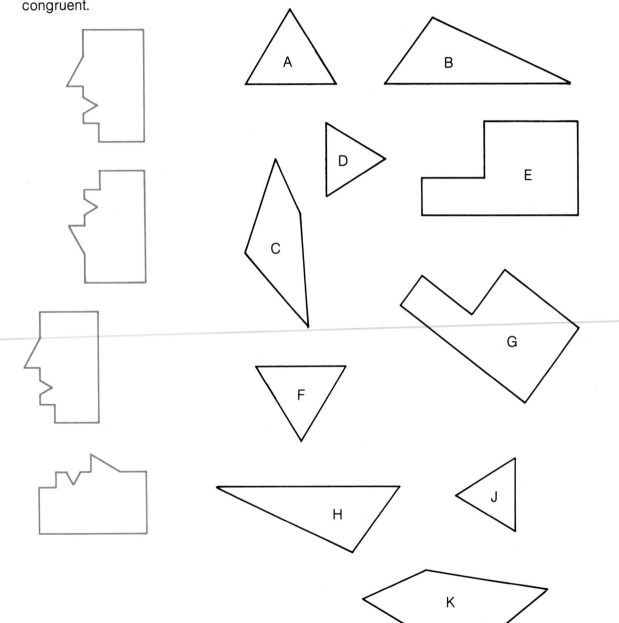

time out

In each exercise, name one pair of congruent triangles.

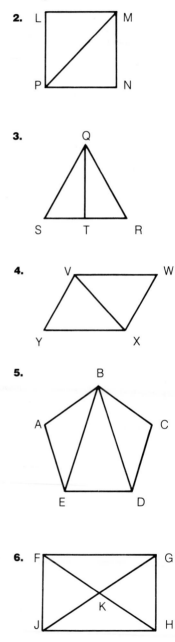

2. L M P N

3. Q S T R

4. V W Y X

5. B A C E D

6. F G J K H

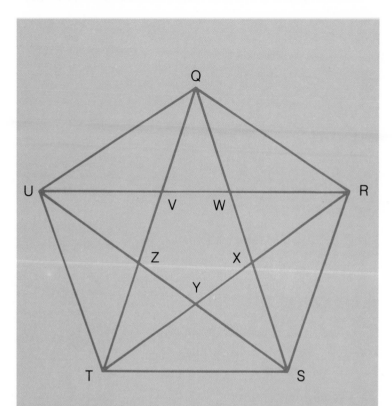

1. Find the four triangles that are congruent to triangle QVW.

2. Find the four triangles that are congruent to triangle QVU.

3. Find all the triangles that are congruent to triangle QRU.

4. Find all the triangles that are congruent to triangle QST.

5. Find all the triangles that are congruent to triangle URY.

6. Find all the triangles that are congruent to triangle QVR.

Circles, page 132

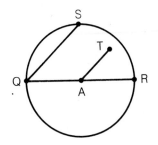

The center of the circle is point A.

1. Name one diameter.

2. Name one radius.

Constructions, pages 133–142

Joan has started two constructions. For exercises 3 and 4, identify each construction.

a. Bisecting an angle

b. Copying an angle

c. Constructing parallel lines

d. Constructing perpendicular lines

3.

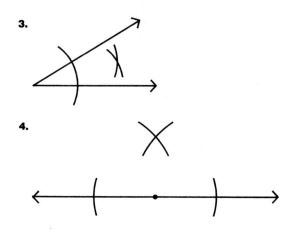

4.

Angle measurement, page 144

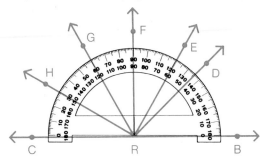

Give the measure of each angle to the nearest degree.

5. ∠HRB **6.** ∠DRB **7.** ∠FRB

Polygons, pages 142, 146–149

8. Which polygon shown below is a parallelogram?

9. Which triangles shown below are congruent?

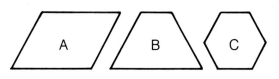

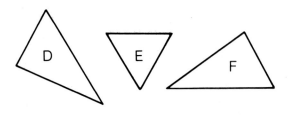

10. Suppose that a regular polygon has 60° in each of its central angles. How many sides does the polygon have?

$$C = \pi d$$

Area of a Rectangle

Mr. Suzuki wanted to cover a floor
that measured 12 feet by 12 feet.

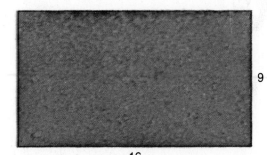

16

He had a rectangular piece of carpet.
It measured 9 feet by 16 feet.

9

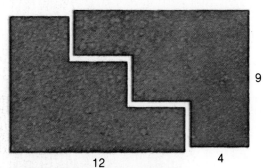

He could see how to cut this carpet
into two pieces—

12   4

and form a 12-foot square.
Can you see how to do this?

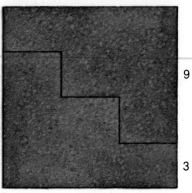

9

Does cutting and rearranging the pieces
change the area?

9 × 16 = 144

12 × 12 = 144

The area is 144 square feet.

3

12

■ *To find the area of a rectangle, multiply the base and the height.*

$$A = bh$$

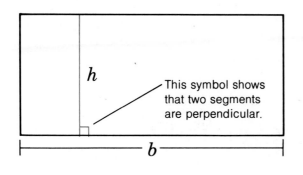

This symbol shows that two segments are perpendicular.

Measure to the nearest millimeter to find the base and the height of each rectangle. Use the formula to find the area of each rectangle in square millimeters.

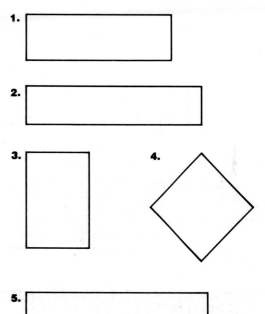

1.

2.

3.   4.

5.

6. **a.** Use grid paper. Draw as many different rectangles as you can that have an area of 24 square units.

   b. Are any of the rectangles also squares?

7. **a.** Use grid paper. Draw as many different rectangles as you can that have an area of 36 square units.

   b. Are any of these rectangles also squares?

Area of a Parallelogram

A parallelogram is a quadrilateral with two pairs of parallel sides. The opposite sides have the same length.

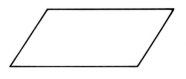

You can cut apart any parallelogram and rearrange the parts to form a rectangle.

Draw this parallelogram on grid paper.
Always measure the height perpendicular to the base.
The base is 7 and the height is 3.

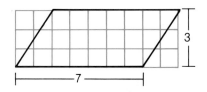

After you draw a segment perpendicular to the base, color the two parts. Cut along the segment.

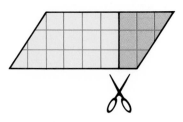

Form a rectangle. Do you change the area of the parallelogram when you rearrange the parts?

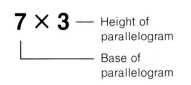

Area of rectangle: **7 × 3**

Area of parallelogram: **7 × 3** —— Height of parallelogram

                                  —— Base of parallelogram

■ *To find the area of a parallelogram, multiply the base and the height.*

$$A = bh$$

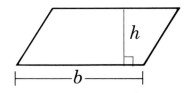

Which numbers do you
multiply to find the area?

Use the formula
to find the area
of each parallelogram.

For each parallelogram,
measure base and height
to the nearest millimeter.
Find the area in
square millimeters.

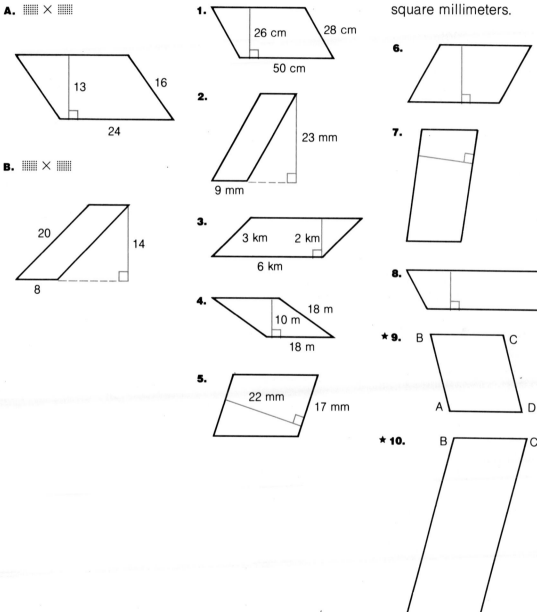

A. ▦ × ▦

13   16

24

B. ▦ × ▦

20   14

8

1.

26 cm   28 cm

50 cm

2.

23 mm

9 mm

3.

3 km   2 km

6 km

4.

18 m

10 m

18 m

5.

22 mm

17 mm

6.

7.

8.

★ 9.   B   C

A   D

★ 10.   B   C

A   D

Area of a Triangle

You can cut apart any triangle and rearrange the parts to form a parallelogram.

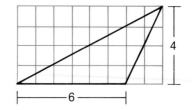

Draw this triangle on grid paper.
What is its base? What is its height?

Find the midpoints of two of the sides.
Join the midpoints.
Color the two parts of the triangle
and cut along the segment you drew.

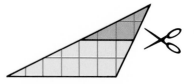

Form a parallelogram. Do you change the area
of the triangle when you rearrange the parts?

Area of parallelogram: **6 × 2**

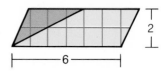

Area of triangle: **6 × 2** —— One-half the height
                                      of triangle
                            Base of triangle

■ *To find the area of a triangle, multiply the*
base and one-half the height.

$$A = b(\tfrac{1}{2}h) \text{ or}$$
$$A = \tfrac{1}{2}bh$$

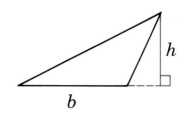

Which numbers do you multiply to find the area?

A. $\frac{1}{2} \times$ ▦ $\times$ ▦

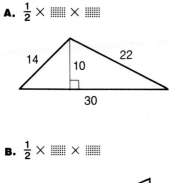

14   22
10
30

B. $\frac{1}{2} \times$ ▦ $\times$ ▦

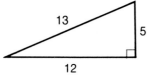

13   5
12

Use the formula to find the area of each triangle.

1.

44 m   24 m
15 m

2.

22 cm   19 cm   22 cm
22 cm

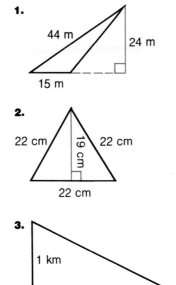

3.

1 km
2 km

4.

12 mm
36 mm

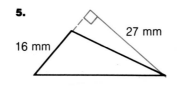

5.

27 mm
16 mm

Measure each base and height to the nearest millimeter. Find each area in square millimeters.

6.

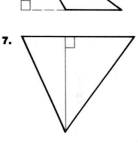

7.

8.

★9.

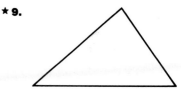

★10.

★11.

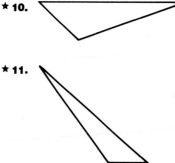

**More practice
Set A, page 190**

Area of a Trapezoid

A *trapezoid* is a quadrilateral that has one pair of parallel sides. The parallel sides are called *bases*.

You can cut any trapezoid into two parts and rearrange the parts to form a parallelogram.

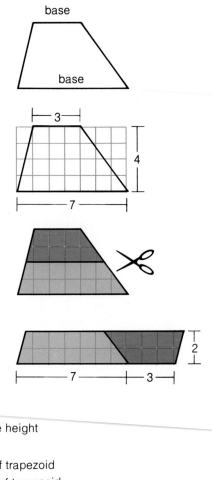

Draw this trapezoid on grid paper.
How long are its two bases? What is its height?

Find the midpoints of the two sides that are not parallel. Join the midpoints.
Color the two parts and cut along the segment.

Form a parallelogram. Do you change the area of the trapezoid when you rearrange the parts?

Area of parallelogram: **(7 + 3) × 2**

Area of trapezoid:
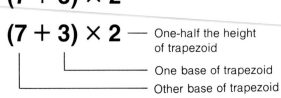

(7 + 3) × 2 ——— One-half the height of trapezoid
                    ——— One base of trapezoid
                    ——— Other base of trapezoid

■ *To find the area of a trapezoid, multiply one-half the height and the sum of the bases.*

$$A = \tfrac{1}{2}h\,(a + b)$$

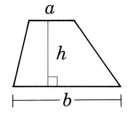

Which numbers do you use in the formula to find the area?

A. $\frac{1}{2} \times$ ▦ $\times$ (▦ + ▦)

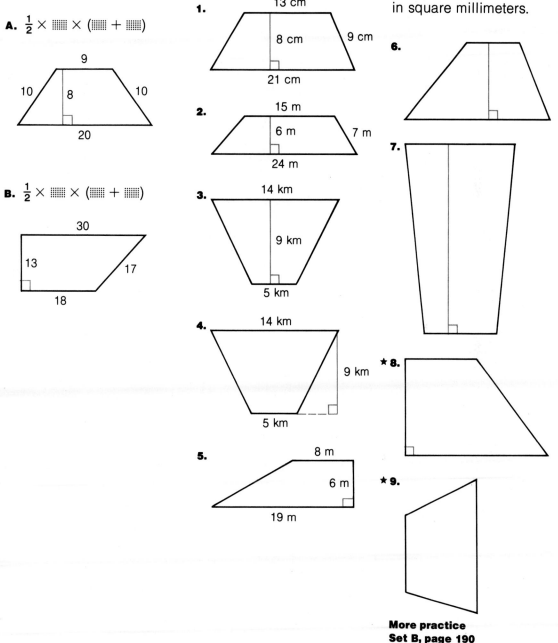

B. $\frac{1}{2} \times$ ▦ $\times$ (▦ + ▦)

Use the formula to find the area of each trapezoid.

1.

13 cm
8 cm   9 cm
21 cm

2.

15 m
6 m   7 m
24 m

3.

14 km
9 km
5 km

4.

14 km
9 km
5 km

5.

8 m
6 m
19 m

For each trapezoid, measure bases and height to the nearest millimeter. Find the area in square millimeters.

6.

7.

★8.

★9.

More practice Set B, page 190

159

side trip

Areas of Designs

Many designs are formed by using one kind of polygon over and over. If you can find the area of one polygon, you will be able to find the area of the entire design.

In each exercise, measure base and height to the nearest millimeter. Then find the approximate area of the design.

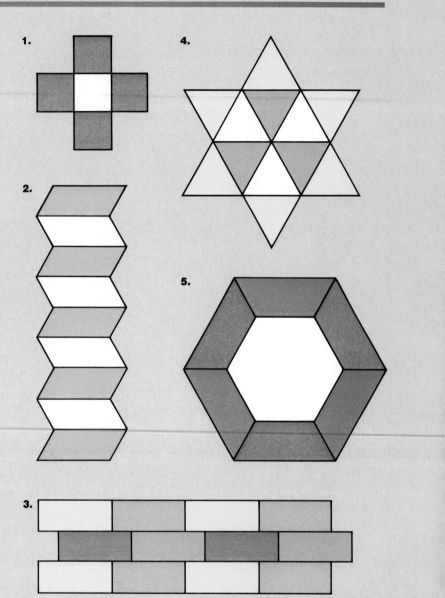

1.

2.

3.

4.

5.

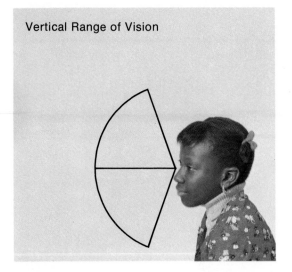

Vertical Range of Vision

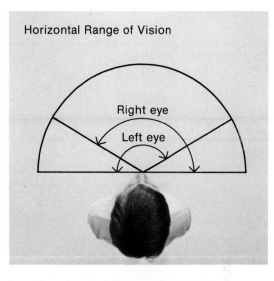

Horizontal Range of Vision

Right eye

Left eye

Optometrist

When you have your eyes examined, your range of vision is checked.

Each eye sees some of the things that the other eye sees, but from a different angle. Each eye also sees things that the other eye does not.

Looking up and down gives the vertical range of vision.

1. Use your protractor. How many degrees above the horizontal can this person see?

2. How many degrees below the horizontal can she see?

3. What is her total vertical range of vision?

Looking from side to side gives the horizontal range of vision.

4. The range of this person's left eye is ▦ degrees.

5. The range of the right eye is ▦ degrees.

6. The range of vision that your eyes share is called your range of binocular sight. The range of this person's binocular sight is ▦ degrees.

7. Ask a friend to help you find your horizontal range of vision. Cover one eye at a time and have the other person move objects in and out of your range. Keep your eyes level with the top of a desk or table.

The Number Pi

Mr. Chinn's class investigated circles by measuring circular objects around school.

Donna measured the *circumference* of a Frisbee®. It was about 78.5 centimeters.

Carlos measured the diameter. It was about 25 centimeters.

Divide the circumference by the diameter. Give your answer to the nearest hundredth.

The students entered their results in a table.

For each object, divide C by d.
Give your answer to the nearest hundredth.

	Object	Circumference C (centimeters)	Diameter d (centimeters)	$C \div d$
1.	Bicycle tire	192	61	
2.	Basketball hoop	143.5	45.7	
3.	Garbage can lid	135.6	43.2	
4.	Record	96.1	30.5	
5.	Telephone dial	23.2	7.4	
6.	Top of paper cup	21.7	6.9	

The quotient $C \div d$ is the same for all circles.
This number is written with the Greek letter pi, or π.

You can think of π as a decimal that never ends
and that has no repeating pattern.

$\pi = $ **3.14159265358979323846264338327950288419716939937510** . . .

For each exercise, carry out your answer to seven
decimal places. Compare it with 3.1415926.

7. $22 \div 7$ **9.** $512 \div 163$

8. $223 \div 71$ **10.** $355 \div 113$

Circumference of a Circle

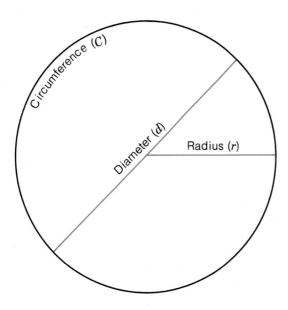

You know that $\pi = C \div d$.
If you know the diameter of a circle,
you can use the following formula
to find the circumference.

$$C = \pi d$$

Since the diameter of a circle is
twice the radius, you can also use
this formula.

$$C = 2\pi r$$

Find the circumference of each circle.
Use 3.14 for π. Give your answer to the
nearest tenth.

1.

1 m

2.

5 cm

3.

10 km

4.

500 m

5.

18 cm

6.

6 km

7. How far does this tire travel
when it goes around once?

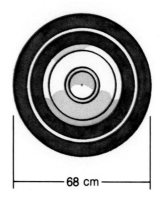

68 cm

8. The circumference of this wooden rod is 3 cm. Will the rod go through the hole? Explain.

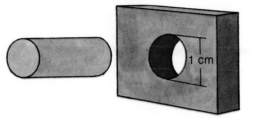

9. How much fencing is needed to enclose the part of the pasture where the goat can graze?

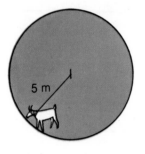

5 m

10. A new water heater is being hauled from the delivery truck into the basement. Which of these straps will fit around the heater?

100 cm   150 cm   200 cm

├─46 cm─┤

**More practice
Set C, page 190**

The caps on fire hydrants are special shapes.

In Middlebury, Vermont, the caps are pentagonal.

This shape, which is formed from arcs of a circle, is called a Reuleaux triangle. In Philadelphia, you would find caps shaped like this.

1. Why do you suppose that caps with unusual shapes are used on fire hydrants?

2. What shape are the caps on the fire hydrants in your neighborhood?

Area of a Circle

Here is a method that should help you understand the formula for the area of a circle.

Cut a circular shape into pie-shaped pieces.

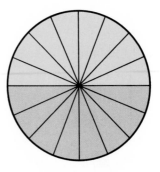

Rearrange the pieces like this.

In this new arrangement, you can locate the radius and the circumference of the circle.

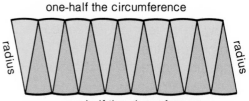

This shape looks almost like a parallelogram. To find its area, multiply the base times the height.

$A = \frac{1}{2} C(r)$

$A = \pi r(r)$, or

$C = 2\pi r$, so
$\frac{1}{2}C = \pi r$

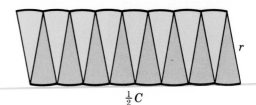

$$A = \pi r^2$$

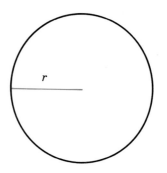

Find the area of each circle.
Use 3.14 for π. Give your answer
to the nearest tenth.

7. How many
square meters
of pasture does
the goat have
for grazing?

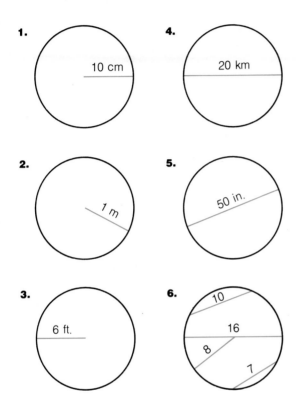

1.

10 cm

4.

20 km

2.

1 m

5.

50 in.

8. A circular
foundation for
a silo is being
prepared. What
is the area of
the foundation?

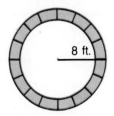

8 ft.

9. Find the area
of this foul
circle on the
basketball
court.

12 ft.

3.

6 ft.

6.

10

16

8

7

**More practice
Set D, page 190**

10. Find the area
of the blue
part of this
design.

★ 11. Find the area
of the white
part.

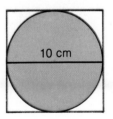

10 cm

time out

Rosita lives 6 miles from Miguel.
Larry lives 4.5 miles from Rosita.
Larry also lives 4.5 miles from Miguel.

Use your compass to help you decide
where Larry's house might be.

Areas of polygons, pages 152–159

Find the area of each polygon.

1. Rectangle

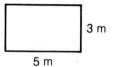

3 m

5 m

2. Parallelogram

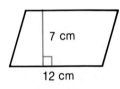

7 cm

12 cm

3. Parallelogram

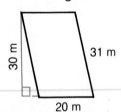

30 m

31 m

20 m

4. Triangle

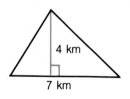

4 km

7 km

5. Triangle

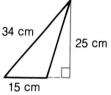

34 cm

25 cm

15 cm

6. Trapezoid

1.5 mm

2 mm

2.5 mm

Circles, pages 162–167

Find the circumference of each circle. Use 3.14 for π. Give your answer to the nearest tenth.

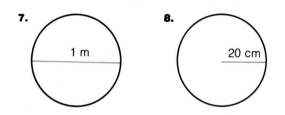

7.

1 m

8.

20 cm

Find the area of each circle. Use 3.14 for π. Give your answer to the nearest tenth.

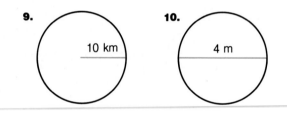

9.

10 km

10.

4 m

$$V = \pi r^{2} h$$

Polyhedrons

Polyhedrons are space figures with all flat surfaces.

Some polyhedrons are *prisms*.

Some polyhedrons are *pyramids*.

A polyhedron has *faces*,

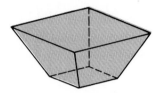

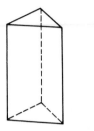
Triangular prism

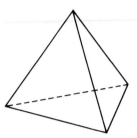
Triangular pyramid

vertices,

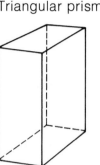
Rectangular prism

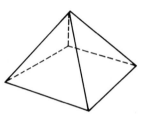
Rectangular pyramid

and *edges*.

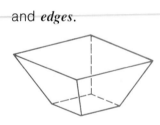

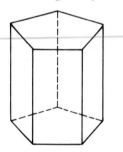
Pentagonal prism

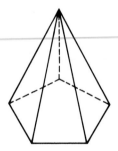
Pentagonal pyramid

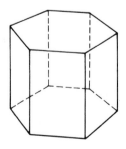
Hexagonal prism

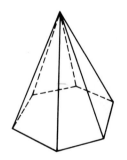
Hexagonal pyramid

In a polyhedron, the sum of the number of vertices and the number of faces is two more than the number of edges.

$$V + F = E + 2$$

In each exercise, count the number of vertices, faces, and edges. Show that when you substitute the numbers in the formula, you get a true statement.

4.

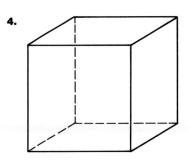

1.

5.

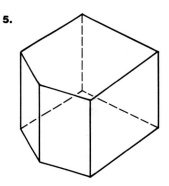

2.

6.

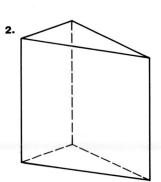

3.

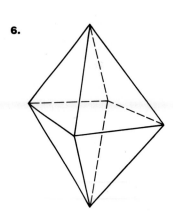

Regular Polyhedrons

There are five *regular polyhedrons*.

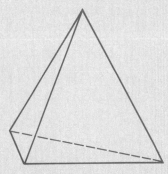

Regular tetrahedron

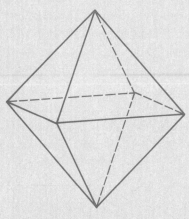

Regular octahedron

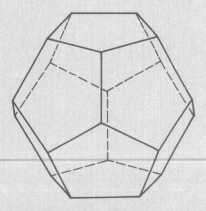

Regular dodecahedron

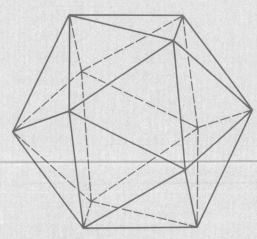

Regular icosahedron

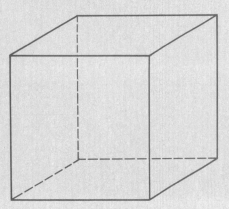

Regular hexahedron, or cube

For each figure on this page, identify the shape of the face and give the total number of faces.

In a regular polyhedron,

a. all the edges are the same length;

b. all the faces are regular polygons and are congruent;

c. the same number of edges meet at each vertex.

Tell why each of the following figures is *not* a regular polyhedron.

1.

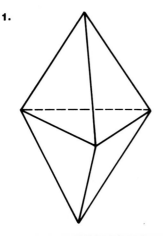

2.

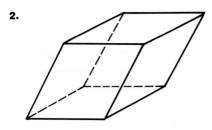

Joan drew a triangle. She put a point A inside the triangle and a point B outside the triangle. She connected A and B with an unbroken curve that crossed each side of the triangle exactly once.

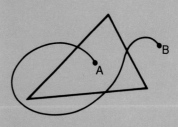

Try Joan's experiment with each of these figures: (1) quadrilateral, (2) pentagon, (3) hexagon, (4) heptagon, and (5) octagon.

In which figures were you able to connect the points? How many vertices does each of these figures have?

In which figures were you unable to connect the points? How many vertices does each of these figures have?

Would you be able to connect points A and B if the figure had 50 sides? 51 sides?

Patterns for Polyhedrons

You can construct a pattern for
a rectangular prism.

First construct a rectangle by using the
endpoints of two diameters of a circle.

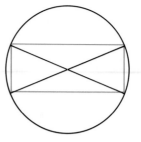

Extend the sides of the rectangle and
mark off segments equal to the length
of the shorter side.

Connect the points to form the faces
of the prism.

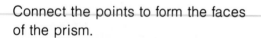

Cut out the pattern and fold it
to make the prism.

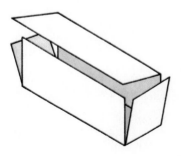

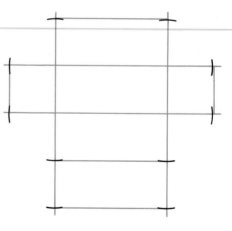

1. Start with a square and construct a pattern for a cube.

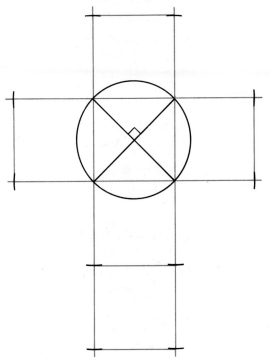

2. Draw a triangle. Bisect each side and join the midpoints.

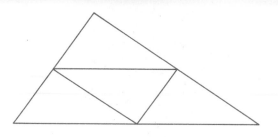

Cut and fold to make a triangular pyramid.

3. Construct a regular hexagon. Then construct an isosceles triangle on each side of the hexagon. In constructing the triangles, use a compass setting greater than the radius of the circle.

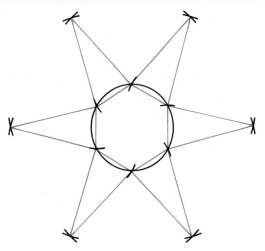

Cut and fold to make a hexagonal pyramid.

4. Construct a pattern for a square pyramid.

Surface Area of Prisms

Ted and his classmates are decorating bricks. They will sell the bricks as book ends, doorstops, and bookshelf dividers.

How much surface does Ted cover when he paints one brick?

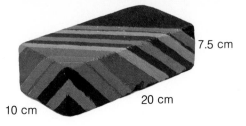

Ted made a pattern to show the six faces. Then he found the area of each face and added.

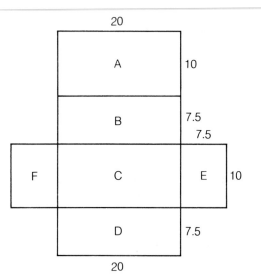

Face	$l \times w$	Area (cm²)
A	20 × 10	200
B	20 × 7.5	150
C	20 × 10	200
D	20 × 7.5	150
E	10 × 7.5	75
F	10 × 7.5	75
Total		850

The total *surface area* of one brick is 850 square centimeters.

Find the total surface area of each prism in square units.

1.

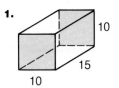

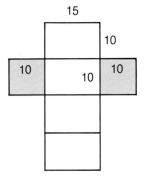

2.

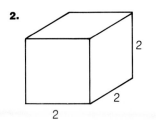

3.

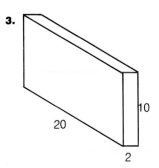

4.

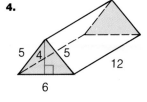

5.

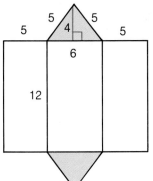

6.

Area of each base:
2.6 square units

Susan and Michiko made these paper models of prisms. The measurements are given in centimeters.

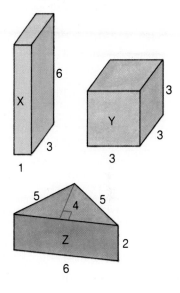

7. Find the surface area of each prism.

8. Which prism requires the most paper?

9. Which requires more paper, two models of prism X or two models of cube Y?

10. Can Michiko make two models of prism Z from a piece of paper that measures 9 cm by 12 cm?

177

Surface Area of Pyramids

A. Sara made a model of an Egyptian pyramid. She painted the square base and the four triangular faces. How many square centimeters of surface did she paint?

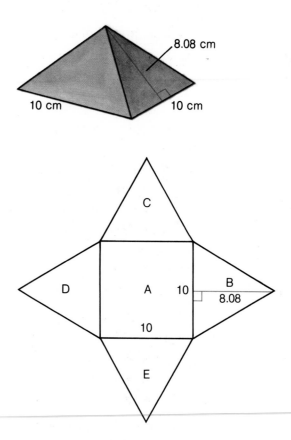

Sara found the area of each face. Then she added.

Face	Finding area	Area (cm²)
A	10 × 10	100
B	$\frac{1}{2}$ × 10 × 8.08	40.4
C	$\frac{1}{2}$ × 10 × 8.08	40.4
D	$\frac{1}{2}$ × ▦ × ▦	▦
E	$\frac{1}{2}$ × ▦ × ▦	▦
	Total	▦

The surface area of Sara's pyramid was ▦ square centimeters.

B. The Pyramid of King Pepi I, which was built about 2400 **B.C.**, also had a square base. What was its surface area in square feet?

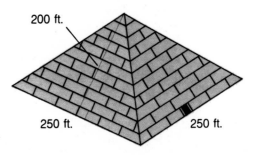

Face	Finding area	Area (sq. ft.)
Base	▦ × ▦	62,500
Face	▦ × ▦ × ▦	▦
Face	▦ × ▦ × ▦	▦
Face	▦ × ▦ × ▦	▦
Face	▦ × ▦ × ▦	▦
	Total	▦

Find the total surface area of each pyramid in square units.

1. Square pyramid

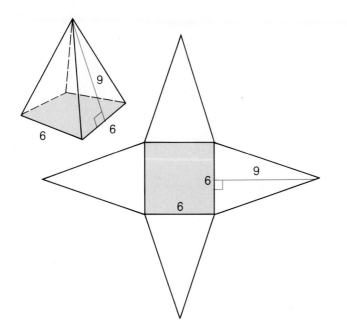

2. Regular tetrahedron

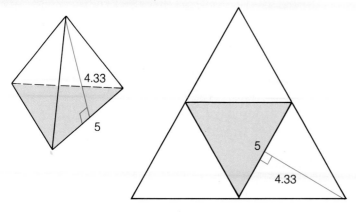

3. Square pyramid

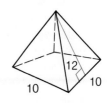

4. Square pyramid

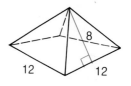

5. Triangular pyramid

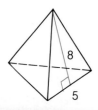

Area of base:
10.25 square units

6. Triangular pyramid

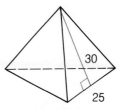

Area of base:
275 square units

Volume of Prisms

A. You already know how to find the volume of a rectangular prism.

$$V = \underbrace{l \times w}_{\text{Area of base}} \times \underbrace{h}_{\text{Height}}$$

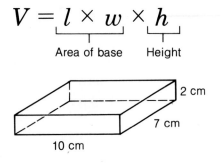

Volume: $10 \times 7 \times 2$
        140 cubic centimeters

B. Find the volume of this cube.

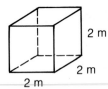

Volume: ▦ × ▦ × ▦
       ▦ cubic meters

C. Find the volume of this triangular prism.

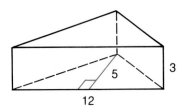

Area of base: $\frac{1}{2} \times 12 \times 5$
Volume: $(\frac{1}{2} \times 12 \times 5) \times$ ▦
      ▦ cubic units

■ *To find the volume of a prism, multiply the area of a base and the height.*

For each of exercises 1–7, find the volume of the prism in cubic units.

1.

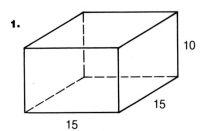

2.

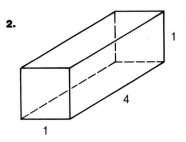

3.

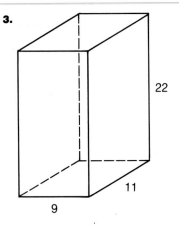

180

4.

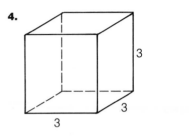

3
3
3

5.

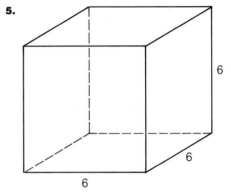

6
6
6

6.

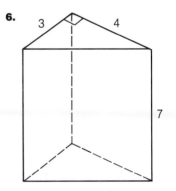

3 4
7

7.

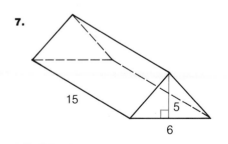

15 5
6

The Dewey-Packum Moving Company has three kinds of boxes.

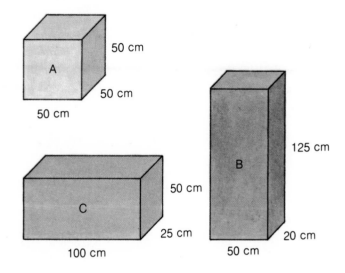

50 cm
A
50 cm
50 cm

B
125 cm
50 cm 20 cm

50 cm
C
25 cm
100 cm

8. Find the volume of each box.

9. Find the surface area of each box.

10. Do boxes with the same volume have to have the same surface area? Which box took the least amount of cardboard to make?

Surface Area of Cylinders

This space figure is a *cylinder*.

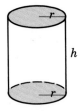

Imagine cutting the cylinder apart. The two bases are circular.

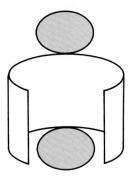

The other surface is rectangular. The length of the rectangle is the same as the circumference of a circular base.

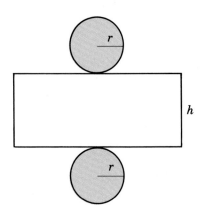

To find the surface area of a cylinder, you can add the areas of the two circles and the rectangle.

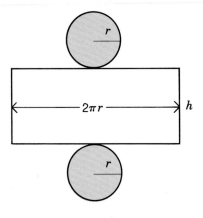

Area of bases: $2\pi r^2$

Area of rectangle: $2\pi rh$

Total surface area: $2\pi r^2 + 2\pi rh$

Find the surface area of each cylinder in square units. Use 3.14 for π and give your answer to the nearest tenth.

2.

4

10

5.

14

6

6.

3

9

1.

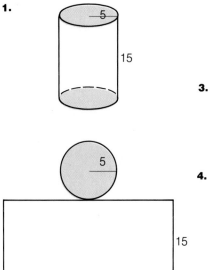

5

15

5

15

5

3.

5

5

4.

5

15   10

Area of bases:
$2 \times 3.14 \times 5 \times 5$

Area of rectangle:
$2 \times 3.14 \times 5 \times 15$

Surface area:
▦ square units

Find the surface area of each object to the nearest square centimeter.

7. Soup can
$r = 3.3$ cm
$h = 10.2$ cm

8. Pineapple can
$r = 4.1$ cm
$h = 11.3$ cm

9. Potato-chip can
$r = 2.6$ cm
$h = 20.9$ cm

10. Coffee can
$r = 7.6$ cm
$h = 16.3$ cm

Volume of Cylinders

What is the volume of this candy tin?

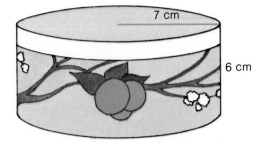

7 cm

6 cm

■ *To find the volume of a cylinder, multiply the area of the base and the height.*

Area of base:
πr^2
$3.14 \times 7 \times 7$
▦ cm²

Volume:
▦ cm² × 6 cm
▦ cm³

Use this formula to find the volume of any cylinder.

$$V = \pi r^2 h$$

Area ⎵ Height
of base

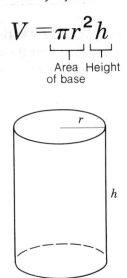

r

h

In exercises 1–6, find the volume of each cylinder. Use 3.14 for π and give your answer to the nearest cubic unit.

1.

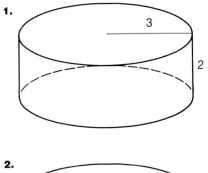

3

2

2.

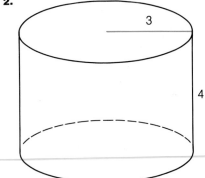

3

4

3.

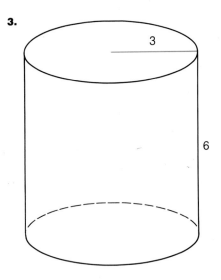

3

6

4.

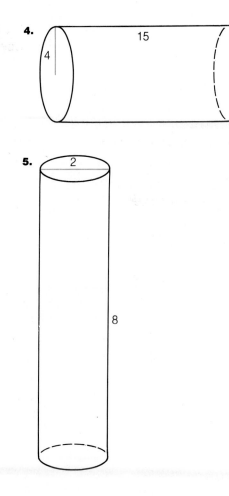

These objects are shaped like cylinders. Find the volume of each. Use 3.14 for π and give your answer to the nearest cubic unit.

7. A swimming pool that is 1.3 meters deep, with a radius of 5 meters

8. A cooking pan with a height of 8 centimeters and a radius of 8.5 centimeters

9. A soft-drink can with a radius of 3.5 centimeters and a height of 8 centimeters

10. A drinking straw with a length of 25 centimeters and a radius of 0.2 centimeter

★ 11. Will the pan in exercise 8 hold the contents of a soup can that has a radius of 6.5 centimeters and a height of 13 centimeters? Explain your answer.

6.

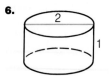

laboratory activity

You can make a one-sided figure called a Moebius strip.

Cut a strip of paper that is about 2 centimeters wide and 27 centimeters long. Place an X on both ends of the strip, on the same side.

Tape the ends together, twisting the paper so that the X's touch.

If an ant is on the paper and a crumb is directly above the ant, it can find a path to the crumb without going around the edge.

Draw the path to see what happens.

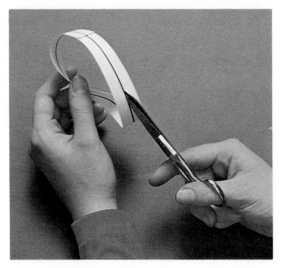

Cut the strip in half by poking your scissors into the path and cutting along the path.

Do you get another Moebius strip? Draw another path to find out.

Constructing a Regular Decagon

Step 1

Draw a circle and two perpendicular radii.

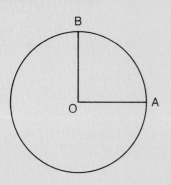

Step 2

Find the midpoint of $\overline{OB}$. Call it M. Draw a circle with its center at M and radius $\overline{OM}$.

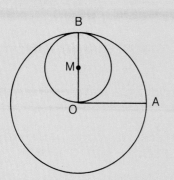

Step 3

Draw $\overline{AM}$. This segment intersects the small circle at D.

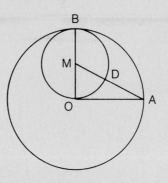

Step 4

Use the length of $\overline{DA}$ as a compass setting to divide the circle into ten equal parts.

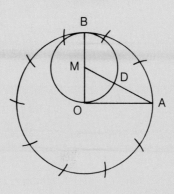

Step 5

Connect the points to make a decagon.

How could you use this construction to make a regular pentagon?

Chapter 9 Test
Measuring Polyhedrons and Cylinders, Pages 170–187

Polyhedrons, pages 170–175

For each polyhedron, tell how many faces, vertices, and edges it has.

1.

3.

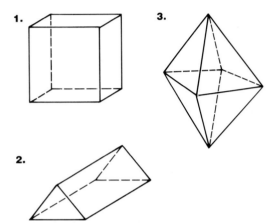

2.

Tell what kind of polyhedron can be made from each pattern.

4.

5.

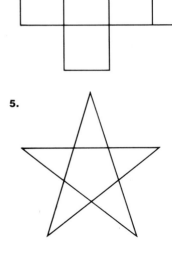

Surface area of prisms and pyramids, pages 176–179

For each figure, find the total surface area in square units.

6.   **7.**

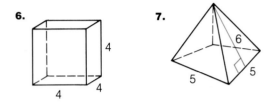

Volume of prisms, pages 180–181

8. Find the volume in cubic units.

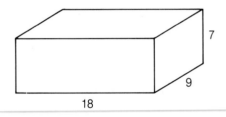

Cylinders, pages 182–185

9. Find the total surface area to the nearest square unit. Use 3.14 for π.

10. Find the volume to the nearest cubic unit.

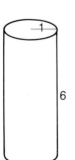
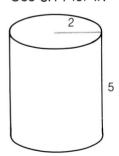

Unit 3 Test

Constructions and angle measurement,
pages 132–149

1. What geometric figure is being
bisected?

Give the measure of each angle to the
nearest degree.

2. ∠ABC   **3.** ∠ABD   **4.** ∠ABF

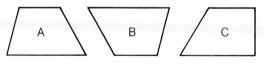

5. Two of these polygons are congruent.
Which ones?

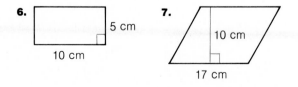

Measuring polygons and circles, pages 152–167

For each of exercises 6–9,
find the area.

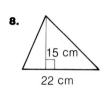

8.

9.

6 cm

9 cm

12 cm

Use 3.14 for π.
Give answers to
the nearest tenth.

10. Find the
circumference.

11. Find the area.

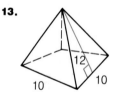

8 in.

Measuring polyhedrons and cylinders,
pages 170–187

For exercises 12 and 13, find the total
surface area in square units.

12.

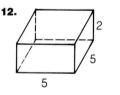

13.

14. Find the
volume in
cubic units.

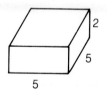

Use 3.14 for π. Give answers
to the nearest unit.

15. Find the
surface area
in square units.

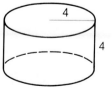

16. Find the
volume in
cubic units.

More Practice

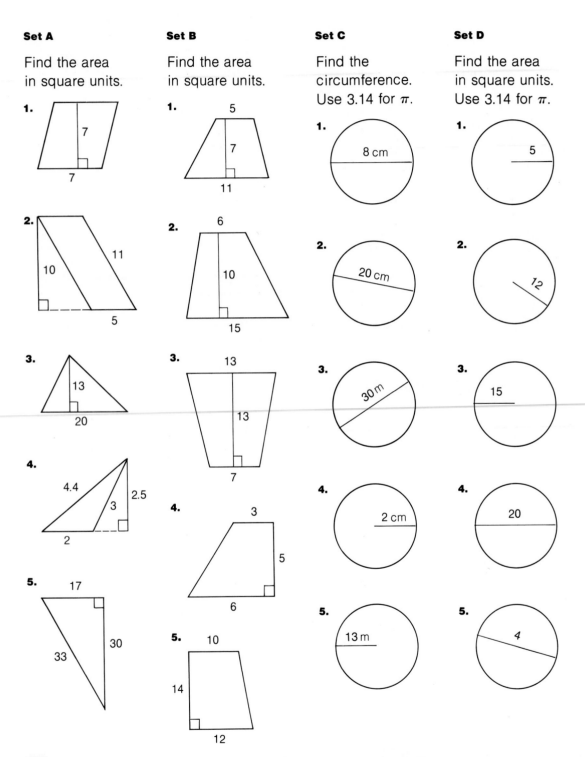

Set A

Find the area
in square units.

1.

7

7

2.

11

10

5

3.

13

20

4.

4.4

3   2.5

2

5.

17

30

33

Set B

Find the area
in square units.

1.

5

7

11

2.

6

10

15

3.

13

13

7

4.

3

5

6

5.

10

14

12

Set C

Find the
circumference.
Use 3.14 for π.

1.

8 cm

2.

20 cm

3.

30 m

4.

2 cm

5.

13 m

Set D

Find the area
in square units.
Use 3.14 for π.

1.

5

2.

12

3.

15

4.

20

5.

4

190

Individualized Skills Maintenance

Diagnosis

A. 6.85 + 2.03

.482 + .398

192 + 27.95

48.4 + 7.382

B. 46.07 − 39.49

.8738 − .4582

.5736 − .35

14 − 1.96

C. .6 × 4.06

.9 × 37.8

D. 6.2 × 31.9

.37 × .83

E. 9.06 × 41.4

.817 × 50.8

F. .06 × .146

.004 × .923

G. .075 × .0983

.0087 × 3.16

Practice

Set A (pp. 92–93)	**Set B** (pp. 94–95)	**Set C** (pp. 104–105)
1. 3.031 + 6.157	**1.** 49.72 − 5.65	**1.** .6 × .43
2. 7.45 + 4.97	**2.** 35.5 − 27.4	**2.** .4 × 9.7
3. 64.4 + 7.4	**3.** .8008 − .5804	**3.** .9 × 26
4. 6.408 + .919	**4.** 5.565 − .059	**4.** .7 × .85
5. 56.01 + 3.32	**5.** 2.81 − .94	**5.** .8 × 4.8
6. .261 + 8.425	**6.** 52.974 − 27.025	**6.** .6 × 57
7. 9.1 + 85.1	**7.** 7.9 − 2.4	**7.** .9 × .468
8. 25.38 + 57.24	**8.** 8.5652 − 5.9299	**8.** .5 × 5.22
9. 410.4 + 36.1	**9.** .815 − .766	**9.** .8 × 37.7
10. 5.156 + 5.541	**10.** .0297 − .0032	**10.** .6 × 491
11. 9.7 + 529.8	**11.** 479.8 − 42.3	**11.** .7 × .969
12. 22.2 + 2.83	**12.** 6.3 − .87	**12.** .5 × 1.77
13. 8.28 + 8.328	**13.** 24 − 8.3	**13.** .8 × 24.5
14. .838 + 15.36	**14.** 2.49 − 1.9	**14.** .6 × 135
15. 73.5 + .082	**15.** 20.963 − 19.7	**15.** .4 × .626
16. 68.9 + 90.45	**16.** 364 − 162.4	**16.** .9 × 7.25
17. 70.915 + 506.2	**17.** 24.1 − 4.246	**17.** .7 × 76.4
18. 6.73 + 4.005	**18.** 2.936 − .77	**18.** .8 × 345
19. 65.4 + 1.451	**19.** 83.72 − 37.753	**19.** .4 × .4364
20. 2.43 + 651.2	**20.** 8 − 2.394	**20.** .9 × 9.709
21. .737 + 36.98	**21.** 31.4 − 9	**21.** .7 × 20.55
22. 6.73 + 34.4	**22.** 2128 − 2.3371	**22.** .5 × 473.5

Individualized Skills Maintenance

Practice *(continued)*

Set D (pp. 104–105)

1. .74 × .88
2. 6.7 × 4.7
3. .37 × 2.3
4. 4.6 × 14
5. .89 × .75
6. 3.7 × .82
7. .49 × 45
8. 2.2 × 1.1
9. .16 × 7.6
10. 1.9 × 9.15
11. .21 × 7.61
12. 6.5 × .952
13. .87 × .565
14. 2.6 × 29.3
15. .43 × 22.4
16. 9.8 × .668
17. .12 × 91.2
18. 7.1 × 6.87
19. .87 × 3.33
20. 2.8 × 63.3
21. .32 × 3.62
22. 8.9 × .598

Set E (pp. 104–105)

1. 67.8 × .252
2. 9.08 × 2.16
3. 81.7 × 67.9
4. .346 × 4.91
5. 7.16 × .137
6. .771 × 86.7
7. 46.1 × .291
8. 5.06 × 4.97
9. 12.2 × .917
10. .686 × 45.4
11. 2.69 × .9404
12. .486 × 3.475
13. 19.5 × 773.1
14. .773 × 55.05
15. 21.5 × .2298
16. 3.51 × 483.8
17. .216 × 32.01
18. 3.93 × 7.024
19. 56.5 × .0365
20. .487 × 244.1
21. 3.05 × 38869
22. 18.9 × 49435

Set F (p. 106)

1. .7 × .14
2. .003 × .33
3. .06 × .016
4. .008 × 1.2
5. .2 × .44
6. .005 × .019
7. .03 × .324
8. .006 × .094
9. .08 × .674
10. .4 × .24
11. .003 × .992
12. .07 × .095
13. .9 × .111
14. .004 × .614
15. .05 × .105
16. .009 × .032
17. .6 × .139
18. .09 × .076
19. .4 × .177
20. .07 × .232
21. .5 × .017
22. .08 × .098

Set G (p. 106)

1. .35 × .274
2. .047 × .088
3. .0076 × 1.27
4. .089 × .41
5. .0093 × 6.07
6. .0074 × .65
7. .033 × 2.92
8. .077 × .082
9. .0049 × 7.16
10. .14 × .35
11. .0012 × 34.8
12. .044 × .033
13. .066 × .974
14. .0027 × 5.6
15. .0088 × .386
16. .019 × .061
17. .41 × .189
18. .0068 × 7.1
19. .026 × .624
20. .047 × .68
21. .0036 × 3.34
22. .054 × .57

Unit 4

Number Theory, Fractions, and Mixed Numbers

Flow Charts and Number Patterns

Flow charts can be used to show the order of steps taken to solve a problem.

These symbols often are used in flow charts.

The circle tells you to start or stop.

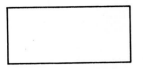

The rectangle specifies an operation or an action.

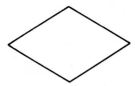

The diamond contains a question that can be answered *yes* or *no*.

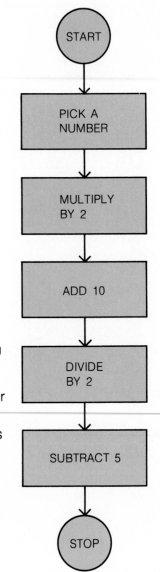

The arrow shows the flow from one step to the next.

Follow the steps in the flow chart at the right for each of these numbers.

1. 7

2. 23

3. 52

4. 207

5. 143

6. In each of exercises 1–5, how does your final answer compare with the number you started with?

7. Pick some other number and follow the steps in the flow chart. Does the same pattern hold?

Follow the steps in the flow chart below for each set of three digits.

8. 1, 6, 7 **11.** 1, 2, 9

9. 4, 6, 8 **12.** 4, 4, 5

10. 1, 3, 5

These numerals are called palindromes.

101   2332   486684

A palindrome reads the same backward or forward.

For some numbers you can follow the steps in this flow chart until the sum is a palindrome.

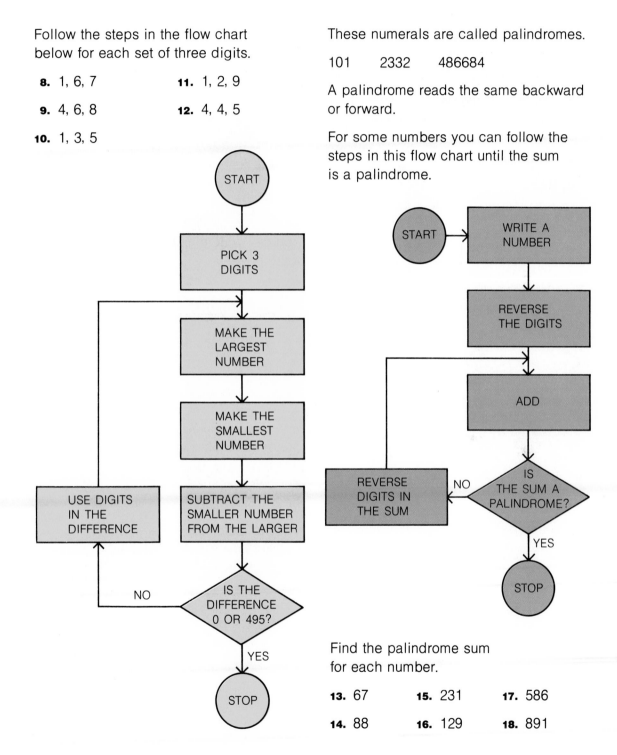

Find the palindrome sum for each number.

13. 67 **15.** 231 **17.** 586

14. 88 **16.** 129 **18.** 891

Factors

Each of these rectangles has an area of 12 square units.

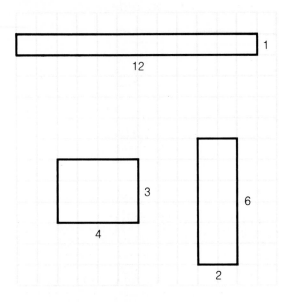

You can write these multiplication sentences for 12. Each sentence shows two *factors* of 12.

$1 \times 12 = 12$ $12 \times 1 = 12$

$2 \times 6 = 12$ $6 \times 2 = 12$

$3 \times 4 = 12$ $4 \times 3 = 12$

The numbers 1, 2, 3, 4, 6, and 12 are all the factors of 12.

Each factor of 12 is also a divisor of 12. The number 12 is *divisible* by each of the numbers 1, 2, 3, 4, 6, and 12.

1. You can use these multiplication sentences to find the factors of 64. List all the factors of 64.

$1 \times 64 = 64$

$2 \times 32 = 64$

$4 \times 16 = 64$

$8 \times 8 = 64$

List all the factors of each number. You can write multiplication sentences to help you.

2. 14	**6.** 42	**10.** 26
3. 21	**7.** 30	**11.** 97
4. 16	**8.** 19	**12.** 100
5. 7	**9.** 81	**13.** 36

In a *perfect number,* the sum of the factors is equal to twice the number itself. For example, 6 is a perfect number, because $1 + 2 + 3 + 6 = 12$, or 2×6.

14. The factors of 496 are 1, 2, 4, 8, 16, 31, 62, 124, 248, and 496. Show that 496 is a perfect number.

15. Is 28 a perfect number?

16. Is 32 a perfect number?

Finding Multiples

When you multiply a whole number by 1, 2, 3, and so on, you obtain the *multiples* of that number.

1×5 $\quad 2 \times 5$ $\quad 3 \times 5$ $\quad 4 \times 5$

5,   10,   15,   20, . . .

The multiples of 5 are 5, 10, 15, and so on. The three dots mean that you can continue finding multiples of 5.

For each exercise, list the next six multiples.

1. Multiples of 6: 6, 12, 18, . . .

2. Multiples of 12: 12, 24, 36, . . .

3. Multiples of 9: 9, 18, 27, . . .

4. Multiples of 14: 14, 28, . . .

5. Multiples of 50: 50, 100, . . .

6. Multiples of 125: 125, 250, . . .

7. Multiples of 300: 300, . . .

8. List the multiples of 7 that are less than 95.

9. List the multiples of 25 that are less than 125.

10. List the multiples of 100 that are less than 1500.

side trip

1. Use these instructions to make a flow chart. You must put the steps in the correct order.

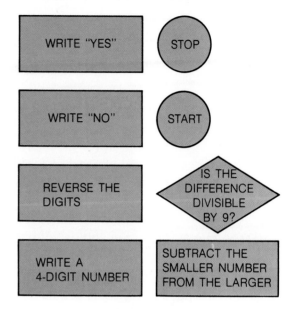

2. Follow the steps in your flow chart with five different 4-digit numbers.

3. Is each difference divisible by 9?

4. Follow the steps in your flow chart with different 5-digit numbers. Is each difference divisible by 9?

Finding Prime and Composite Numbers

A. Conchita could form only one rectangle with an area of 13 square units.

$1 \times 13 = 13$

$13 \times 1 = 13$

The number 13 has only two factors, 1 and 13.

■ *A positive number that has exactly two different factors is a **prime number**.*

B. Grace formed these rectangles with an area of 16 square units.

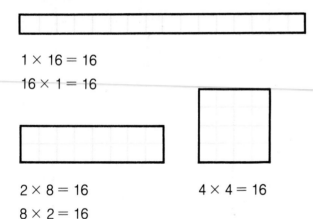

$1 \times 16 = 16$

$16 \times 1 = 16$

$2 \times 8 = 16$ $4 \times 4 = 16$

$8 \times 2 = 16$

The number 16 has five factors, 1, 2, 4, 8, and 16.

■ *A positive number that has more than two different factors is a **composite number**.*

The number 1 is neither prime nor composite.

For each exercise, tell if the number is prime or composite.

1. 33   11. 29

2. 19   12. 50

3. 7   13. 89

4. 18   14. 41

5. 21   15. 65

6. 13   16. 47

7. 57   17. 81

8. 38   18. 127

9. 25   19. 242

10. 11   20. 317

21. List the numbers from 2 to 50. Circle the prime numbers.

● **Discuss** The number 2 is prime. Are there any other even prime numbers? How do you know?

Using Sums of Primes

The First One Hundred Prime Numbers

2	3	5	7	11	13	17	19	23	29	31	37	41	43	47
53	59	61	67	71	73	79	83	89	97	101	103	107	109	113
127	131	137	139	149	151	157	163	167	173	179	181	191	193	197
199	211	223	227	229	233	239	241	251	257	263	269	271	277	281
283	293	307	311	313	317	331	337	347	349	353	359	367	373	379
383	389	397	401	409	419	421	431	433	439	443	449	457	461	463
467	479	487	491	499	503	509	521	523	541					

Christian Goldbach, an eighteenth-century Russian mathematician, suggested that every even number greater than 4 can be expressed as the sum of two odd primes. For example, $14 = 7 + 7$, and $40 = 17 + 23$.

Express each number as the sum of two odd primes.

1. 6
2. 8
3. 18
4. 26
5. 32
6. 84
7. 100
8. 318
9. 540

Goldbach also suggested that every odd number greater than 7 can be expressed as the sum of three odd primes. For example, $15 = 5 + 5 + 5$.

Express each number as the sum of three odd primes.

10. 9
11. 13
12. 17
13. 23
14. 35
15. 41
16. 75
17. 193
18. 381

Tests for Divisibility

People have devised ways to find whether one number is divisible by another. Here are tests for divisibility by 2, 5, and 10.

- *A number is divisible by 2 if the digit in the ones place is 0, 2, 4, 6, or 8.*

- *A number is divisible by 5 if the digit in the ones place is 0 or 5.*

- *A number is divisible by 10 if the digit in the ones place is 0.*

Use the nine numbers below for exercises 1, 2, and 3.

485	5950	5,645,435
356	10,935	8,359,654
4892	329,458	3,465,470

1. Which numbers are divisible by 2?

2. Which numbers are divisible by 5?

3. Which numbers are divisible by 10?

4. If a number is divisible by both 2 and 5, is it divisible by 10?

5. If a number is divisible by 10, is it divisible by both 2 and 5?

Use this flow chart to test for divisibility by 3.

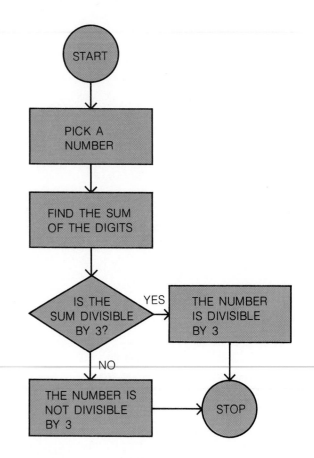

Complete the table.

	Number	Sum of digits	Is the number divisible by 3?
6.	342		
7.	78,431		
8.	64,259		
9.	2,324,508		
10.	111,111,111		

Use this flow chart to test for divisibility by 9.

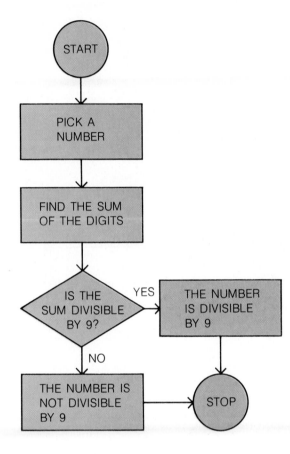

Complete the table.

	Number	Sum of digits	Is the number divisible by 9?
11.	774		
12.	86,517		
13.	432,865		
14.	1,326,672		
15.	2,347,869		

16. Write a 5-digit number that is divisible by 9.

17. Write a 7-digit number that has a remainder of 4 when divided by 9.

18. Write a 5-digit number that is divisible by 3 but not by 9.

19. Can you write a number that is divisible by 9 but not by 3?

Complete the table. Check if the number is divisible.

Number	Divisible by				
	2	3	5	9	10
1245		✓	✓		
20. 3924					
21. 2472					
22. 56,835					
23. 284,310					
24. 45,936					
25. 28,180					
26. 739,472					
27. 852,975					
28. 2,418,630					

Finding Prime Factors

Every composite number can be expressed as the product of primes.

"Factor trees" can be used to find the prime factors of a number.

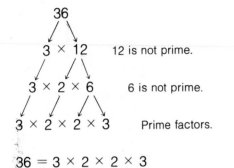

3 × 12   12 is not prime.

3 × 2 × 6   6 is not prime.

3 × 2 × 2 × 3   Prime factors.

36 = 3 × 2 × 2 × 3

The *prime factorization* of 36 is 3 × 2 × 2 × 3.

You can express the prime factorization by using exponents.

$3 \times 2 \times 2 \times 3 = 2^2 \times 3^2$

2.

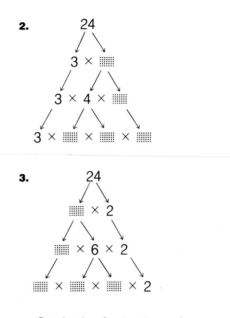

3.

4. Study the factor trees in exercises 1, 2, and 3. Did each tree end with the same set of factors?

5. Write the prime factorization of 24.

Complete the factor trees.

1.

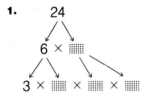

3 × ▦ × ▦ × ▦

For each number, find the prime factorization. Use the table of primes on page 201.

6. 18   **10.** 150   **14.** 1000

7. 98   **11.** 958   **15.** 2406

8. 100   **12.** 194   **16.** 2300

9. 315   **13.** 490   **17.** 2796

Prime Factor Darts

Notice that the numbers in the rings are prime. Multiply the numbers hit to find the total score.

Judy threw three darts, hitting 3, 3, and 7. Her score was $3 \times 3 \times 7 = 63$.

For each player, find the number of darts thrown and where they hit.

Player	Score	Number of darts thrown	Rings hit
Maria	308	4	2, 2, 7, 11
18. Chuck	420		
19. Earl	294		
20. Sally	360		

21. Is 68 a possible score?

22. Is 39 a possible score?

23. Is 200 a possible score?

Finding Greatest Common Factors

A. List the factors of 12 and 30.

12: 1, 2, 3, 4, 6, 12

30: 1, 2, 3, 5, 6, 10, 15, 30

The *common factors* of 12 and 30 are 1, 2, 3, and 6.

The *greatest common factor* (GCF) of 12 and 30 is 6.

Find the GCF of each pair of numbers. You can list the factors of each number.

1. 18 and 27
2. 24 and 32
3. 12 and 23
4. 8 and 40
5. 28 and 16

6. 15 and 18
7. 10 and 25
8. 18 and 24
9. 9 and 13
10. 18 and 36

● **Discuss** Can the GCF of a pair of numbers be greater than either number?

Every pair of whole numbers has at least one common factor. What is it?

You can use prime factorization to find greatest common factors. Study these examples.

B. The GCF of 18 and 24 is 6.

$$24 = 2 \times 2 \times 2 \times 3$$
$$18 = \qquad 2 \times 3 \times 3$$
$$\qquad\qquad 2 \times 3 \quad = 6$$

C. The GCF of 48 and 180 is 12.

$$48 = 2 \times 2 \times 2 \times 2 \times 3$$
$$180 = \qquad 2 \times 2 \times 3 \times 3 \times 5$$
$$\qquad\qquad 2 \times 2 \times 3 \quad = 12$$

D. The GCF of 16 and 23 is 1.

$$16 = 2 \times 2 \times 2 \times 2$$
$$23 = \qquad\qquad\qquad 23$$

There are no common prime factors. The GCF is 1.

For each exercise, use prime factorization to find the GCF.

11. 60 and 140
12. 45 and 81
13. 12 and 96

14. 18 and 32
★ 15. 12, 20, and 30
★ 16. 9, 27, and 45

Finding Least Common Multiples

A. List the multiples of 3 and 4.

3: 3, 6, 9, 12, 15, 18, 21, 24, . . .

4: 4, 8, 12, 16, 20, 24, . . .

The *common multiples* of 3 and 4 are 12, 24, 36, 48, ...

The *least common multiple* (LCM) of 3 and 4 is 12.

B. Find the LCM of 9 and 15.

List the multiples of 15 until you find the first multiple of 15 that is also a multiple of 9.

15, 30, 45

The LCM of 9 and 15 is 45.

Find the LCM of each pair of numbers.

1. 10 and 25

2. 6 and 20

3. 5 and 7

4. 8 and 12

5. 7 and 28

6. 9 and 12

7. 4 and 22

8. 3 and 8

9. 20 and 30

10. 24 and 36

● **Discuss** Can the LCM of 5 and 7 be less than 7?

You can use prime factorization to find the LCM. Study these examples.

C. The LCM of 40 and 60 is 120.

$$40 = 2 \times 2 \times 2 \times 5$$
$$60 = \quad\quad 2 \times 2 \times 5 \times 3$$
$$2 \times 2 \times 2 \times 5 \times 3 = 120$$

D. The LCM of 30 and 315 is 630.

$$315 = 3 \times 3 \times 5 \times 7$$
$$30 = \quad\quad 3 \times 5 \quad\quad \times 2$$
$$3 \times 3 \times 5 \times 7 \times 2 = 630$$

E. The LCM of 13 and 24 is 312.

$$13 = 13$$
$$24 = \quad\quad 2 \times 2 \times 2 \times 3$$
$$13 \times 2 \times 2 \times 2 \times 3 = 312$$

For each exercise, use prime factorization to find the LCM.

11. 24 and 40

12. 36 and 81

13. 35 and 42

★ **14.** 5, 8, and 10

★ **15.** 15, 21, and 42

★ **16.** 6, 20, and 38

time out

Jack, Nora, Ed, Ray, and Sally all eat lunch in the same restaurant. All of them are eating there today; however, only one of them eats in this restaurant every day.

Jack eats there every day.

Nora eats there every other day.

Ed eats there every third day.

Ray eats there every fourth day.

Sally eats there every fifth day.

The next time they are all together again in this restaurant, they will have a big celebration. How many days from today will the celebration take place?

Finding factors and multiples, pages 198–199

For each exercise, list all the factors.

1. 9 **3.** 30

2. 16 **4.** 56

For each number, list the first five multiples.

5. 2 **7.** 10

6. 7 **8.** 15

Prime and composite numbers, pages 200–201, 204–205

Tell whether the number is prime or composite.

9. 19 **12.** 37

10. 42 **13.** 54

11. 12 **14.** 26

For each exercise, write the prime factorization.

15. 12 **17.** 72

16. 30 **18.** 105

Finding greatest common factors and least common multiples, pages 206–207

Find the GCF.

19. 5 and 15

20. 8 and 20

21. 16 and 24

Find the LCM.

22. 8 and 12

23. 4 and 5

24. 6 and 15

Meaning of Fractions

A. Fifteen minutes is what fraction of an hour?

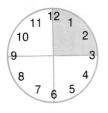

$\frac{1}{4}$ one-fourth

Fifteen minutes is $\frac{1}{4}$ hour.

B. Seven days is what fraction of the month of April?

April

S	M	T	W	T	F	S
	1	2	3	4	5	6
7	8	9	10	11	12	13
14	15	16	17	18	19	20
21	22	23	24	25	26	27
28	29	30				

$\frac{7}{30}$ seven-thirtieths

Seven days is $\frac{7}{30}$ of April.

Numbers like $\frac{1}{4}$ and $\frac{7}{30}$ are *fractions*. A fraction has a *numerator* and a *denominator*. The denominator is never zero.

$\frac{7}{30}$ —— Numerator
—— Denominator

Give the fractions.

1. Teresa slept 11 hours. This is what fraction of a day?

2. A box of cereal weighs 12 ounces. This is what fraction of a pound?

3. Brian ran home in 30 seconds. This is what fraction of a minute?

4. The ten digits are 0, 1, 2, 3, 4, 5, 6, 7, 8, and 9. What fraction of the digits are

   a. even numbers?

   b. odd numbers?

   c. greater than 5?

5. Mary cut a cake into 12 equal pieces. Five pieces were eaten. What fraction of the cake was eaten?

6. Fran cut a pizza into four pieces and ate one of them. Can you be sure that she ate $\frac{1}{4}$ of the pizza?

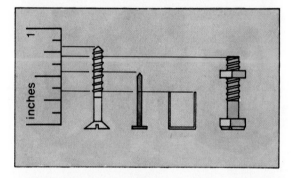

Monday A.M. Feeder Count

Cardinal	///
Wren	/
Blue Jay	//////
Starling	/////////
Martin	/
Sparrow	///
Total	23

What fraction of the birds at the feeder were

7. cardinals?

8. blue jays?

9. starlings?

10. robins?

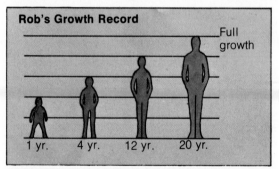

Give the length of each object to the nearest $\frac{1}{8}$ inch.

11. screw

12. nail

13. staple

14. bolt

Rob's Growth Record

At what age did Rob reach

15. $\frac{4}{5}$ of full growth?

16. $\frac{2}{5}$ of full growth?

17. $\frac{5}{5}$ of full growth?

18. $\frac{3}{5}$ of full growth?

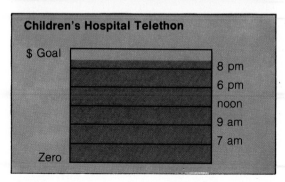

Children's Hospital Telethon

What fraction of the telethon goal was reached at

19. 7 A.M.?

20. noon?

21. 6 P.M.?

22. 8 P.M.?

Meaning of Mixed Numbers

A. $2 + \frac{1}{2}$

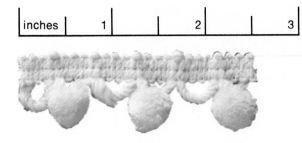

$2\frac{1}{2}$

two and one-half inches

B. $1 + \frac{1}{3}$

$1\frac{1}{3}$

one and one-third dozen

Numbers like $2\frac{1}{2}$ and $1\frac{1}{3}$
are *mixed numbers*.
A mixed number has a
whole-number part and
a fraction part.

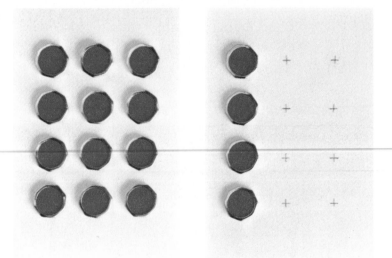

Give the length of each object to the
nearest $\frac{1}{8}$ inch. Use a mixed number.

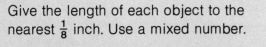

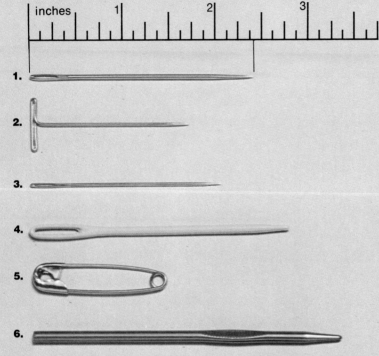

1.

2.

3.

4.

5.

6.

7.

8.

Give the mixed numbers.

Here's how

90 min. = ▦ hr.

$\frac{90}{60} = 1\frac{30}{60} = 1\frac{1}{2}$

9. 20 oz. = ▦ lb.

10. 36 hr. = ▦ da.

11. 7 ft. = ▦ yd.

12. 5 pt. = ▦ qt.

13. 11 qt. = ▦ gal.

14. 72 sec. = ▦ min.

15. 18 in. = ▦ ft.

16. 10 da. = ▦ wk.

17. 130 min. = ▦ hr.

18. 40 oz. = ▦ lb.

careers

Doctor's Assistant

When Lisa goes to the doctor's office for her yearly checkup, the doctor's assistant weighs Lisa and measures her height. Then the assistant may show the height and weight on a graph.

The graph at the right shows Lisa's height record through her present age of 12. For example, the graph shows that Lisa was $43\frac{3}{4}$ inches tall at age 5.

1. List Lisa's heights from age 1 through age 12.

2. Lisa weighed $7\frac{1}{2}$ pounds when she was born. Her weights from age 1 through age 12 are listed below. Be a doctor's assistant and make a graph showing this information.

Age	Weight	Age	Weight
1	$22\frac{1}{4}$ lb.	7	50 lb.
2	29 lb.	8	$52\frac{1}{4}$ lb.
3	$34\frac{1}{2}$ lb.	9	$60\frac{3}{4}$ lb.
4	$37\frac{3}{4}$ lb.	10	$69\frac{1}{2}$ lb.
5	$40\frac{3}{4}$ lb.	11	$74\frac{1}{2}$ lb.
6	$42\frac{1}{2}$ lb.	12	$83\frac{1}{4}$ lb.

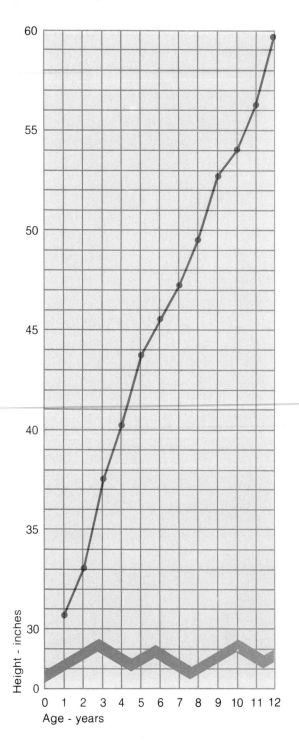

Finding Equal Fractions

A.

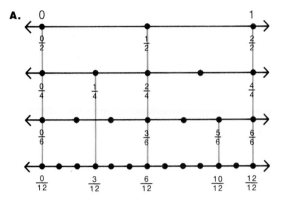

$$\frac{0}{12} \quad \frac{3}{12} \quad \frac{6}{12} \quad \frac{10}{12} \quad \frac{12}{12}$$

The number lines show *equal fractions.*
For example,

$$\frac{1}{2} = \frac{2}{4} = \frac{3}{6} = \frac{6}{12}.$$

B. You can multiply the numerator and the denominator of $\frac{1}{2}$ by 6 to get $\frac{6}{12}$.

C. You can divide the numerator and the denominator of $\frac{3}{6}$ by 3 to get $\frac{1}{2}$.

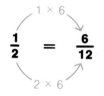

■ *You can multiply or divide the numerator and the denominator of a fraction by the same number (not zero) to find an equal fraction.*

Find equal fractions. Multiply or divide each numerator and denominator by the number given.

Multiply by 4.

1. $\frac{3}{5}$ **2.** $\frac{1}{4}$ **3.** $\frac{5}{8}$

Divide by 2.

4. $\frac{8}{10}$ **5.** $\frac{12}{16}$ **6.** $\frac{10}{20}$

Divide by 3.

7. $\frac{3}{6}$ **8.** $\frac{9}{12}$ **9.** $\frac{6}{15}$

Multiply by 2.

10. $\frac{1}{5}$ **11.** $\frac{2}{3}$ **12.** $\frac{7}{10}$

Multiply by 5.

13. $\frac{2}{3}$ **14.** $\frac{3}{4}$ **15.** $\frac{4}{7}$

For each exercise, write four fractions equal to the given fraction.

16. $\frac{3}{4} = \frac{\text{▦}}{8} = \frac{\text{▦}}{12} = \frac{\text{▦}}{\text{▦}} = \frac{\text{▦}}{\text{▦}}$

17. $\frac{2}{5}$ **20.** $\frac{1}{2}$ **23.** $\frac{4}{3}$

18. $\frac{1}{7}$ **21.** $\frac{1}{6}$ **24.** $\frac{2}{9}$

19. $\frac{3}{8}$ **22.** $\frac{7}{8}$ **25.** $\frac{5}{2}$

Reducing Fractions to Lowest Terms

A fraction can be *reduced* if you can divide the numerator and the denominator by a common factor greater than 1.

A fraction is in *lowest terms* when it cannot be reduced.

Two ways to reduce $\frac{16}{24}$ to lowest terms are shown below.

Long way	Short way
Divide 16 and 24 by 4. Divide 4 and 6 by 2.	Divide 16 and 24 by 8.

$$16 \div 4 \qquad 4 \div 2 \qquad 16 \div 8$$

$$\frac{16}{24} = \frac{4}{6} = \frac{2}{3} \qquad\qquad \frac{16}{24} = \frac{2}{3}$$

$$24 \div 4 \qquad 6 \div 2 \qquad 24 \div 8$$

The fraction $\frac{2}{3}$ is in lowest terms since it cannot be reduced.

Reduce each fraction to lowest terms.

1. $\frac{6}{8}$ 13. $\frac{8}{28}$

2. $\frac{8}{10}$ 14. $\frac{50}{60}$

3. $\frac{3}{18}$ 15. $\frac{9}{36}$

4. $\frac{5}{15}$ 16. $\frac{15}{20}$

5. $\frac{10}{4}$ 17. $\frac{20}{25}$

6. $\frac{6}{27}$ 18. $\frac{28}{32}$

7. $\frac{12}{18}$ 19. $\frac{3}{24}$

8. $\frac{45}{50}$ 20. $\frac{21}{28}$

9. $\frac{8}{24}$ 21. $\frac{2}{16}$

10. $\frac{9}{18}$ 22. $\frac{8}{20}$

11. $\frac{8}{12}$ 23. $\frac{50}{100}$

12. $\frac{10}{16}$ 24. $\frac{7}{49}$

time out

In the addition example at the right, replace each letter by a digit. All identical letters must be replaced by the same digit. All different letters must be replaced by different digits.

Hint: Replace each D by 5.

```
  DONALD
+ GERALD
  ROBERT
```

216

Finding Missing Numbers in Equal Fractions

You can find a missing numerator or denominator in equal fractions.

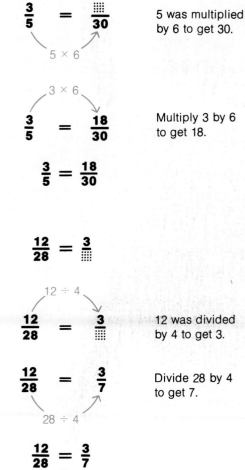

A. $\dfrac{3}{5} = \dfrac{\text{▦}}{30}$

$\dfrac{3}{5} = \dfrac{\text{▦}}{30}$ — 5 was multiplied by 6 to get 30.

5×6

3×6

$\dfrac{3}{5} = \dfrac{18}{30}$ — Multiply 3 by 6 to get 18.

$\dfrac{3}{5} = \dfrac{18}{30}$

B. $\dfrac{12}{28} = \dfrac{3}{\text{▦}}$

$12 \div 4$

$\dfrac{12}{28} = \dfrac{3}{\text{▦}}$ — 12 was divided by 4 to get 3.

$\dfrac{12}{28} = \dfrac{3}{7}$ — Divide 28 by 4 to get 7.

$28 \div 4$

$\dfrac{12}{28} = \dfrac{3}{7}$

Find each missing number.

1. $\dfrac{1}{2} = \dfrac{\text{▦}}{6}$

2. $\dfrac{4}{12} = \dfrac{\text{▦}}{3}$

3. $\dfrac{4}{10} = \dfrac{\text{▦}}{5}$

4. $\dfrac{3}{4} = \dfrac{12}{\text{▦}}$

5. $\dfrac{7}{8} = \dfrac{\text{▦}}{16}$

6. $\dfrac{12}{15} = \dfrac{4}{\text{▦}}$

7. $\dfrac{2}{3} = \dfrac{12}{\text{▦}}$

8. $\dfrac{3}{21} = \dfrac{\text{▦}}{7}$

9. $\dfrac{6}{20} = \dfrac{3}{\text{▦}}$

10. $\dfrac{5}{6} = \dfrac{\text{▦}}{30}$

11. $\dfrac{4}{9} = \dfrac{8}{\text{▦}}$

12. $\dfrac{2}{5} = \dfrac{\text{▦}}{25}$

13. $\dfrac{5}{45} = \dfrac{1}{\text{▦}}$

14. $\dfrac{5}{8} = \dfrac{15}{\text{▦}}$

15. $\dfrac{10}{60} = \dfrac{1}{\text{▦}}$

16. $\dfrac{7}{6} = \dfrac{\text{▦}}{42}$

17. $\dfrac{18}{21} = \dfrac{\text{▦}}{7}$

18. $\dfrac{4}{7} = \dfrac{16}{\text{▦}}$

19. Find a fraction that is equal to $\dfrac{1}{4}$ and has a denominator of 12.

20. Find a fraction that is equal to $\dfrac{2}{3}$ and has a denominator of 9.

21. Find a fraction that is equal to $\dfrac{12}{16}$ and has a denominator of 4.

Mixed Numbers as Quotients

You can write the answers to some division problems as mixed numbers.

Ms. Takata estimates that she watches 650 hours of television per year. This is an average of how many hours per week?

Find 650 ÷ 52.   Write the answer as a mixed number.

$$
\begin{array}{r}
12 \\
52\overline{)650} \\
-52 \\
\hline
130 \\
-104 \\
\hline
26
\end{array}
$$

$12\frac{26}{52}$ —— Remainder
—— Divisor

$12\frac{26}{52} = 12\frac{1}{2}$

Ms. Takata watches an average of $12\frac{1}{2}$ hours of television per week.

Divide. Write each answer as a mixed number.

1. $4\overline{)57}$

2. $6\overline{)92}$

3. $4\overline{)163}$

4. $16\overline{)136}$

5. $9\overline{)168}$

6. $6\overline{)723}$

7. $18\overline{)105}$

8. $25\overline{)210}$

9. $15\overline{)140}$

10. $62\overline{)557}$

11. $24\overline{)304}$

12. $75\overline{)892}$

13. Brad cut 100 yards of drapery fabric into 32 equal pieces. How long was each piece?

14. A bakery uses 500 dozen eggs per month (30 days). This is an average of how many dozen eggs per day?

15. A company mailed 12 boxes, all the same weight. If the total weight was 429 pounds, what was the weight of each box?

laboratory activity

Maria decided to find out what fraction of her favorite television program was taken up by commercials.

She used a watch with a second hand and recorded the number of seconds each commercial lasted. Then she made a table of the results.

The Crazy Quilts
Channel 6, Monday 7–7:30 pm

Commercial	Seconds	Minutes
Shampoo ✓	30 sec.	$\frac{1}{2}$ min.
Cars	60 sec.	
Soap ✓	30 sec.	
Cereal	90 sec.	
Toothpaste	30 sec.	
Records ✓	120 sec.	

Few things in life work as well as a Volkswagen.

1. Complete Maria's table.

2. What fraction of the 30 minutes was devoted to commercials?

3. Maria checked the commercials she liked. What fraction of the total commercial time did Maria like?

4. What fraction of your favorite television program is devoted to commercials?

Changing Fractions to Mixed Numbers

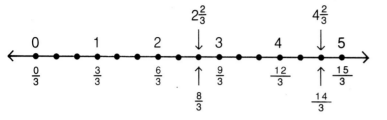

A fraction is greater than 1 if the numerator is greater than the denominator.

Every fraction greater than 1 can be written as a mixed number or a whole number.

A. Change $\frac{14}{3}$ to a mixed number.

Look at the number line. $\frac{14}{3} = 4\frac{2}{3}$

Divide 14 by 3. $14 \div 3 = 4\frac{2}{3}$

To find a mixed number equal to $\frac{14}{3}$, you can divide 14 by 3 and write the answer as a mixed number.

$$\frac{14}{3} = \left(14 \div 3 \right) = 4\frac{2}{3}$$

B. Change $\frac{87}{6}$ to a mixed number.

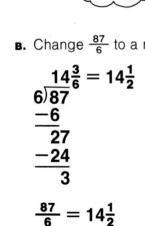

$$\frac{87}{6} = 14\frac{1}{2}$$

Change each fraction to a mixed number or a whole number.

1. $\frac{7}{2}$	**9.** $\frac{38}{6}$
2. $\frac{26}{3}$	**10.** $\frac{32}{3}$
3. $\frac{37}{2}$	**11.** $\frac{92}{5}$
4. $\frac{28}{7}$	**12.** $\frac{65}{10}$
5. $\frac{89}{8}$	**13.** $\frac{29}{5}$
6. $\frac{68}{3}$	**14.** $\frac{76}{3}$
7. $\frac{51}{4}$	**15.** $\frac{153}{4}$
8. $\frac{109}{8}$	**16.** $\frac{108}{9}$

Express each quotient as a fraction or a mixed number.

17. $9 \div 6 = \frac{9}{6} = $ ▦

18. $12 \div 7$

19. $8 \div 3$

20. $2 \div 5$

21. $10 \div 6$

22. $25 \div 8$

Changing Mixed Numbers to Fractions

Every whole number and mixed number can be written as a fraction.

Write each number as a fraction.

1. $1\frac{7}{8}$ **9.** $8\frac{1}{6}$ **17.** $5\frac{3}{10}$

A. Change $4\frac{2}{3}$ to a fraction.

2. $4\frac{1}{3}$ **10.** $7\frac{3}{5}$ **18.** $8\frac{5}{9}$

Here is one way to find the fraction.

3. $2\frac{3}{4}$ **11.** $9\frac{1}{2}$ **19.** $15\frac{1}{2}$

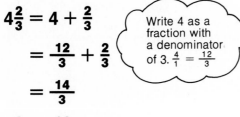

$$4\frac{2}{3} = 4 + \frac{2}{3}$$

Write 4 as a fraction with a denominator of 3. $\frac{4}{1} = \frac{12}{3}$

$$= \frac{12}{3} + \frac{2}{3}$$

$$= \frac{14}{3}$$

$$4\frac{2}{3} = \frac{14}{3}$$

4. $6\frac{1}{5}$ **12.** $5\frac{3}{8}$ **20.** $10\frac{3}{5}$

5. $3\frac{5}{6}$ **13.** 11 **21.** $33\frac{1}{3}$

6. $1\frac{9}{10}$ **14.** $8\frac{1}{2}$ **22.** $21\frac{3}{4}$

7. 6 **15.** $6\frac{1}{4}$ **23.** 27

Here is a shortcut.

8. $5\frac{7}{9}$ **16.** $9\frac{2}{3}$ **24.** $18\frac{3}{10}$

$$4\frac{2}{3} = \frac{14}{3}$$

Multiply 3 and 4. Then add 2.

B. Change $14\frac{1}{2}$ to a fraction.

$$14\frac{1}{2} = \frac{29}{2}$$

Multiply 2 and 14. Then add 1.

© 1966 United Feature Syndicate, Inc.

Finding Common Denominators

Fractions that have the same
denominator are said to have a
common denominator.

A. Find a common denominator
of $\frac{5}{6}$ and $\frac{3}{8}$.

A common denominator of $\frac{5}{6}$ and $\frac{3}{8}$
is a common multiple of 6 and 8.

$$\frac{5}{6} \qquad \frac{3}{8}$$

$$\begin{array}{c} \uparrow \\ 8 \\ 16 \\ 24 \end{array}$$

24 is a common multiple of 6 and 8.
It is a common denominator
of $\frac{5}{6}$ and $\frac{3}{8}$.

Since 24 is the least common multiple
of 6 and 8, it is the *least common
denominator* of $\frac{5}{6}$ and $\frac{3}{8}$.

B. Now find fractions that are equal
to $\frac{5}{6}$ and $\frac{3}{8}$ and that have a
denominator of 24.

$$\frac{5}{6} = \frac{20}{24} \qquad \frac{3}{8} = \frac{9}{24}$$

To find a common denominator, list the
multiples of the larger denominator
until you find a common multiple of all
the denominators.

c. Sometimes the larger denominator
is a common denominator.

$$\frac{3}{4} \qquad \frac{5}{16}$$

16 is a common denominator.

Find a fraction that is equal to $\frac{3}{4}$
and that has a denominator of 16.

$$\frac{3}{4} = \frac{\text{▦}}{16}$$

D. The product of the denominators
is always a common denominator.

$$\frac{2}{9} \qquad \frac{1}{6} \qquad 9 \times 6 = 54$$

54 is a common denominator.

Find fractions that are equal to $\frac{2}{9}$
and $\frac{1}{6}$ and that have a denominator
of 54.

$$\frac{2}{9} = \frac{\text{▦}}{54} \qquad \frac{1}{6} = \frac{\text{▦}}{54}$$

Is 54 the least common denominator
of $\frac{2}{9}$ and $\frac{1}{6}$?

Write these fractions with a common denominator.

1. $\frac{1}{3}$ $\frac{1}{6}$

2. $\frac{5}{8}$ $\frac{1}{2}$

3. $\frac{7}{15}$ $\frac{3}{5}$

4. $\frac{1}{2}$ $\frac{2}{3}$

5. $\frac{2}{3}$ $\frac{4}{5}$

6. $\frac{1}{4}$ $\frac{5}{6}$

7. $\frac{1}{2}$ $\frac{3}{7}$

8. $\frac{5}{9}$ $\frac{3}{4}$

9. $\frac{2}{3}$ $\frac{5}{12}$

10. $\frac{3}{8}$ $\frac{7}{12}$

11. $\frac{1}{3}$ $\frac{7}{8}$

12. $\frac{4}{5}$ $\frac{5}{6}$

13. $\frac{10}{21}$ $\frac{3}{7}$

14. $\frac{3}{8}$ $\frac{5}{6}$

15. $\frac{5}{9}$ $\frac{2}{5}$

16. $\frac{7}{10}$ $\frac{3}{15}$

17. $\frac{2}{5}$ $\frac{1}{6}$ $\frac{3}{10}$

Hint: Find multiples of 10 until you find a common multiple of 5, 6, and 10.

18. $\frac{1}{2}$ $\frac{3}{4}$ $\frac{7}{8}$

19. $\frac{1}{3}$ $\frac{5}{6}$ $\frac{1}{2}$

20. $\frac{1}{2}$ $\frac{3}{14}$ $\frac{2}{7}$

21. $\frac{3}{8}$ $\frac{1}{3}$ $\frac{5}{6}$

22. $\frac{2}{3}$ $\frac{3}{4}$ $\frac{1}{6}$

Suppose you were given 1 billion dollars and were told to spend the money at the rate of 1 dollar per second. How long would it take you to spend the 1 billion dollars? Give your answer in days, hours, minutes, and seconds.

223

Comparing Fractions and Mixed Numbers

A. Which cake uses more milk?

Compare $\frac{1}{3}$ and $\frac{2}{3}$.

To compare fractions that have a common denominator, compare the numerators.

$$\frac{2}{3} > \frac{1}{3}$$

The crumb cake uses more milk.

B. Which cake uses less butter?

Compare $\frac{2}{3}$ and $\frac{3}{4}$.

First find equal fractions that have a common denominator. Then compare the new fractions.

$$\frac{2}{3} \qquad \frac{3}{4}$$

$$\frac{8}{12} < \frac{9}{12}, \text{ so } \frac{2}{3} < \frac{3}{4}.$$

The velvet cake uses less butter.

C. Which cake uses more flour?

Compare $2\frac{1}{2}$ and $2\frac{1}{3}$.

First compare the whole numbers. If the whole numbers are equal, compare the fractions.

$$2\frac{1}{2} \qquad 2\frac{1}{3}$$

$$2\frac{3}{6} > 2\frac{2}{6},$$
$$\text{so } 2\frac{1}{2} > 2\frac{1}{3}.$$

The velvet cake uses more flour.

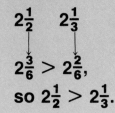

Velvet Cake	Crumb Cake
$2\frac{1}{2}$ cups flour	$2\frac{1}{3}$ cups flour
2 teaspoons baking powder	2 teaspoons baking powder
$\frac{3}{8}$ teaspoon salt	$\frac{1}{8}$ teaspoon salt
$1\frac{1}{4}$ cups sugar	$1\frac{1}{2}$ cups sugar
$\frac{2}{3}$ cup butter	$\frac{3}{4}$ cup butter
3 eggs	2 eggs
$\frac{1}{3}$ cup milk	$\frac{2}{3}$ cup milk
1 teaspoon vanilla	1 teaspoon vanilla

Compare the numbers.
Use >, <, or =.

1. $\frac{1}{2}$ ● $\frac{7}{8}$

2. $\frac{9}{10}$ ● $\frac{4}{5}$

3. $1\frac{2}{3}$ ● $1\frac{5}{6}$

4. $2\frac{3}{4}$ ● $2\frac{2}{3}$

5. $5\frac{1}{2}$ ● $5\frac{3}{5}$

6. $\frac{3}{9}$ ● $\frac{1}{3}$

7. $\frac{3}{4}$ ● $\frac{7}{10}$

8. $8\frac{6}{7}$ ● $8\frac{13}{14}$

9. $6\frac{2}{3}$ ● $6\frac{1}{2}$

10. $1\frac{1}{6}$ ● $2\frac{2}{9}$

11. $\frac{4}{5}$ ● $\frac{5}{6}$

12. $3\frac{7}{8}$ ● $3\frac{11}{16}$

13. $\frac{5}{12}$ ● $\frac{1}{4}$

14. $9\frac{1}{2}$ ● $9\frac{4}{8}$

15. $4\frac{4}{9}$ ● $4\frac{1}{2}$

16. $\frac{4}{5}$ ● $\frac{3}{4}$

17. $1\frac{5}{8}$ ● $1\frac{5}{6}$

18. $7\frac{3}{4}$ ● $7\frac{5}{7}$

Tell if the nail is long
enough to go through
the board.

Length of nail	Thickness of board
19. $\frac{5}{6}$ in.	$\frac{3}{4}$ in.
20. $\frac{7}{8}$ in.	$\frac{5}{6}$ in.
21. $1\frac{1}{4}$ in.	$1\frac{3}{8}$ in.
22. $2\frac{1}{4}$ in.	3 in.
23. $2\frac{5}{8}$ in.	$2\frac{1}{2}$ in.
24. $3\frac{3}{4}$ in.	$3\frac{7}{8}$ in.

In each exercise, write
the numbers in order
from least to greatest.

25. $\frac{3}{4}$ $\frac{5}{8}$ $\frac{1}{2}$

26. $\frac{3}{16}$ $\frac{3}{8}$ $\frac{1}{4}$

27. $2\frac{1}{2}$ $2\frac{1}{4}$ $1\frac{1}{2}$

28. $1\frac{1}{3}$ $1\frac{5}{6}$ $1\frac{1}{2}$

29. $\frac{1}{2}$ $\frac{1}{3}$ $\frac{3}{4}$ $\frac{5}{6}$

30. $\frac{2}{3}$ $\frac{4}{5}$ $\frac{5}{6}$ $\frac{1}{2}$

Adding Fractions

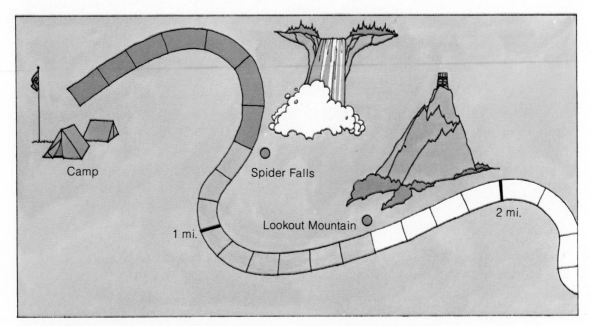

Camp

Spider Falls

Lookout Mountain

1 mi.

2 mi.

A. One day, Rachel hiked $\frac{7}{10}$ of a mile to Spider Falls and then $\frac{9}{10}$ of a mile to Lookout Mountain. How many miles did she hike?

Find $\frac{7}{10} + \frac{9}{10}$.

To add fractions that have the same denominator, add the numerators.

$$\begin{array}{r} \frac{7}{10} \\ + \frac{9}{10} \\ \hline \frac{16}{10} = 1\frac{6}{10} = 1\frac{3}{5} \end{array}$$

Rachel hiked $1\frac{3}{5}$ miles.

B. It took Rachel $\frac{1}{4}$ hour to hike from camp to Spider Falls and then $\frac{2}{3}$ hour to hike to Lookout Mountain. What fraction of an hour did she spend hiking?

Find $\frac{1}{4} + \frac{2}{3}$.

To add fractions with different denominators, first find equal fractions that have the same denominator.

12 is a common denominator.

$$\begin{array}{r} \frac{1}{4} = \frac{3}{12} \\ + \frac{2}{3} = \frac{8}{12} \\ \hline \frac{11}{12} \end{array}$$

Rachel spent $\frac{11}{12}$ of an hour hiking.

Add.

1. $\frac{1}{8} = \frac{\text{▦}}{8}$
    $+ \frac{3}{4} = \frac{\text{▦}}{8}$

2. $\frac{1}{4} = \frac{\text{▦}}{12}$
    $+ \frac{1}{6} = \frac{\text{▦}}{12}$

3. $\frac{2}{3} = \frac{\text{▦}}{15}$
    $+ \frac{4}{5} = \frac{\text{▦}}{15}$

4. $\frac{3}{4}$
    $+ \frac{3}{4}$

5. $\frac{5}{8}$
    $+ \frac{1}{2}$

6. $\frac{3}{4}$
    $+ \frac{7}{8}$

7. $\frac{1}{4}$
    $+ \frac{1}{5}$

8. $\frac{1}{3}$
    $+ \frac{5}{8}$

9. $\frac{7}{10}$
    $+ \frac{3}{4}$

10. $\frac{5}{6} + \frac{1}{2}$

11. $\frac{5}{16} + \frac{5}{8}$

12. $\frac{9}{10} + \frac{1}{6}$

13. $\frac{5}{9} + \frac{1}{2}$

14. $\frac{3}{4} + \frac{4}{5}$

15. $\frac{3}{8} + \frac{1}{3}$

16. $\frac{5}{6} + \frac{2}{3}$

17. $\frac{3}{10} + \frac{1}{2}$

18. $\frac{1}{2} + \frac{1}{4} + \frac{1}{8}$

19. $\frac{2}{5} + \frac{7}{10} + \frac{1}{2}$

20. $\frac{1}{2} + \frac{3}{4} + \frac{2}{3}$

21. $\frac{1}{8} + \frac{1}{3} + \frac{1}{6}$

**More practice
Set A, page 254**

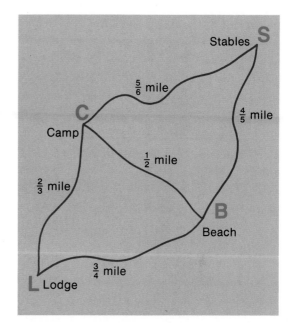

Find each distance in miles.

22. From L to B to C

23. From L to C to S

24. From C to L to B

25. From L to B to S

26. From S to C to B to L

27. From L to C to B to L

28. From S to C to B to S

Adding Mixed Numbers

A. How long is Twin Mountain Trail?

Find $10\frac{3}{4} + 11\frac{1}{4}$.

To add mixed numbers, add the fractions. Then add the whole numbers.

$$10\frac{3}{4}$$
$$+ 11\frac{1}{4}$$
$$\overline{ 21\frac{4}{4} = 22}$$

$21\frac{4}{4} = 21 + \frac{4}{4}$
$= 21 + 1$
$= 22$

Twin Mountain Trail is 22 miles long.

B. How long is Split Rock Trail?

Find $5\frac{1}{2} + 15\frac{2}{3}$.

6 is a common denominator.

$$5\frac{1}{2} = 5\frac{3}{6}$$
$$+ 15\frac{2}{3} = 15\frac{4}{6}$$
$$\overline{\phantom{+ 15\frac{2}{3} = } 20\frac{7}{6} = 21\frac{1}{6}}$$

$20\frac{7}{6} = 20 + \frac{7}{6}$
$= 20 + 1\frac{1}{6}$
$= 21\frac{1}{6}$

Split Rock Trail is $21\frac{1}{6}$ miles long.

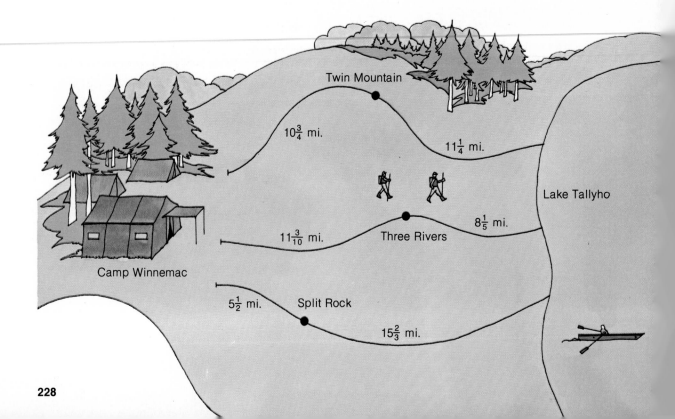

Twin Mountain

$10\frac{3}{4}$ mi.

$11\frac{1}{4}$ mi.

Lake Tallyho

$11\frac{3}{10}$ mi.

Three Rivers

$8\frac{1}{5}$ mi.

Camp Winnemac

$5\frac{1}{2}$ mi.

Split Rock

$15\frac{2}{3}$ mi.

c. How long is Three Rivers Trail?

Find $11\frac{3}{10} + 8\frac{1}{5}$.

10 is a common denominator.

$$11\frac{3}{10} = 11\frac{3}{10}$$
$$+ \ 8\frac{1}{5} = \ 8\frac{2}{10}$$
$$\overline{\phantom{+ \ 8\frac{1}{5} = \ }19\frac{5}{10} = 19\frac{1}{2}}$$

Three Rivers Trail is $19\frac{1}{2}$ miles long.

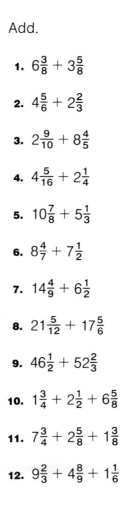

Add.

1. $6\frac{3}{8} + 3\frac{5}{8}$

2. $4\frac{5}{6} + 2\frac{2}{3}$

3. $2\frac{9}{10} + 8\frac{4}{5}$

4. $4\frac{5}{16} + 2\frac{1}{4}$

5. $10\frac{7}{8} + 5\frac{1}{3}$

6. $8\frac{4}{7} + 7\frac{1}{2}$

7. $14\frac{4}{9} + 6\frac{1}{2}$

8. $21\frac{5}{12} + 17\frac{5}{6}$

9. $46\frac{1}{2} + 52\frac{2}{3}$

10. $1\frac{3}{4} + 2\frac{1}{2} + 6\frac{5}{8}$

11. $7\frac{3}{4} + 2\frac{5}{8} + 1\frac{3}{8}$

12. $9\frac{2}{3} + 4\frac{8}{9} + 1\frac{1}{6}$

13. José hiked to Twin Mountain with a $3\frac{1}{2}$-pound sleeping bag and a $9\frac{3}{4}$-pound backpack. What was the total weight of these two items?

14. Lou is hiking up Three Rivers Trail. She hiked $2\frac{1}{5}$ miles in the morning and $3\frac{7}{10}$ miles in the afternoon. How many miles in all did she hike?

15. It took Yoshio $1\frac{2}{3}$ hours to ride his bicycle from camp to Split Rock. He stayed at Split Rock for $2\frac{1}{2}$ hours and then rode back in $\frac{3}{4}$ of an hour. How long was he gone?

16. It is $15\frac{2}{3}$ miles from Split Rock to Lake Tallyho. How many miles is a round trip?

More practice Set B, page 254

Subtracting Fractions

A. Ramón wants to buy the lightest utensils for his backpack. A large frying pan weighs $\frac{7}{8}$ pound, and a small one weighs $\frac{3}{8}$ pound. How much less does the small frying pan weigh?

Find $\frac{7}{8} - \frac{3}{8}$.

To subtract fractions that have the same denominator, subtract the numerators.

$$
\begin{array}{r}
\frac{7}{8} \\
- \frac{3}{8} \\
\hline
\frac{4}{8} = \frac{1}{2}
\end{array}
$$

The small pan weighs $\frac{1}{2}$ pound less.

B. A set of metal dishes weighs $\frac{5}{8}$ pound. A plastic set weighs $\frac{3}{16}$ pound. How much less does the plastic set weigh?

Find $\frac{5}{8} - \frac{3}{16}$.

To subtract fractions with different denominators, first find equal fractions that have the same denominator.

16 is a common denominator.

$$
\begin{array}{r}
\frac{5}{8} = \frac{10}{16} \\
- \frac{3}{16} = \frac{3}{16} \\
\hline
\frac{7}{16}
\end{array}
$$

The plastic set weighs $\frac{7}{16}$ pound less.

Knife $\frac{1}{8}$ lb.   Spoon $\frac{1}{32}$ lb.   Fork $\frac{1}{32}$ lb.

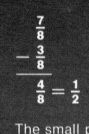

Plate $\frac{1}{8}$ lb.

Frying pan $\frac{7}{8}$ lb.

1. $\frac{6}{7} - \frac{4}{7}$

2. $\frac{3}{4} - \frac{1}{2}$

3. $\frac{2}{3} - \frac{1}{6}$

4. $\frac{7}{8} - \frac{1}{2}$

5. $\frac{2}{3} - \frac{1}{2}$

6. $\frac{5}{6} - \frac{3}{4}$

7. $\frac{2}{3} - \frac{2}{9}$

8. $\frac{15}{16} - \frac{1}{4}$

9. $\frac{4}{5} - \frac{3}{10}$

10. $\frac{7}{9} - \frac{1}{6}$

11. $\frac{11}{12} - \frac{3}{4}$

12. $\frac{7}{10} - \frac{1}{3}$

13. $\frac{9}{10} - \frac{1}{2}$

14. $\frac{1}{2} - \frac{2}{5}$

15. $\frac{3}{8} - \frac{1}{3}$

16. $\frac{6}{7} - \frac{1}{2}$

17. $\frac{15}{16} - \frac{5}{8}$

18. $\frac{3}{5} - \frac{1}{4}$

19. $\frac{1}{2} - \frac{2}{9}$

20. $\frac{5}{8} - \frac{3}{5}$

21. $\frac{4}{5} - \frac{1}{3}$

22. $\frac{3}{4} - \frac{2}{3}$

23. $\frac{5}{6} - \frac{2}{5}$

24. $\frac{7}{8} - \frac{1}{7}$

**More practice
Set C, page 254**

Which weighs more? How much more?

25. Coffeepot or cup

26. Cup or plate

27. Knife or spoon

28. Frying pan or kettle

29. Coffeepot or kettle

30. Bowl or plate

Coffeepot $\frac{5}{8}$ lb.

Bowl $\frac{1}{4}$ lb.

Kettle $\frac{1}{2}$ lb.

Cup $\frac{3}{16}$ lb.

231

Subtracting Mixed Numbers

A "mummy" style sleeping bag weighs $4\frac{3}{4}$ pounds. A backpack sleep pad weighs $1\frac{1}{2}$ pounds. How much less does the sleep pad weigh?

Find $4\frac{3}{4} - 1\frac{1}{2}$.

To subtract mixed numbers, subtract the fractions. Then subtract the whole numbers.

4 is a common denominator.

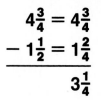

$$4\frac{3}{4} = 4\frac{3}{4}$$
$$-1\frac{1}{2} = 1\frac{2}{4}$$
$$\overline{\qquad 3\frac{1}{4}}$$

The sleep pad weighs $3\frac{1}{4}$ pounds less.

Subtract.

1. $2\frac{4}{5} - 1\frac{1}{5}$

2. $3\frac{3}{4} - 1\frac{1}{2}$

3. $5\frac{5}{6} - 2\frac{1}{3}$

4. $1\frac{2}{3} - \frac{1}{2}$

5. $11\frac{7}{8} - 8\frac{3}{4}$

6. $4\frac{4}{5} - 2\frac{1}{3}$

7. $9\frac{2}{3} - 6\frac{1}{4}$

8. $7\frac{6}{7} - 3\frac{2}{3}$

9. $15\frac{9}{10} - 4\frac{3}{4}$

10. $9\frac{1}{3} - 2\frac{1}{5}$

11. $6\frac{5}{8} - 4\frac{7}{16}$

12. $13\frac{3}{4} - 7\frac{2}{5}$

13. $4\frac{7}{9} - 3\frac{1}{6}$

14. $6\frac{1}{4} - 1\frac{1}{6}$

15. $10\frac{5}{7} - 8\frac{1}{2}$

16. $11\frac{5}{6} - 2\frac{4}{5}$

17. $7\frac{7}{8} - 5\frac{1}{3}$

18. $12\frac{9}{10} - 10\frac{2}{3}$

Renaming to Subtract Mixed Numbers

A. Sometimes you need to rename a whole number before you subtract.

Find $13 - 6\frac{3}{4}$.

Rename 13 to show a fraction in fourths.

$$13 = 12\frac{4}{4}$$
$$- \ 6\frac{3}{4} = \ 6\frac{3}{4}$$
$$\overline{ \ 6\frac{1}{4}}$$

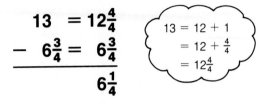

$13 = 12 + 1$
$= 12 + \frac{4}{4}$
$= 12\frac{4}{4}$

B. Sometimes you may need to rename a mixed number.

Find $9\frac{1}{6} - 4\frac{5}{6}$.

Rename $9\frac{1}{6}$ to show more sixths.

$$9\frac{1}{6} = 8\frac{7}{6}$$
$$- \ 4\frac{5}{6} = 4\frac{5}{6}$$
$$\overline{ \ 4\frac{2}{6} = 4\frac{1}{3}}$$

$9\frac{1}{6} = 9 \ + \frac{1}{6}$
$= 8\frac{6}{6} + \frac{1}{6}$
$= 8\frac{7}{6}$

Rename each whole number. Then subtract.

1. $\quad 4 = 3\frac{}{2}$
$\quad - 1\frac{1}{2} = 1\frac{1}{2}$

2. $\quad 9 = 8\frac{}{6}$
$\quad - 4\frac{5}{6} = 4\frac{5}{6}$

3. $\quad 18 = 17\frac{}{3}$
$\quad - 10\frac{1}{3} = 10\frac{1}{3}$

4. $7 - 3\frac{1}{8}$

5. $1 - \frac{4}{5}$

6. $10 - 4\frac{3}{7}$

7. $5 - 4\frac{2}{9}$

8. $12 - 6\frac{3}{4}$

9. $15 - 8\frac{3}{10}$

10. $3 - 2\frac{5}{8}$

Rename each mixed number. Then subtract.

11. $\quad 7\frac{3}{8} = 6\frac{}{8}$
$\quad - 4\frac{5}{8} = 4\frac{5}{8}$

12. $\quad 3\frac{4}{9} = 2\frac{}{9}$
$\quad - 2\frac{5}{9} = 2\frac{5}{9}$

13. $\quad 15\frac{1}{4} = 14\frac{}{4}$
$\quad - \ 9\frac{3}{4} = \ 9\frac{3}{4}$

14. $8\frac{1}{6} - 5\frac{5}{6}$

15. $4\frac{3}{5} - 1\frac{4}{5}$

16. $6\frac{3}{10} - 2\frac{7}{10}$

17. $3\frac{1}{7} - 1\frac{4}{7}$

18. $5\frac{2}{5} - 1\frac{3}{5}$

19. $12\frac{1}{3} - 9\frac{2}{3}$

20. $19\frac{5}{8} - 13\frac{7}{8}$

**More practice
Set D, page 254**

Subtracting Mixed Numbers with Renaming

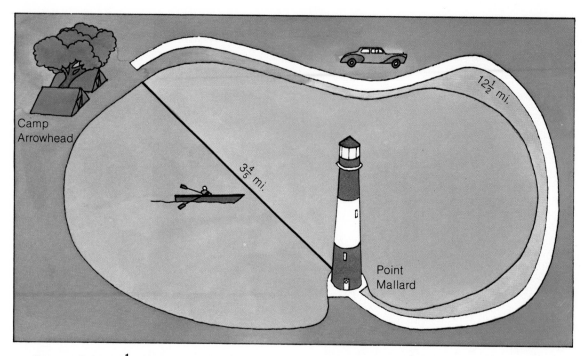

Camp
Arrowhead

$3\frac{4}{5}$ mi.

$12\frac{1}{2}$ mi.

Point
Mallard

A. By car it is $12\frac{1}{2}$ miles from Camp Arrowhead to Point Mallard. By boat it is $3\frac{4}{5}$ miles. How many miles shorter is the boat trip?

Find $12\frac{1}{2} - 3\frac{4}{5}$.

10 is a common denominator.

Rename $12\frac{5}{10}$ to show more tenths.

$$12\frac{1}{2} = 12\frac{5}{10} = 11\frac{15}{10}$$
$$- \ 3\frac{4}{5} = \ 3\frac{8}{10} = \ 3\frac{8}{10}$$
$$\overline{\qquad\qquad\qquad\qquad\ 8\frac{7}{10}}$$

The boat trip is $8\frac{7}{10}$ miles shorter.

B. It took Bud $1\frac{1}{3}$ hours to row a boat from Camp Arrowhead to Point Mallard. It took Terry $\frac{1}{2}$ hour to go by car. How much longer did it take Bud to go by boat?

Find $1\frac{1}{3} - \frac{1}{2}$.

6 is a common denominator.

$$1\frac{1}{3} = 1\frac{\square}{6} = \frac{\square}{6}$$
$$- \ \frac{1}{2} = \ \frac{\square}{6} = \frac{\square}{6}$$
$$\overline{\qquad\qquad\qquad\ \frac{\square}{6}}$$

It took Bud $\frac{\square}{6}$ hour longer.

Did you hear about the boy who stayed up all night to see where the sun went down? What do you think happened?

Do exercises 1–20. Then assign a letter from the code to the whole-number part of each answer.

Code	
1	D
2	A
3	O
4	I
5	T
6	F
7	H
8	L
9	E
10	M
11	W
12	Y
13	N

Subtract.

1. $9\frac{1}{2} = 9\frac{4}{8} = 8\frac{}{8}$
   $-2\frac{7}{8} = 2\frac{7}{8} = 2\frac{7}{8}$

2. $10\frac{1}{3} = 10\frac{4}{12} = 9\frac{}{12}$
   $-5\frac{3}{4} = 5\frac{9}{12} = 5\frac{9}{12}$

3. $21\frac{3}{8} = 21\frac{9}{24} = 20\frac{}{24}$
   $-7\frac{5}{6} = 7\frac{20}{24} = 7\frac{20}{24}$

4. $3\frac{2}{3}$
   $-1\frac{1}{2}$

5. 12
   $-3\frac{4}{5}$

6. $14\frac{1}{4}$
   $-5\frac{7}{8}$

7. $15\frac{1}{3}$
   $-2\frac{1}{2}$

8. $9\frac{2}{3} - 5\frac{1}{6}$

9. $7 - 1\frac{2}{3}$

10. $6\frac{1}{5} - 4\frac{5}{6}$

11. $10\frac{3}{4} - 8\frac{2}{5}$

12. $17 - 5\frac{5}{8}$

13. $14\frac{1}{3} - \frac{3}{5}$

14. $15\frac{4}{5} - 6\frac{1}{2}$

15. $9\frac{3}{4} - 7\frac{5}{6}$

16. $8 - 4\frac{6}{7}$

17. $19\frac{1}{3} - 6\frac{1}{8}$

18. $8\frac{5}{6} - 1\frac{1}{7}$

19. $7\frac{4}{5} - 3\frac{4}{7}$

20. $17\frac{1}{4} - 6\frac{5}{9}$

Fractions and mixed numbers, pages 210–225

1. How full is the gasoline tank?

2. Write four fractions equal to $\frac{2}{3}$.

Find each missing number.

3. $\frac{3}{5} = \frac{}{15}$

4. $\frac{8}{12} = \frac{2}{}$

Reduce to lowest terms.

5. $\frac{8}{10}$

6. $\frac{9}{24}$

Divide. Give each answer as a mixed number.

7. $4\overline{)58}$

8. $7\overline{)100}$

Write each mixed number as a fraction.

9. $2\frac{1}{3}$

10. $7\frac{5}{6}$

Write each fraction as a mixed number.

11. $\frac{12}{5}$

12. $\frac{25}{3}$

Write these fractions with a common denominator.

13. $\frac{3}{4}, \frac{1}{3}$

14. $\frac{1}{2}, \frac{4}{7}$

Compare the numbers. Use > or <.

15. $\frac{1}{2}$ ⬤ $\frac{3}{5}$

16. $1\frac{2}{3}$ ⬤ $1\frac{5}{6}$

17. $7\frac{3}{4}$ ⬤ $7\frac{2}{3}$

Adding fractions and mixed numbers, pages 226–229

Add.

18. $\frac{1}{3} + \frac{1}{6}$

19. $\frac{3}{4} + \frac{3}{8}$

20. $1\frac{5}{7} + 3\frac{2}{7}$

21. $6\frac{1}{2} + 2\frac{2}{3}$

22. $4\frac{3}{8} + 5\frac{1}{6}$

Subtracting fractions and mixed numbers, pages 230–235

Subtract.

23. $\frac{7}{8} - \frac{5}{8}$

24. $10\frac{3}{4} - 4\frac{1}{6}$

25. $6 - \frac{4}{5}$

26. $5\frac{1}{2} - 4\frac{3}{4}$

27. $7\frac{1}{3} - 3\frac{1}{2}$

Problem solving, pages 218, 226–235

28. Lee's tent weighs $9\frac{7}{8}$ pounds. The tent case weighs $3\frac{1}{2}$ pounds. What is the total weight?

29. Len hiked $4\frac{1}{2}$ miles and Anita hiked $6\frac{7}{10}$ miles. How much farther did Anita hike?

30. Gail cut a 27-inch sausage into 4 equal pieces. Each piece was how many inches long?

$$\frac{4}{5} \div 8 = n$$

Multiplying Fractions

Deluxe Hamburger

$\frac{3}{4}$ pound ground beef

$\frac{1}{2}$ pound ground veal

$\frac{3}{4}$ tablespoon minced onion

$\frac{3}{4}$ teaspoon salt

$\frac{1}{4}$ teaspoon garlic salt

$\frac{1}{4}$ teaspoon ginger

$\frac{1}{4}$ teaspoon pepper

A. Tony is cutting this recipe in half. How much ground beef should he use?

The pictures show one way to find the answer.

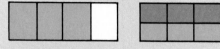

$\frac{3}{4}$ pound $\frac{1}{2}$ of $\frac{3}{4}$ pound

What fraction of a pound should he use?

$\frac{1}{2}$ of $\frac{3}{4}$ is $\frac{3}{8}$.

$\frac{1}{2} \times \frac{3}{4} = \frac{3}{8}$

He should use $\frac{3}{8}$ pound of beef.

B. How much ground veal should Tony use?

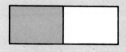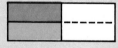

$\frac{1}{2}$ pound $\frac{1}{2}$ of $\frac{1}{2}$ pound

What fraction of a pound should he use?

$\frac{1}{2}$ of $\frac{1}{2}$ is $\frac{1}{4}$.

$\frac{1}{2} \times \frac{1}{2} = \frac{1}{4}$

He should use $\frac{1}{4}$ pound of veal.

To multiply fractions, first multiply the numerators. Then multiply the denominators.

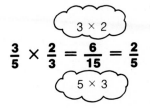

$$\frac{3}{5} \times \frac{2}{3} = \frac{6}{15} = \frac{2}{5}$$

Multiply.

1. $\frac{1}{3} \times \frac{1}{2}$

2. $\frac{3}{5} \times \frac{5}{9}$

3. $\frac{1}{4} \times \frac{1}{4}$

4. $\frac{2}{3} \times \frac{5}{6}$

5. $\frac{1}{8} \times \frac{3}{4}$

6. $\frac{7}{10} \times \frac{1}{2}$

7. $\frac{4}{5} \times \frac{1}{6}$

8. $\frac{5}{7} \times \frac{1}{5}$

9. $\frac{4}{9} \times \frac{3}{4}$

10. $\frac{7}{12} \times \frac{3}{7}$

11. $\frac{1}{3} \times \frac{5}{8}$

12. $\frac{1}{2} \times \frac{1}{9}$

13. $\frac{2}{5} \times \frac{3}{4}$

14. $\frac{6}{7} \times \frac{1}{2}$

15. $\frac{8}{9} \times \frac{1}{4}$

16. $\frac{1}{6} \times \frac{3}{7}$

17. $\frac{1}{5} \times \frac{1}{5}$

18. $\frac{3}{8} \times \frac{3}{8}$

19. $\frac{5}{16} \times \frac{2}{3}$

20. $\frac{9}{10} \times \frac{5}{6}$

21. $\frac{1}{2} \times \frac{1}{2} \times \frac{1}{2}$

22. $\frac{2}{3} \times \frac{1}{2} \times \frac{3}{4}$

23. $\frac{1}{2} \times \frac{1}{4} \times \frac{3}{4}$

24. $\frac{5}{6} \times \frac{1}{5} \times \frac{3}{4}$

Some students were asked which potato chips, Crispies or Crunchies, they liked best. Here are the results.

Crispies

Preferred by $\frac{3}{8}$ of those surveyed.
Of these, $\frac{1}{3}$ were girls; $\frac{2}{3}$ were boys.

Crunchies

Preferred by $\frac{1}{2}$ of those surveyed.
Of these, $\frac{3}{5}$ were girls; $\frac{2}{5}$ were boys.

No Preference

$\frac{1}{8}$ of those surveyed.
Of these, $\frac{1}{2}$ were girls; $\frac{1}{2}$ were boys.

What fraction of all students surveyed were

25. girls who preferred Crispies? (Find $\frac{1}{3}$ of $\frac{3}{8}$, or $\frac{1}{3} \times \frac{3}{8}$.)

26. boys who preferred Crispies?

27. girls who preferred Crunchies?

28. boys who preferred Crunchies?

29. girls having no preference?

30. boys having no preference?

Multiplying Fractions: A Shortcut

A. Find $\frac{5}{6} \times \frac{7}{10}$.

$$\frac{5}{6} \times \frac{7}{10} = \frac{35}{60} = \frac{7}{12}$$

Sometimes you can use a shortcut when you multiply.

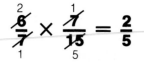

A numerator, 5, and a denominator, 10, were divided by 5.

B. Find $\frac{6}{7} \times \frac{7}{15}$.

Sometimes you can use the shortcut more than once.

$$\frac{\cancel{6}^{\,2}}{\cancel{7}_{\,1}} \times \frac{\cancel{7}^{\,1}}{\cancel{15}_{\,5}} = \frac{2}{5}$$

A numerator, 6, and a denominator, 15, were divided by 3.

Each 7 was divided by 7.

Multiply.

1. $\frac{2}{3} \times \frac{1}{4}$

2. $\frac{3}{5} \times \frac{1}{3}$

3. $\frac{1}{2} \times \frac{4}{7}$

4. $\frac{7}{8} \times \frac{4}{5}$

5. $\frac{2}{3} \times \frac{6}{7}$

6. $\frac{9}{10} \times \frac{5}{8}$

7. $\frac{5}{6} \times \frac{3}{4}$

8. $\frac{5}{12} \times \frac{8}{9}$

9. $\frac{6}{7} \times \frac{1}{9}$

10. $\frac{4}{5} \times \frac{3}{10}$

11. $\frac{1}{6} \times \frac{5}{9}$

12. $\frac{4}{9} \times \frac{3}{8}$

13. $\frac{3}{4} \times \frac{1}{12}$

14. $\frac{5}{8} \times \frac{8}{15}$

15. $\frac{2}{3} \times \frac{9}{10}$

16. $\frac{5}{8} \times \frac{4}{5}$

17. $\frac{5}{14} \times \frac{14}{5}$

18. $\frac{1}{2} \times \frac{7}{9}$

19. $\frac{6}{7} \times \frac{4}{9}$

20. $\frac{4}{5} \times \frac{5}{16}$

21. $\frac{7}{8} \times \frac{3}{14}$

22. $\frac{11}{12} \times \frac{9}{10}$

23. $\frac{15}{16} \times \frac{8}{9}$

24. $\frac{1}{2} \times \frac{2}{3} \times \frac{3}{4}$

25. $\frac{2}{7} \times \frac{1}{4} \times \frac{7}{8}$

26. $\frac{3}{10} \times \frac{5}{6} \times \frac{2}{3}$

27. $\frac{1}{3} \times \frac{5}{12} \times \frac{3}{5}$

28. $\frac{3}{4} \times \frac{2}{3} \times \frac{4}{3}$

29. $\frac{2}{3} \times \frac{2}{3} \times \frac{2}{3}$

30. $\frac{3}{8} \times \frac{5}{6} \times \frac{4}{5}$

**More practice
Set E, page 255**

Multiplying Fractions and Whole Numbers

LEMONADE FOR 100 PEOPLE

Boil 8 cups of sugar in 4 cups water
for 10 minutes. Cool. Then add 7 cups
lemon juice and 9 cans frozen juice
concentrate. Stir and add 8 sliced
oranges and 4 gallons of cold water.

A. Yvonne made $\frac{2}{3}$ of this recipe.
How many cups of sugar did she use?

Find $\frac{2}{3}$ of 8, or $\frac{2}{3} \times 8$.

$\frac{2}{3} \times 8$

$\frac{2}{3} \times \frac{8}{1} = \frac{16}{3} = 5\frac{1}{3}$

She used $5\frac{1}{3}$ cups of sugar.

B. About how many people will $\frac{2}{3}$ of the recipe serve?

Find $\frac{2}{3}$ of 100, or $\frac{2}{3} \times 100$.

$\frac{2}{3} \times 100$

$\frac{2}{3} \times \frac{100}{1} = \frac{200}{3} = 66\frac{2}{3}$

Two-thirds of the recipe will serve about 67 people.

Multiply to find each answer.

1. $\frac{1}{2}$ of 14
2. $\frac{3}{10}$ of 20
3. $\frac{2}{5}$ of 35
4. $\frac{3}{4}$ of 16
5. $\frac{5}{8}$ of 40
6. $\frac{2}{3}$ of 2
7. $\frac{8}{9}$ of 10
8. $\frac{7}{10}$ of 15
9. $\frac{4}{5}$ of 32
10. $\frac{1}{6}$ of 51
11. $\frac{3}{4}$ of 75
12. $\frac{3}{5}$ of 250
13. $\frac{1}{3}$ of 600
14. $\frac{1}{4}$ of 332
15. $\frac{7}{8}$ of 150
16. $\frac{1}{9}$ of 100
17. $\frac{5}{6}$ of 475
18. $\frac{3}{8}$ of 125

19. Paul is making $\frac{3}{4}$ of the lemonade recipe. Tell how much of each ingredient he should use.

20. About how many people will $\frac{3}{4}$ of the recipe serve?

21. Caroline invited 60 people to a party. Four-fifths of them came. How many people came to the party?

Multiplying Mixed Numbers

Pancakes (36 medium sized)

5 cups pancake mix
$3\frac{1}{3}$ cups milk
4 eggs
$4\frac{1}{2}$ tablespoons melted shortening

This is the recipe the students at Mills School will use for their pancake supper. They will make $2\frac{1}{2}$ times the recipe.

A. How many cups of pancake mix will they need?

Find $2\frac{1}{2} \times 5$. First write $2\frac{1}{2}$ and 5 as fractions.

$$2\frac{1}{2} \times 5$$
$$\frac{5}{2} \times \frac{5}{1} = \frac{25}{2} = 12\frac{1}{2}$$

They will need $12\frac{1}{2}$ cups of pancake mix.

B. How many cups of milk will they need?

Find $2\frac{1}{2} \times 3\frac{1}{3}$.

$$2\frac{1}{2} \times 3\frac{1}{3}$$
$$\frac{5}{2} \times \frac{10^{5}}{3} = \frac{25}{3} = 8\frac{1}{3}$$

They will need $8\frac{1}{3}$ cups of milk.

C. How many eggs will they need? How many tablespoons of shortening?

Multiply.

1. $1\frac{1}{3} \times 3\frac{1}{2}$

2. $7 \times 1\frac{3}{4}$

3. $2\frac{2}{3} \times \frac{3}{5}$

4. $4\frac{1}{2} \times 1\frac{1}{3}$

5. $3\frac{2}{5} \times 1\frac{1}{4}$

6. $1\frac{1}{8} \times 2\frac{2}{3}$

7. $1\frac{3}{4} \times 6$

8. $2\frac{2}{3} \times 2\frac{1}{2}$

9. $6\frac{1}{2} \times \frac{2}{13}$

10. $2\frac{5}{8} \times \frac{1}{7}$

11. $1\frac{8}{9} \times 1\frac{4}{5}$

12. $1\frac{2}{3} \times 8$

13. $4\frac{1}{2} \times 4\frac{1}{2}$

14. $3\frac{3}{10} \times 3\frac{1}{3}$

15. $3\frac{7}{8} \times \frac{8}{9}$

16. $1\frac{1}{2} \times 2\frac{1}{3} \times \frac{3}{4}$

17. $1\frac{2}{3} \times \frac{3}{5} \times 1\frac{7}{8}$

18. $2\frac{1}{4} \times 3\frac{1}{2} \times 2\frac{2}{3}$

Reciprocals

Find each answer.

19. A bread slicer cut a loaf of French bread into 12 slices, each $1\frac{7}{8}$ inches thick. How long was the loaf of bread?

20. Norma used $1\frac{1}{3}$ cups of popped popcorn to make one popcorn ball. How many cups of popped popcorn did she need for 25 popcorn balls?

21. A box of cereal contains 11 servings of $1\frac{1}{4}$ ounces each. How much do the contents of the box of cereal weigh?

22. Mel uses $\frac{3}{8}$ pound of ground meat for one large hamburger. How many pounds of meat does he need for 15 large hamburgers?

23. A chili recipe calls for $2\frac{3}{4}$ teaspoons of chili powder for every pound of ground beef. How many teaspoons of chili powder are needed for $5\frac{1}{2}$ pounds of meat?

24. A cookie recipe calls for $2\frac{3}{4}$ cups of flour. How much flour is needed for $2\frac{1}{2}$ times the recipe?

25. The cookie recipe makes $4\frac{1}{2}$ dozen cookies. How many cookies does $2\frac{1}{2}$ times the recipe make?

More practice
Set F, page 255

Two numbers whose product is 1 are *reciprocals*.

A. $\frac{4}{9}$ and $\frac{9}{4}$ are reciprocals.

$$\frac{4}{9} \times \frac{9}{4} = \frac{36}{36} = 1$$

B. $2\frac{2}{3}$ and $\frac{3}{8}$ are reciprocals.

$$2\frac{2}{3} = \frac{8}{3}$$
$$\downarrow$$
$$\frac{8}{3} \times \frac{3}{8} = \frac{24}{24} = 1$$

C. 5 and $\frac{1}{5}$ are reciprocals.

$$5 = \frac{5}{1}$$
$$\downarrow$$
$$\frac{5}{1} \times \frac{1}{5} = \frac{5}{5} = 1$$

Give the reciprocal of each number.

1. $\frac{3}{5}$ **6.** $3\frac{1}{4}$ **11.** $\frac{4}{7}$ **16.** $\frac{1}{3}$

2. $\frac{2}{3}$ **7.** $\frac{5}{6}$ **12.** $\frac{9}{10}$ **17.** $10\frac{1}{2}$

3. 6   **8.** 9   **13.** $1\frac{9}{10}$ **18.** 1

4. $\frac{1}{2}$ **9.** $\frac{7}{8}$ **14.** $2\frac{1}{3}$ **19.** $2\frac{3}{5}$

5. $1\frac{1}{2}$ **10.** $4\frac{2}{3}$ **15.** $3\frac{5}{8}$ **20.** $5\frac{3}{4}$

Using Multiplication: Area

A. Find the area of the shaded rectangle.

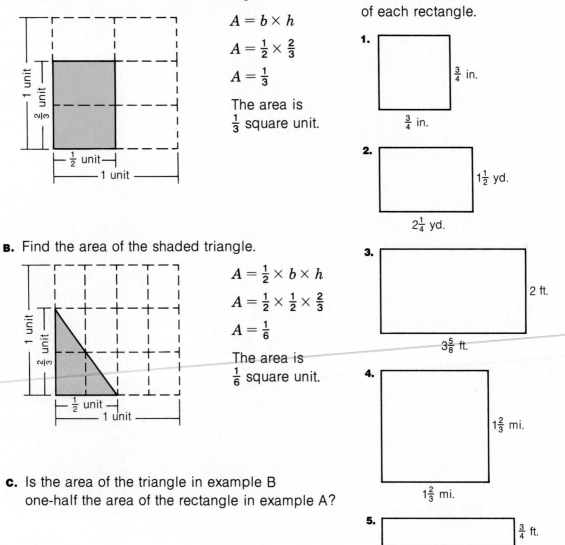

$$A = b \times h$$

$$A = \tfrac{1}{2} \times \tfrac{2}{3}$$

$$A = \tfrac{1}{3}$$

The area is
$\tfrac{1}{3}$ square unit.

Find the area
of each rectangle.

1.

$\tfrac{3}{4}$ in.

$\tfrac{3}{4}$ in.

2.

$1\tfrac{1}{2}$ yd.

$2\tfrac{1}{4}$ yd.

B. Find the area of the shaded triangle.

$$A = \tfrac{1}{2} \times b \times h$$

$$A = \tfrac{1}{2} \times \tfrac{1}{2} \times \tfrac{2}{3}$$

$$A = \tfrac{1}{6}$$

The area is
$\tfrac{1}{6}$ square unit.

3.

2 ft.

$3\tfrac{5}{8}$ ft.

4.

$1\tfrac{2}{3}$ mi.

$1\tfrac{2}{3}$ mi.

C. Is the area of the triangle in example B
one-half the area of the rectangle in example A?

5.

$\tfrac{3}{4}$ ft.

$3\tfrac{2}{3}$ ft.

side trip

Find the area
of each triangle.

6.

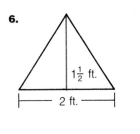

$1\frac{1}{2}$ ft.

2 ft.

7.

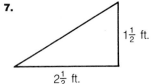

$1\frac{1}{2}$ ft.

$2\frac{1}{2}$ ft.

8.

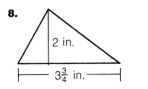

2 in.

$3\frac{3}{4}$ in.

9.

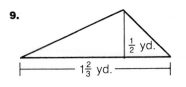

$\frac{1}{2}$ yd.

$1\frac{2}{3}$ yd.

10.

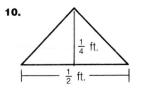

$\frac{1}{4}$ ft.

$\frac{1}{2}$ ft.

Is There a Least Fraction?

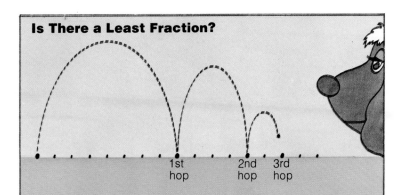

1st hop   2nd hop   3rd hop

A flea saw a dog's nose a long way away. The flea hopped $\frac{1}{2}$ of the distance to the nose. Then it grew cautious and hopped only $\frac{1}{2}$ of the remaining distance. It continued this way, covering just $\frac{1}{2}$ of the remaining distance with each hop.

What fraction of the distance remained

1. after the first hop? $\frac{1}{2} \times 1 = \frac{1}{2}$

2. after the second hop? $\frac{1}{2} \times \frac{1}{2} = \frac{1}{4}$

3. after the third hop?

4. after the fourth hop?

5. after the tenth hop?

6. The fractions in exercises 1–5 are getting smaller and smaller. If you continued, do you think you would get a fraction that is equal to zero?

7. Ask a friend to name the least fraction that he or she can think of. The fraction should be greater than zero. Then name a fraction that is less than your friend's fraction.

Dividing by Fractions

Shelly is making a beaded belt. The design repeats approximately every $\frac{3}{8}$ inch, and the bands of color are $\frac{3}{4}$ inch wide.

A. The design occurs 16 times in 6 inches of belt.

$$6 \div \frac{3}{8} = 16$$

You can find the answer by counting the designs in 6 inches of belt.

$$6 \times \frac{8}{3} = 16$$

B. How many bands of color are in $4\frac{1}{2}$ inches of belt?

$$4\frac{1}{2} \div \frac{3}{4} = \text{▦}$$

Count the bands in $4\frac{1}{2}$ inches.

$$4\frac{1}{2} \times \frac{4}{3} = \text{▦}$$

There are ▦ bands of color.

C. How many designs are in $\frac{3}{4}$ inch of belt?

$$\frac{3}{4} \div \frac{3}{8} = \text{▦}$$

Count the designs in $\frac{3}{4}$ inch of belt.

$$\frac{3}{4} \times \frac{8}{3} = \text{▦}$$

There are ▦ designs.

D. How do reciprocals help you divide by fractions?

■ *Dividing by a number is the same as multiplying by its reciprocal.*

$1\frac{2}{5} \div \frac{9}{10}$

$1\frac{2}{5} \times \frac{10}{9} = \frac{7}{\underset{1}{5}} \times \frac{\overset{2}{10}}{9} = \frac{14}{9} = 1\frac{5}{9}$

Complete the computation.

1. $\frac{5}{8} \div \frac{3}{4} = \frac{5}{8} \times \frac{4}{3}$

2. $\frac{2}{3} \div \frac{1}{3} = \frac{2}{3} \times \frac{\text{▦}}{1}$

3. $3\frac{3}{7} \div \frac{2}{3} = 3\frac{3}{7} \times \frac{3}{\text{▦}}$

4. $1\frac{3}{4} \div \frac{5}{6} = 1\frac{3}{4} \times \frac{\text{▦}}{5}$

Divide.

5. $\frac{9}{10} \div \frac{1}{5}$

6. $\frac{5}{6} \div \frac{1}{3}$

7. $1\frac{1}{2} \div \frac{3}{4}$

8. $\frac{7}{8} \div \frac{1}{6}$

9. $2\frac{3}{4} \div \frac{3}{8}$

10. $8 \div \frac{2}{3}$

11. $3\frac{1}{3} \div \frac{5}{7}$

12. $\frac{3}{5} \div \frac{9}{10}$

13. $\frac{7}{12} \div \frac{3}{4}$

14. $\frac{8}{9} \div \frac{5}{6}$

15. $4\frac{1}{2} \div \frac{3}{5}$

16. $6\frac{2}{3} \div \frac{1}{2}$

17. $1\frac{2}{3} \div \frac{7}{8}$

18. $12 \div \frac{4}{5}$

19. $15 \div \frac{5}{8}$

20. $3\frac{1}{2} \div \frac{2}{3}$

21. $2\frac{1}{7} \div \frac{3}{4}$

22. $\frac{15}{16} \div \frac{5}{8}$

Give each answer.

23. Sarah had $1\frac{7}{8}$ yards of quilted gingham. How many complete purses can she make if she uses $\frac{1}{3}$ yard of fabric for each purse?

Find $1\frac{7}{8} \div \frac{1}{3}$.

24. Gary has $3\frac{1}{2}$ yards of man-made leather fabric. How many complete vests can he make if he uses $\frac{5}{8}$ yard for each vest?

25. June is making a 36-inch string of beads. Each bead is $\frac{3}{8}$ inch long. How many beads will she need?

26. How many beads, each $\frac{1}{32}$ inch long, are needed to make a 1-inch string of beads?

27. Ruth is braiding strips of material for a rug. How many strips, each $\frac{3}{4}$ inch wide, can she cut from 54 inches of material?

28. Dianne can paint decorations on a shirt in $\frac{2}{3}$ hour. How many shirts can she decorate in 5 hours?

**More practice
Set G, page 255**

Dividing Mixed Numbers

A. Tom uses a strip of leather $2\frac{2}{3}$ feet long to make a belt. How many belts can he make from a 16-foot strip of leather?

Find $16 \div 2\frac{2}{3}$.

$$16 \div 2\frac{2}{3}$$

$$\frac{16}{1} \div \frac{8}{3} = \frac{\overset{2}{\cancel{16}}}{1} \times \frac{3}{\cancel{8}} = \frac{6}{1} = 6$$

He can make 6 belts from a 16-foot strip.

B. It takes Tom $1\frac{1}{2}$ hours to decorate one belt. How many belts can he decorate in $3\frac{3}{4}$ hours?

Find $3\frac{3}{4} \div 1\frac{1}{2}$.

$$3\frac{3}{4} \div 1\frac{1}{2}$$

$$\frac{15}{4} \div \frac{3}{2} = \frac{\overset{5}{\cancel{15}}}{\underset{2}{\cancel{4}}} \times \frac{\overset{1}{\cancel{2}}}{\underset{1}{\cancel{3}}} = \frac{5}{2} = 2\frac{1}{2}$$

He can decorate $2\frac{1}{2}$ belts in $3\frac{3}{4}$ hours.

Divide.

1. $5 \div 3\frac{1}{3}$

2. $1\frac{3}{4} \div 2\frac{1}{2}$

3. $4\frac{1}{6} \div 7\frac{1}{2}$

4. $6\frac{1}{2} \div 4$

5. $4\frac{2}{3} \div 1\frac{1}{3}$

6. $2\frac{5}{8} \div 7$

7. $5\frac{1}{3} \div 2\frac{2}{3}$

8. $8 \div 2\frac{2}{3}$

9. $2\frac{2}{7} \div 5\frac{1}{3}$

10. $9 \div 6\frac{3}{4}$

11. $3\frac{3}{4} \div 3\frac{3}{4}$

12. $6\frac{2}{3} \div 5$

13. $1\frac{7}{8} \div 1\frac{2}{3}$

14. $7\frac{1}{2} \div 2$

15. $10 \div 4\frac{3}{8}$

16. $2\frac{4}{5} \div 1\frac{3}{4}$

17. $8\frac{1}{4} \div 1\frac{1}{2}$

18. $3\frac{1}{4} \div 1\frac{1}{6}$

Give each answer.

19. $6\frac{3}{4}$ ounces of yarn.
$2\frac{1}{4}$ ounces for each scarf.
How many scarfs?

20. $13\frac{3}{4}$ pounds of wax.
$2\frac{3}{4}$ pounds of wax for each candle.
How many candles?

21. 39 inches of string.
$6\frac{1}{2}$ inches for each candlewick.
How many candlewicks?

22. $5\frac{1}{4}$ ounces of silver.
$1\frac{3}{4}$ ounces for each belt buckle.
How many buckles?

23. $11\frac{1}{2}$ yards of fabric.
$2\frac{7}{8}$ yards for each costume.
How many costumes?

24. $8\frac{1}{8}$ yards of felt.
$1\frac{5}{8}$ yards for each jacket.
How many jackets?

**More practice
Set H, page 255**

Plan a party for 48 people.

1. Decide what refreshments you are going to serve; for example, fruit punch and cookies.

2. Find recipes for the refreshments you have to make.

3. Decide how many times you will have to make each recipe so that you will have enough. If you are using a dessert recipe that serves 18, for example, you will probably want to make 3 times the recipe.

$$48 \div 18 = 2\frac{2}{3} \approx 3$$

4. For each recipe, list how much of each ingredient you will need. For example, suppose that a cake recipe calls for $2\frac{1}{4}$ cups of flour, and you are going to make 3 cakes. Then you will need $3 \times 2\frac{1}{4}$, or $6\frac{3}{4}$, cups of flour.

Changing Fractions to Decimals

You can use division to express a fraction as a decimal.

A. Sometimes you can divide until the remainder is zero.

To express $\frac{5}{16}$ as a decimal, divide 5 by 16. Divide until the remainder is 0.

$$
\begin{array}{r}
.3125 \\
16)\overline{5.0000} \\
-48 \\
\hline
20 \\
-16 \\
\hline
40 \\
-32 \\
\hline
80 \\
-80 \\
\hline
0
\end{array}
$$

$\frac{5}{16} = .3125$

B. Sometimes you will never get a remainder of zero.

To express $\frac{3}{11}$ as a decimal, divide 3 by 11. Give your answer to the nearest thousandth.

$$
\begin{array}{r}
.2727 \\
11)\overline{3.0000} \\
-22 \\
\hline
80 \\
-77 \\
\hline
30 \\
-22 \\
\hline
80 \\
-77 \\
\hline
3
\end{array}
$$

$\frac{3}{11}$ is .273 to the nearest thousandth.

$\frac{3}{11} \approx .273$

Divide to express each fraction as a decimal. For exercises 1–12, continue dividing until the remainder is zero.

1. $\frac{3}{4}$

2. $\frac{1}{2}$

3. $\frac{7}{8}$

4. $\frac{3}{10}$

5. $\frac{4}{5}$

6. $\frac{29}{100}$

7. $\frac{1}{5}$

8. $\frac{9}{10}$

9. $\frac{7}{20}$

10. $\frac{3}{8}$

11. $\frac{6}{25}$

12. $\frac{15}{16}$

For exercises 13–24, give your answers to the nearest thousandth.

13. $\frac{1}{3}$

14. $\frac{1}{12}$

15. $\frac{1}{9}$

16. $\frac{2}{7}$

17. $\frac{5}{6}$

18. $\frac{4}{13}$

19. $\frac{7}{12}$

20. $\frac{4}{9}$

21. $\frac{2}{3}$

22. $\frac{1}{7}$

23. $\frac{9}{11}$

24. $\frac{1}{6}$

careers

Salesperson

Sometimes fabrics are sold by the yard, and a customer will buy a fraction of a yard. In determining the total price, the salesperson either uses a chart or multiplies the number of yards by the price per yard. Any fraction of a cent is rounded up to the next whole number.

How would you find the cost of $1\frac{7}{8}$ yards of fabric that sells for $2.29 per yard?

Think of $2.29 as 229 cents.

$$1\frac{7}{8} \times 229$$

Multiply.

$$\frac{15}{8} \times \frac{229}{1} = \frac{3435}{8} = 429\frac{3}{8}$$

Round the answer up to the next whole number. 430 cents is $4.30.

The fabric would cost $4.30.

For each exercise, find the total price.

1. $2\frac{1}{4}$ yards of corduroy at $1.79 per yard

2. $5\frac{1}{3}$ yards of ribbon at $.39 per yard

3. $6\frac{2}{3}$ yards of gingham at $1.29 per yard

4. $14\frac{1}{2}$ yards of drapery fabric at $2.25 per yard

5. $3\frac{1}{8}$ yards of wool suiting at $8.49 per yard

Chapter 12 Test
Multiplying and Dividing Fractions and Mixed Numbers, Pages 238–251

Multiplying fractions and mixed numbers, pages 238–243

Multiply.

1. $\frac{3}{4} \times \frac{3}{4}$

2. $\frac{5}{6} \times \frac{9}{10}$

3. $1\frac{1}{3} \times 6$

4. $2\frac{1}{2} \times \frac{3}{4}$

5. $1\frac{2}{3} \times 1\frac{4}{5}$

6. $2\frac{1}{4} \times \frac{1}{3} \times 1\frac{1}{2}$

7. Find $\frac{3}{5}$ of 25.

8. Find $\frac{3}{8}$ of 60.

Give the reciprocal of each number.

9. $\frac{5}{8}$

10. 3

11. $1\frac{1}{3}$

Dividing fractions and mixed numbers, pages 246–249

Divide.

12. $\frac{2}{3} \div \frac{5}{6}$

13. $\frac{7}{8} \div \frac{3}{4}$

14. $\frac{1}{2} \div \frac{1}{5}$

15. $9 \div \frac{3}{5}$

16. $1\frac{1}{3} \div 8$

17. $1\frac{3}{8} \div \frac{7}{8}$

18. $5\frac{1}{4} \div 1\frac{3}{4}$

19. $2\frac{1}{2} \div 3\frac{1}{3}$

Changing fractions to decimals, page 250

20. Express $\frac{3}{4}$ as a decimal.

21. Express $\frac{2}{3}$ as a decimal to the nearest thousandth.

Problem solving, pages 238–239, 241–249

Find each answer.

22. A pudding recipe calls for $2\frac{1}{2}$ cups of milk. Bradley made $1\frac{1}{2}$ times the recipe. How much milk did he use?

23. A punch recipe calls for $4\frac{1}{2}$ quarts of ginger ale. Stella made $\frac{1}{3}$ of the recipe. How many quarts of ginger ale did she use?

24. How many $\frac{3}{4}$-inch notebooks will make a stack $5\frac{1}{4}$ inches high?

25. A glass holds $1\frac{1}{2}$ cups of juice. How many glasses can be filled with 10 cups of juice?

Find each area.

26.
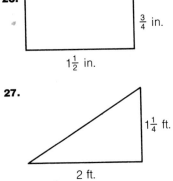
$\frac{3}{4}$ in.

$1\frac{1}{2}$ in.

27.
$1\frac{1}{4}$ ft.

2 ft.

Unit 4 Test

Number theory, pages 196–207

1. List all of the factors of 18.

2. List the first five multiples of 3.

Tell whether the number is prime or composite.

3. 4   4. 13   5. 35

6. Write the prime factorization of 54.

7. Find the GCF of 12 and 32.

8. Find the LCM of 9 and 15.

Adding and subtracting fractions and mixed numbers, pages 210–235

9. Write four fractions equal to $\frac{3}{4}$.

10. Reduce $\frac{6}{16}$ to lowest terms.

11. Find $129 \div 5$ and give the answer as a mixed number.

12. Write $5\frac{1}{3}$ as a fraction.

13. Write $\frac{25}{4}$ as a mixed number.

14. Write $\frac{5}{6}$ and $\frac{3}{4}$ with a common denominator.

Replace ● with > or <.

15. $4\frac{2}{3}$ ● $4\frac{3}{4}$

Find each answer.

16. $\frac{2}{7} + \frac{1}{2}$

17. $1\frac{5}{8} + 2\frac{3}{4}$

18. $5\frac{3}{5} + 3\frac{1}{3}$

19. $\frac{5}{6} - \frac{3}{8}$

20. $8\frac{4}{5} - 4\frac{3}{10}$

21. $5\frac{1}{2} - 1\frac{2}{3}$

22. Jean was $51\frac{3}{4}$ inches tall at the beginning of the year. She has grown $2\frac{3}{4}$ inches. How tall is she now?

23. It is 18 miles from Summit to Redsands. Mrs. Ortega has driven $10\frac{7}{10}$ miles. How much farther does she have to go?

Multiplying and dividing fractions and mixed numbers, pages 238–251

24. Give the reciprocal of $1\frac{2}{3}$.

25. Express $\frac{5}{6}$ as a decimal to the nearest thousandth.

26. Find $\frac{2}{7}$ of 25.

Find each answer.

27. $\frac{4}{5} \times \frac{3}{10}$

28. $1\frac{1}{2} \times 2\frac{3}{4}$

29. $2\frac{2}{5} \times 4\frac{1}{6}$

30. $\frac{2}{3} \div \frac{3}{8}$

31. $8 \div \frac{4}{9}$

32. $3\frac{3}{4} \div 2\frac{1}{2}$

33. A rectangle is $4\frac{1}{4}$ feet long and $3\frac{1}{2}$ feet wide. Find the area.

34. Yesterday Tony drank $1\frac{1}{2}$ quarts of milk. Stanley drank $1\frac{1}{2}$ times as much. How much milk did Stanley drink?

More Practice

Set A

1. $\frac{2}{3} + \frac{2}{3}$

2. $\frac{5}{8} + \frac{7}{8}$

3. $\frac{4}{15} + \frac{7}{15}$

4. $\frac{2}{3} + \frac{1}{2}$

5. $\frac{1}{2} + \frac{7}{10}$

6. $\frac{5}{8} + \frac{11}{16}$

7. $\frac{7}{9} + \frac{1}{3}$

8. $\frac{5}{12} + \frac{4}{9}$

9. $\frac{3}{4} + \frac{1}{3}$

10. $\frac{7}{10} + \frac{1}{4}$

11. $\frac{1}{2} + \frac{5}{7}$

12. $\frac{7}{12} + \frac{5}{6}$

13. $\frac{3}{10} + \frac{4}{5}$

14. $\frac{3}{5} + \frac{7}{15}$

15. $\frac{5}{6} + \frac{3}{8}$

16. $\frac{9}{16} + \frac{3}{4}$

17. $\frac{3}{5} + \frac{1}{2} + \frac{5}{6}$

18. $\frac{2}{3} + \frac{1}{6} + \frac{3}{4}$

Set B

1. $3\frac{3}{10} + 8\frac{4}{5}$

2. $7\frac{1}{2} + 25\frac{5}{6}$

3. $4\frac{7}{10} + 9\frac{1}{5}$

4. $8\frac{5}{9} + 6\frac{1}{3}$

5. $4\frac{2}{7} + 9\frac{4}{7}$

6. $12\frac{1}{4} + 5\frac{3}{8}$

7. $6\frac{1}{3} + 50\frac{3}{7}$

8. $9\frac{7}{10} + 4\frac{5}{8}$

9. $7\frac{3}{4} + 20\frac{5}{6}$

10. $8\frac{2}{5} + 10\frac{1}{2}$

11. $30\frac{2}{3} + 7\frac{1}{6}$

12. $10\frac{5}{10} + 6\frac{9}{10}$

13. $15\frac{1}{3} + 23\frac{3}{5}$

14. $29\frac{2}{9} + 47\frac{5}{9}$

15. $38\frac{5}{12} + 61\frac{3}{4}$

16. $7\frac{3}{8} + 1\frac{2}{3} + 4\frac{1}{2}$

17. $3\frac{5}{6} + 8\frac{1}{2} + 5\frac{3}{4}$

18. $6\frac{2}{3} + 9\frac{4}{9} + 2\frac{1}{6}$

Set C

1. $\frac{7}{9} - \frac{4}{9}$

2. $\frac{7}{8} - \frac{3}{4}$

3. $\frac{2}{3} - \frac{3}{7}$

4. $\frac{5}{6} - \frac{1}{3}$

5. $\frac{7}{10} - \frac{1}{5}$

6. $\frac{4}{7} - \frac{3}{14}$

7. $\frac{5}{12} - \frac{1}{4}$

8. $\frac{3}{10} - \frac{1}{8}$

9. $\frac{4}{5} - \frac{7}{10}$

10. $\frac{1}{2} - \frac{2}{7}$

11. $\frac{7}{8} - \frac{3}{8}$

12. $\frac{2}{3} - \frac{2}{5}$

13. $\frac{5}{7} - \frac{1}{3}$

14. $\frac{3}{4} - \frac{1}{6}$

15. $\frac{6}{7} - \frac{1}{4}$

16. $\frac{2}{3} - \frac{1}{9}$

17. $\frac{5}{8} - \frac{1}{7}$

18. $\frac{3}{5} - \frac{1}{10}$

Set D

1. $8 - 4\frac{2}{5}$

2. $13 - 7\frac{1}{2}$

3. $4 - 1\frac{5}{8}$

4. $11 - 9\frac{3}{4}$

5. $16 - 3\frac{4}{7}$

6. $2 - 1\frac{1}{3}$

7. $9 - \frac{5}{6}$

8. $14 - 5\frac{4}{5}$

9. $6 - 2\frac{2}{3}$

10. $12\frac{1}{4} - 4\frac{3}{4}$

11. $7\frac{1}{7} - 2\frac{5}{7}$

12. $14\frac{3}{10} - 9\frac{7}{10}$

13. $9\frac{1}{6} - 1\frac{5}{6}$

14. $11\frac{3}{8} - 7\frac{5}{8}$

15. $2\frac{5}{12} - 1\frac{7}{12}$

16. $8\frac{2}{9} - 5\frac{5}{9}$

17. $10\frac{1}{3} - 3\frac{2}{3}$

18. $25\frac{2}{5} - 16\frac{4}{5}$

More Practice

Set E	Set F	Set G	Set H

Set E

1. $\frac{1}{3} \times \frac{3}{7}$

2. $\frac{2}{5} \times \frac{5}{8}$

3. $\frac{3}{10} \times \frac{5}{6}$

4. $\frac{1}{2} \times \frac{4}{9}$

5. $\frac{2}{7} \times \frac{7}{8}$

6. $\frac{3}{4} \times \frac{5}{9}$

7. $\frac{5}{12} \times \frac{4}{5}$

8. $\frac{2}{9} \times \frac{3}{7}$

9. $\frac{2}{3} \times \frac{9}{14}$

10. $\frac{7}{12} \times \frac{9}{14}$

11. $\frac{3}{8} \times \frac{4}{15}$

12. $\frac{3}{5} \times \frac{10}{17}$

13. $\frac{7}{20} \times \frac{20}{7}$

14. $\frac{2}{3} \times \frac{5}{8} \times \frac{4}{5}$

15. $\frac{1}{2} \times \frac{1}{3} \times \frac{6}{7}$

16. $\frac{3}{4} \times \frac{5}{6} \times \frac{4}{7}$

17. $\frac{3}{7} \times \frac{1}{4} \times \frac{8}{9}$

18. $\frac{2}{5} \times \frac{3}{8} \times \frac{5}{9}$

Set F

1. $3\frac{1}{3} \times 2\frac{2}{5}$

2. $8 \times 4\frac{5}{6}$

3. $1\frac{3}{4} \times 6\frac{2}{7}$

4. $5\frac{1}{2} \times 3\frac{3}{5}$

5. $2\frac{1}{3} \times \frac{4}{7}$

6. $4\frac{4}{11} \times 1\frac{3}{8}$

7. $3\frac{1}{8} \times \frac{4}{5}$

8. $5\frac{1}{4} \times 2\frac{2}{3}$

9. $4\frac{5}{8} \times 4$

10. $1\frac{3}{7} \times 3\frac{1}{2}$

11. $9\frac{1}{5} \times 5\frac{5}{6}$

12. $2\frac{1}{12} \times 8\frac{2}{5}$

13. $3\frac{4}{15} \times 4\frac{2}{7}$

14. $1\frac{5}{7} \times 1\frac{1}{6}$

15. $4\frac{1}{6} \times 2\frac{7}{10}$

16. $1\frac{2}{3} \times 5\frac{1}{7} \times 2\frac{4}{5}$

17. $\frac{3}{4} \times 3\frac{1}{5} \times 1\frac{3}{8}$

18. $4\frac{1}{6} \times 1\frac{3}{5} \times \frac{3}{10}$

Set G

1. $\frac{5}{8} \div \frac{5}{6}$

2. $\frac{7}{9} \div \frac{7}{12}$

3. $9 \div \frac{3}{7}$

4. $3\frac{1}{2} \div \frac{7}{8}$

5. $\frac{2}{3} \div \frac{4}{9}$

6. $11\frac{3}{8} \div \frac{1}{4}$

7. $\frac{4}{9} \div \frac{2}{3}$

8. $8\frac{3}{5} \div \frac{2}{5}$

9. $12 \div \frac{3}{4}$

10. $5\frac{1}{3} \div \frac{4}{5}$

11. $\frac{3}{4} \div \frac{3}{5}$

12. $1\frac{5}{9} \div \frac{1}{6}$

13. $\frac{7}{12} \div \frac{5}{8}$

14. $6\frac{1}{4} \div \frac{1}{2}$

15. $16 \div \frac{8}{9}$

16. $9\frac{5}{6} \div \frac{1}{3}$

17. $\frac{4}{5} \div \frac{2}{5}$

18. $7\frac{2}{5} \div \frac{1}{5}$

Set H

1. $3\frac{3}{5} \div 9$

2. $5\frac{1}{3} \div 4$

3. $4 \div 3\frac{1}{5}$

4. $8\frac{1}{5} \div 6\frac{3}{5}$

5. $2\frac{5}{6} \div 1\frac{4}{9}$

6. $1\frac{3}{4} \div 3\frac{1}{2}$

7. $6 \div 4\frac{2}{7}$

8. $3\frac{5}{8} \div 5\frac{3}{4}$

9. $4\frac{1}{2} \div 3$

10. $1\frac{4}{5} \div 2\frac{1}{4}$

11. $9\frac{3}{8} \div 8\frac{1}{3}$

12. $12 \div 6\frac{6}{7}$

13. $4\frac{2}{3} \div 7$

14. $5\frac{1}{6} \div 3\frac{2}{9}$

15. $7\frac{3}{5} \div 2\frac{2}{3}$

16. $9 \div 4\frac{1}{2}$

17. $2\frac{1}{4} \div 7\frac{1}{8}$

18. $6\frac{7}{8} \div 1\frac{4}{7}$

Individualized Skills Maintenance

Diagnosis

A. $7\overline{)3.605}$

$46\overline{)86.02}$

B. $.8\overline{)68.48}$

$.7\overline{)4.0306}$

C. $6.3\overline{)308.7}$

$.89\overline{)2162.7}$

D. $.312\overline{)6.1152}$

$40.7\overline{)256.41}$

E. Round each quotient to the nearest hundredth.

$2.5\overline{)9.063}$

$296\overline{)414}$

Practice

Set A (pp. 110–111)

1. $7\overline{)4.823}$

2. $9\overline{)47.61}$

3. $6\overline{)142.2}$

4. $8\overline{)7.552}$

5. $35\overline{)129.5}$

6. $21\overline{)159.6}$

7. $49\overline{)46.06}$

8. $57\overline{)21.66}$

Set B (pp. 112–113)

1. $.4\overline{)2.952}$

2. $.9\overline{)58.95}$

3. $.7\overline{).4382}$

4. $.9\overline{)17.028}$

5. $.3\overline{).4137}$

6. $.8\overline{)22.584}$

7. $.4\overline{).7388}$

8. $.6\overline{)9.426}$

Set C (pp. 112–113)

1. $3.8\overline{)311.6}$

2. $.49\overline{)22.393}$

3. $9.3\overline{)103.23}$

4. $.27\overline{)2.052}$

5. $8.9\overline{)809.9}$

6. $.76\overline{)465.88}$

7. $5.1\overline{)46.92}$

8. $.32\overline{)18.016}$

Set D (pp. 112–113)

1. $26.9\overline{)51.11}$

2. $.486\overline{).10206}$

3. $1.92\overline{)59.52}$

4. $.773\overline{)7.2662}$

5. $21.1\overline{)605.57}$

6. $3.51\overline{)4.3173}$

7. $61.3\overline{)3126.3}$

8. $3.93\overline{)21.222}$

Set E (pp. 116–117)

Round each quotient to the nearest hundredth.

1. $6\overline{)7}$

2. $.9\overline{)1.3}$

3. $7\overline{)9.7}$

4. $.8\overline{).73}$

5. $43\overline{)82}$

6. $.97\overline{)5.1}$

7. $2.6\overline{)5.45}$

8. $83\overline{)86.5}$

9. $4.8\overline{)45.19}$

10. $.57\overline{)2.985}$

11. $468\overline{)775}$

12. $5.22\overline{)80.3}$

13. $37.7\overline{)31.42}$

14. $.491\overline{).5724}$

15. $17.7\overline{)816.7}$

Unit 5

Ratio, Proportion, and Percent

$$\frac{1}{25} = \frac{16}{b}$$ — scale model
— actual car

Writing Equal Ratios

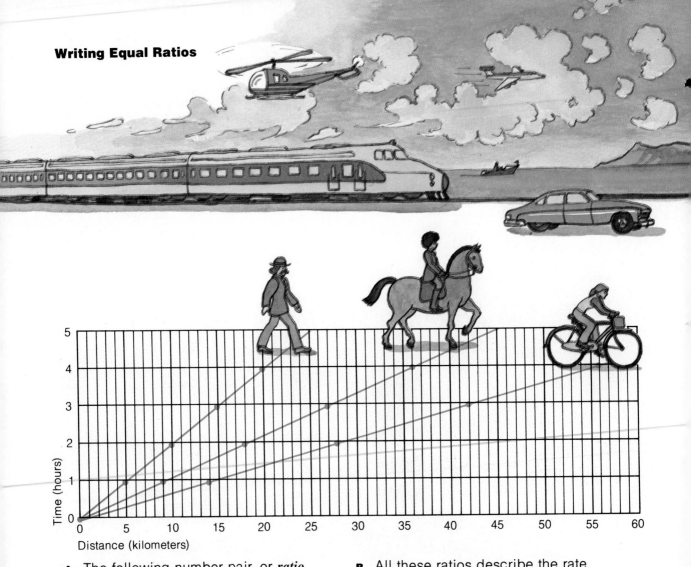

A. The following number pair, or *ratio*, describes the speed at which the person is walking.

$$\frac{15}{3}$$ — Kilometers
— Hours

15 to 3

B. All these ratios describe the rate of speed at which the person is walking. They are *equal ratios*.

$$\frac{5}{1} = \frac{10}{2} = \frac{15}{3} = \frac{20}{4}$$

c. Complete this ratio
for the speed of the horse.

$$\frac{\text{▦}}{1} \quad\begin{matrix}\text{— Kilometers}\\ \\ \text{— Hours}\end{matrix}$$

You can multiply to find equal ratios.

$$\frac{9}{1} = \overset{9 \times 2}{\underset{1 \times 2}{\frac{18}{2}}} = \overset{9 \times 3}{\underset{1 \times 3}{\frac{\text{▦}}{\text{▦}}}} = \overset{9 \times 4}{\underset{1 \times 4}{\frac{\text{▦}}{\text{▦}}}}$$

D. Complete this ratio
for the speed of the bicycle.

$$\frac{\text{▦}}{4} \quad\begin{matrix}\text{— Kilometers}\\ \\ \text{— Hours}\end{matrix}$$

You can divide to find equal ratios.
To find the speed of the bicycle per
hour, divide both 56 and 4 by 4.

$$\frac{56}{4} = \overset{56 \div 4}{\underset{4 \div 4}{\frac{\text{▦}}{1}}}$$

Multiply to complete each list
of equal ratios.

1. $\dfrac{2}{3} = \dfrac{4}{6} = \dfrac{\text{▦}}{\text{▦}} = \dfrac{\text{▦}}{\text{▦}} = \dfrac{\text{▦}}{\text{▦}}$

2. $\dfrac{4}{5} = \dfrac{8}{10} = \dfrac{\text{▦}}{\text{▦}} = \dfrac{\text{▦}}{\text{▦}} = \dfrac{\text{▦}}{\text{▦}}$

3. $\dfrac{5}{7} = \dfrac{10}{14} = \dfrac{\text{▦}}{\text{▦}} = \dfrac{\text{▦}}{\text{▦}} = \dfrac{\text{▦}}{\text{▦}}$

4. $\dfrac{9}{2} = \dfrac{18}{4} = \dfrac{\text{▦}}{\text{▦}} = \dfrac{\text{▦}}{\text{▦}} = \dfrac{\text{▦}}{\text{▦}}$

5. $\dfrac{8}{5} = \dfrac{16}{10} = \dfrac{\text{▦}}{\text{▦}} = \dfrac{\text{▦}}{\text{▦}} = \dfrac{\text{▦}}{\text{▦}}$

For each exercise, find the rate
of speed per hour.

6. Propeller airplane
1200 kilometers in 3 hours

7. Helicopter
300 kilometers in 2 hours

8. Train
400 kilometers in 4 hours

9. Boat
250 kilometers in 5 hours

10. For each of exercises 6–9, write
three equal ratios for the rate
of speed. Then use these ratios
to make a graph like the one
on page 260.

Cross-Products and Proportions

These ratios are equal.

$$\frac{2}{3} = \frac{4}{6} = \frac{6}{9} = \frac{8}{12} = \frac{10}{15}$$

Two ratios are equal and form a *proportion* if the cross-products are equal.

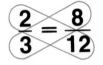

$$2 \times 12 \qquad 3 \times 8$$

$$24 \qquad 24$$

The cross-products are equal.

$\frac{2}{3} = \frac{8}{12}$ is a proportion.

Find the cross-products for each proportion.

1. $\frac{2}{7} = \frac{6}{21}$ **5.** $\frac{4}{10} = \frac{22}{55}$

2. $\frac{18}{3} = \frac{12}{2}$ **6.** $\frac{14}{21} = \frac{16}{24}$

3. $\frac{39}{26} = \frac{3}{2}$ **7.** $\frac{12}{28} = \frac{18}{42}$

4. $\frac{2}{6} = \frac{28}{84}$ **8.** $\frac{9}{42} = \frac{24}{112}$

Tell whether the ratios form a proportion. Find cross-products to help you decide.

9. $\frac{8}{12} \quad \frac{10}{15}$ **14.** $\frac{9}{32} \quad \frac{12}{48}$

10. $\frac{15}{25} \quad \frac{3}{5}$ **15.** $\frac{24}{52} \quad \frac{8}{18}$

11. $\frac{4}{6} \quad \frac{20}{24}$ **16.** $\frac{22}{14} \quad \frac{33}{21}$

12. $\frac{2}{6} \quad \frac{17}{51}$ **17.** $\frac{12}{15} \quad \frac{20}{25}$

13. $\frac{12}{21} \quad \frac{10}{15}$ **18.** $\frac{18}{14} \quad \frac{54}{42}$

More practice
Set A, page 318

Solving Proportions

You can use cross-products to find the missing number in a proportion.

Use a letter for the missing number.

$$\frac{6}{9} = \frac{b}{15}$$

Write the cross-products.

$$6 \times 15 = 9 \times b$$

$$90 = 9b$$

Find b.

$$10 = b$$

Use cross-products to solve these proportions.

1. $\frac{1}{2} = \frac{m}{16}$ **3.** $\frac{3}{4} = \frac{s}{16}$

2. $\frac{a}{4} = \frac{9}{1}$ **4.** $\frac{7}{5} = \frac{h}{10}$

5. $\frac{t}{5} = \frac{9}{15}$ **12.** $\frac{m}{9} = \frac{40}{12}$

6. $\frac{5}{n} = \frac{20}{16}$ **13.** $\frac{5}{n} = \frac{20}{8}$

7. $\frac{5}{8} = \frac{15}{x}$ **14.** $\frac{35}{5} = \frac{42}{a}$

8. $\frac{6}{8} = \frac{h}{20}$ **15.** $\frac{6}{12} = \frac{s}{50}$

9. $\frac{6}{21} = \frac{r}{70}$ **16.** $\frac{x}{10} = \frac{18}{4}$

10. $\frac{8}{7} = \frac{32}{n}$ **17.** $\frac{13}{26} = \frac{5}{b}$

11. $\frac{4}{10} = \frac{22}{b}$ **18.** $\frac{28}{n} = \frac{14}{21}$

More practice Set B, page 318

time out

You have two pails. One pail holds 9 liters. The other holds 4 liters. You need 6 liters of water. How can you use these two pails to measure 6 liters of water?

263

Using Proportions: Heartbeats

An elephant's heart beats about 9 times in 15 seconds. How many times does it beat in 60 seconds?

Write a proportion. Use a letter for the number of heartbeats in 60 seconds.

$$\frac{9}{15} = \frac{c}{60} \quad \begin{array}{l} \text{— Heartbeats} \\ \text{— Seconds} \end{array}$$

Write the cross-products.

$$9 \times 60 = 15 \times c$$

$$540 = 15c$$

Find c.

$$36 = c$$

Answer the question.

An elephant's heart beats about 36 times in 60 seconds.

For each exercise in the table, find
the number of heartbeats in 60 seconds.

	Animal	Heartbeats	Time
1.	Horse	10	15 sec.
2.	Lion	3	4 sec.
3.	Sheep	25	20 sec.
4.	Cat	65	30 sec.
5.	Rabbit	5	2 sec.
6.	Rat	43	6 sec.
7.	Mouse	115	12 sec.
8.	Canary	130	12 sec.
9.	Hummingbird	15	1 sec.
10.	Human	8	6 sec.

How long does it take for

11. a cat's heart to beat 13 times?

12. a horse's heart to beat 2 times?

13. a canary's heart to beat 1300 times?

14. a sheep's heart to beat 1000 times?

15. a mouse's heart to beat 1150 times?

★ 16. Find about how many heartbeats a
human has in 5 seconds.

   a. At rest, 80 per minute

   b. Walking fast, 105 per minute

   c. Running, 180 per minute

   d. Chopping wood, 200 per minute

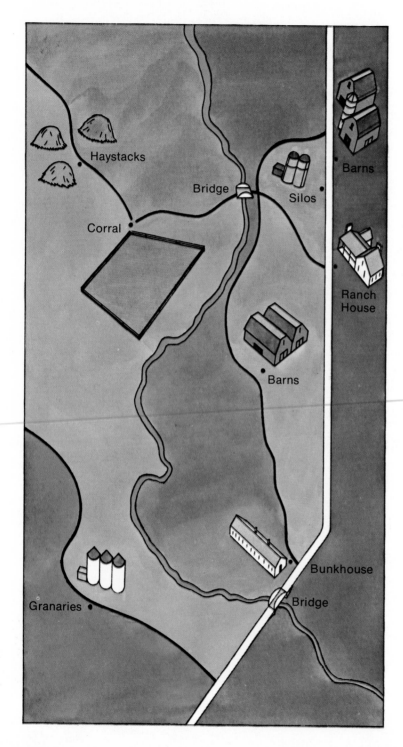

This is an aerial drawing of a large ranch. On the drawing, 2 centimeters represents an actual distance of 75 meters.

The scale is
2 centimeters = 75 meters.

On the drawing, it is 5 centimeters from the bunkhouse to the nearest barn. Use a proportion to find the actual distance.

$$\frac{2}{75} = \frac{5}{n}$$ — Centimeters
— Meters

$$2 \times n = 75 \times 5$$

$$2n = 375$$

$$n = 187.5$$

The actual distance is about 187.5 meters.

Find the actual distance between the two places in meters. Measure on the drawing to the nearest centimeter.

1. Haystacks and corral

2. Silos and nearest barns

3. One group of barns and the other

4. Bunkhouse and ranch house by way of the road

5. Granaries and silos by way of the road

6. About how many meters of fencing are needed to go around the corral?

7. A new house will be built on the river about 150 meters from the present house. How many centimeters would this be on the drawing?

★8. Suppose you walked along the river from one bridge to the other. About how many meters would you have walked?

careers

Architect

Architects plan and design many kinds of buildings. Plans are drawn to scale to show how the rooms will be arranged and how the buildings will look.

Here is an architect's floor plan of a house.

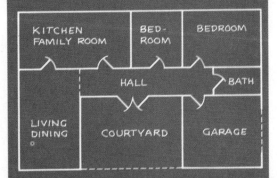

The architect used the scale 10 millimeters = 3 meters.

1. Measure each of the rooms in millimeters and find the dimensions to a tenth of a meter.

2. The new ranch house is to have these rooms all on one floor: living room, dining room, family room, kitchen, four bedrooms, and two baths.

Be an architect and design a plan for the house. Use the scale 10 millimeters = 2 meters.

Using Proportions: Atmospheric Pressure

These depths were reached during explorations under the sea.

Breath-held diving
250 feet (1971)

Scuba diving
437 feet (1968)

Salvage-observation chamber
1060 feet (1956)

Simulated chamber dive
2001 feet (1972)

Cable-controlled Underwater
Research Vehicle (CURV)
2850 feet (1966)

Bathyscaphe
35,802 feet (1960)

At sea level the pressure of the air is about 15 pounds per square inch. For every 33 feet you descend in salt water, there is an increase in pressure of about 15 pounds per square inch.

Find the pressure at 100 feet below sea level.

First use a proportion to find the increase in pressure from sea level to 100 feet below sea level. Round to the nearest whole number.

$$\frac{15}{33} = \frac{t}{100}$$
— Increase in pressure
— Feet below sea level

$$t \approx 45$$

The increase in pressure is about 45 pounds per square inch.

Now find the total pressure per square inch at 100 feet below sea level.

Pressure at sea level	Increase in pressure	Total
15	+ 45	= 60

The pressure at 100 feet below sea level is about 60 pounds per square inch.

Find the total pressure in pounds per square inch at each of these depths. Round your answers to the nearest whole number.

1. 10 feet below sea level

2. 33 feet below sea level

3. 50 feet below sea level

4. Breath-held diving: 250 feet below sea level

5. Scuba diving: 437 feet below sea level

6. Salvage-observation chamber: 1060 feet below sea level

7. Simulated chamber dive: 2001 feet below sea level

8. Cable-controlled Underwater Research Vehicle: 2850 feet below sea level

9. Bathyscaphe: 35,802 feet below sea level

★10. Ralph is 14 years old and has a body surface of about 2000 square inches. What would the total pressure on his body be at sea level? At 33 feet below sea level?

Using Proportions: Maps

The scale for this map is
1 centimeter = 300 kilometers.

The distance on the map between
Moose Factory and Yellowknife
is 7.9 centimeters. Find the
actual air distance.

$$\frac{1}{300} = \frac{7.9}{r} \begin{array}{l} \text{— Centimeters} \\ \text{— Kilometers} \end{array}$$

$$1 \times r = 300 \times 7.9$$

$$r = 2370$$

The air distance is
about 2370 kilometers.

For each exercise, find the approximate
air distance between the places. Measure
on the map to a tenth of a centimeter.

1. Yellowknife and Chilliwack

2. Medicine Hat and Moonbeam

3. Inuvik and Flin Flon

4. Flin Flon and Moose Factory

5. Chilliwack and St. Louis du Ha Ha

6. St. Louis du Ha Ha and Biggar

7. Come-by-Chance and Inuvik

8. One coast of Canada to the other

The scale for this map is 2 cm = 53 km.

For each exercise, find the approximate distance between the towns. Measure on the map to the nearest tenth of a centimeter. Round your answer to the nearest kilometer.

9. Grand Forks and Fargo

10. Bemidji and Crookston

11. Fargo and Winnipeg

12. Crookston and Emerson

13. Detroit Lakes and Bemidji

14. Portage La Prairie and Grand Forks

15. Thief River Falls and Fargo

Suppose you traveled at a speed of 88 kilometers per 60 minutes (1 hour). For each exercise, find about how many minutes it would take to go between the towns.

16. Grand Forks and Fargo

17. Bemidji and Crookston

18. Fargo and Winnipeg

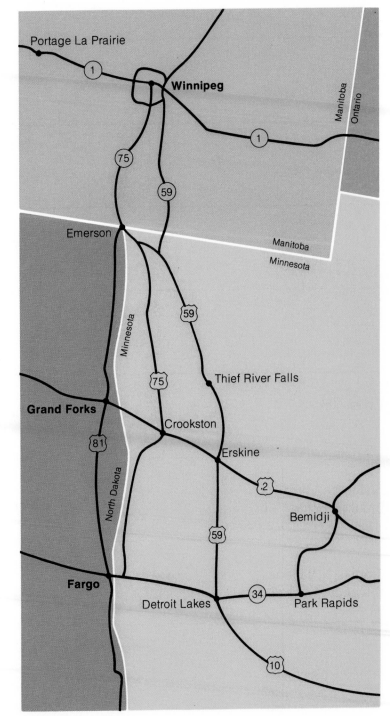

Using Proportions: Comparing Prices

Super Stores		Bargain Mart
Hamburger buns package of 6 - 38¢		Hamburger buns package of 8 - 57¢
Orange juice 16 ounces - 63¢		Orange juice 6 ounces - 28¢
Sweet rolls package of 4 - 51¢		Sweet rolls package of 6 - 85¢
Flashcubes 3 for $1.28		Flashcubes 12 for $4.80
Color film 12 exposures - $1.25		Color film 20 exposures - $1.79
Shampoo 8-ounce bottle - $1.69		Shampoo 12-ounce bottle - $2.29
Transistor batteries 2 for 68¢		Transistor batteries 6 for $2.10
Cola 12 pack - $1.59		Cola 8 pack - 99¢

Which is a better buy, 12 ounces of shampoo at Bargain Mart or 8 ounces at Super Stores?

For each bottle, find the price per ounce to the nearest cent.

$$\frac{12}{2.29} = \frac{1}{n} \quad \begin{array}{l} \text{— Ounces} \\ \text{— Dollars} \end{array}$$

$$n \approx .19$$

$$\frac{8}{1.69} = \frac{1}{n} \quad \begin{array}{l} \text{— Ounces} \\ \text{— Dollars} \end{array}$$

$$n \approx .21$$

The 12-ounce bottle is a better buy because the price per ounce is less.

For each item, tell which store offers the better buy.

1. Hamburger buns
2. Flashcubes
3. Color film
4. Sweet rolls
5. Orange juice
6. Cola
7. Transistor batteries

laboratory activity

1. You can use proportions to enlarge pictures. Find a picture you would like to enlarge. Lightly draw a grid of square centimeters over the picture.

2. Decide on a scale for enlarging the picture. For example, you might use 3 centimeters to represent 1 centimeter. On a piece of paper, make a grid of squares each 3 centimeters on a side.

3. Copy the part of the picture in each square centimeter in the corresponding square on the larger grid.

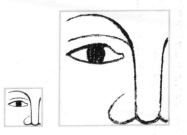

4. How would you reduce a picture?

Chapter 13 Test
Ratio and Proportion, Pages 260–273

Writing equal ratios, pages 260–261

1. Luis walked 10 kilometers in 2 hours. What was his rate of speed per hour?

2. Gail earned $48 in 6 weeks. At this rate, how much did she earn in 1 week?

Complete each list of equal ratios.

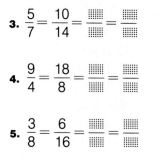

3. $\dfrac{5}{7} = \dfrac{10}{14} = \dfrac{}{} = \dfrac{}{}$

4. $\dfrac{9}{4} = \dfrac{18}{8} = \dfrac{}{} = \dfrac{}{}$

5. $\dfrac{3}{8} = \dfrac{6}{16} = \dfrac{}{} = \dfrac{}{}$

Cross-products and proportions, pages 262–263

Find the cross-products for each proportion.

6. $\dfrac{6}{9} = \dfrac{8}{12}$

7. $\dfrac{20}{16} = \dfrac{15}{12}$

Tell whether each pair of ratios forms a proportion.

8. $\dfrac{2}{5} \quad \dfrac{14}{35}$

10. $\dfrac{8}{26} \quad \dfrac{12}{39}$

9. $\dfrac{15}{25} \quad \dfrac{5}{8}$

11. $\dfrac{3}{100} \quad \dfrac{6}{175}$

Solve these proportions.

12. $\dfrac{n}{6} = \dfrac{20}{8}$

14. $\dfrac{15}{s} = \dfrac{6}{14}$

13. $\dfrac{2}{9} = \dfrac{n}{36}$

15. $\dfrac{n}{30} = \dfrac{22}{12}$

Problem solving, pages 264–273

16. On a map, the distance between two cities is 9.2 centimeters. The scale of the map is 2 centimeters = 3 kilometers. What is the actual distance between the cities?

17. In a drawing, the height of a building is 5.1 centimeters. The scale of the drawing is 3 centimeters = 25 meters. What is the actual height of the building?

18. Your heart beats 180 times per minute when you are running. How many times would it beat if you ran for 3 minutes?

19. A dozen licorice sticks cost 59¢. What is the cost of one licorice stick? Round to the nearest cent.

20. Three phonograph records cost $6.87. What is the cost of one record?

NOW EARN

REGULAR
PASSBOOKS   5%

GOLDEN INCOME
PASSBOOKS $5\frac{1}{2}$%

1 YEAR ($1000)
C.D.'S   6%

Percent

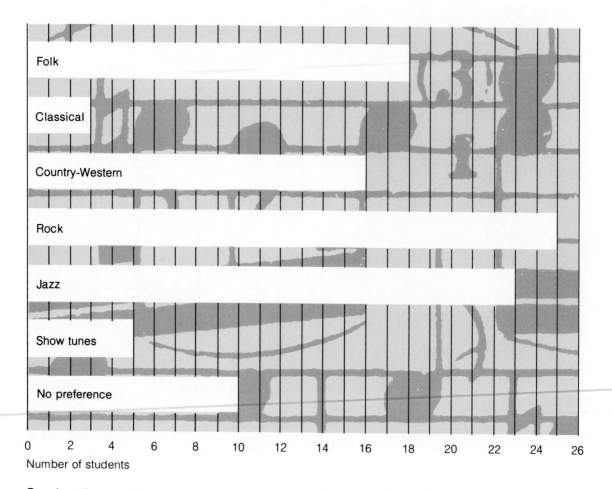

Number of students

One hundred junior-high-school students were surveyed. The graph shows the kinds of music they like best.

23 out of 100 students like jazz best. You can think of "23 out of 100" as $\frac{23}{100}$, or as 23 *percent*.

Percent means "hundredths." The symbol for percent is %.

$$\frac{23}{100} = 23\%$$

Use the graph. What percent of the students chose each of these as their favorite kind of music?

1. Folk

2. Show tunes

3. Rock

4. Classical

5. Country and Western

6. What percent had no preference?

7. List the kinds of music in order of preference, beginning with the most popular.

Write each fraction as a percent.

8. $\frac{83}{100}$

9. $\frac{41}{100}$

10. $\frac{9}{100}$

11. $\frac{95}{100}$

12. $\frac{50}{100}$

13. $\frac{12}{100}$

14. $\frac{38}{100}$

15. $\frac{100}{100}$

The table gives the ages of 100 junior-high-school students. Complete the table.

	Age in years	Number	Fraction	Percent
	Under 11	0	$\frac{0}{100}$	0%
16.	11	8	$\frac{8}{100}$	
17.	12		$\frac{35}{100}$	
18.	13	29	$\frac{}{100}$	
19.	14		$\frac{}{100}$	21%
20.	Over 14		$\frac{7}{100}$	

21. Forty-three out of the 100 students are either 11 or 12 years old. What percent of the students are 11 or 12?

22. What percent of the students are 12 or 13?

23. What percent of the students are 11, 12, 13, or 14?

24. What percent of the students are 11 or over 11?

Percents and Fractions

A. Last month $\frac{2}{3}$ of all the records sold at the Spinning Disc Shop were rock, folk, and jazz records. What percent of the sales were rock, folk, and jazz records?

$$\frac{t}{100} = \frac{2}{3}$$

Write the cross-products.

$$t \times 3 = 100 \times 2$$
$$3t = 200$$

Find t.

$$t = 66\frac{2}{3}$$

Answer the question.

$66\frac{2}{3}\%$ of the records sold were rock, folk, and jazz records.

B. 20% of all the record sales were current hit tunes. What fraction of the sales were hit tunes?

$$20\% = \frac{20}{100} = \frac{1}{5}$$

$\frac{1}{5}$ of the sales were hit tunes.

Write each fraction as a percent.

1. $\frac{2}{5}$ **4.** $\frac{3}{4}$ **7.** $\frac{1}{6}$ **10.** $\frac{5}{6}$

2. $\frac{3}{10}$ **5.** $\frac{1}{3}$ **8.** $\frac{7}{8}$ **11.** $\frac{25}{25}$

3. $\frac{1}{2}$ **6.** $\frac{19}{20}$ **9.** $\frac{27}{50}$ **12.** $\frac{1}{8}$

Write each percent as a fraction in lowest terms.

13. 25%   **16.** 32%   **19.** 14%   **22.** 75%

14. 60%   **17.** 80%   **20.** 5%   **23.** 2%

15. 45%   **18.** 68%   **21.** 17%   **24.** 12%

**More practice
Set C, page 318**

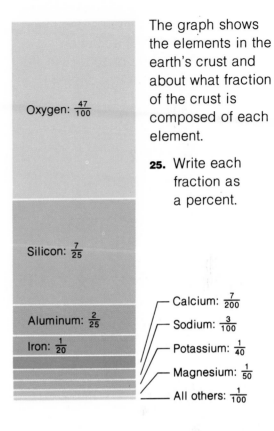

Oxygen: $\frac{47}{100}$

Silicon: $\frac{7}{25}$

Aluminum: $\frac{2}{25}$

Iron: $\frac{1}{20}$

Calcium: $\frac{7}{200}$

Sodium: $\frac{3}{100}$

Potassium: $\frac{1}{40}$

Magnesium: $\frac{1}{50}$

All others: $\frac{1}{100}$

The graph shows the elements in the earth's crust and about what fraction of the crust is composed of each element.

25. Write each fraction as a percent.

laboratory activity

1. Decide what you want to survey, such as favorite TV programs.

2. Decide what items you want to list for your survey, such as these kinds of TV programs:

Comedy
Mystery
Western
Sports
News
No preference

3. Decide who should be asked to participate in your survey; for example, the first 25 people you see in the schoolyard.

4. After you take your survey, tally the results. Then find what percent of the people chose the different items.

Percents and Decimals

A. To change a percent to a decimal, write the percent as a fraction with a denominator of 100. Then change the fraction to a decimal.

$$13\% = \frac{13}{100} = .13$$

$$2\% = \frac{2}{100} = .02$$

$$\left(\frac{82.5}{100} = 82.5 \div 100 \right)$$

$$82.5\% = \frac{82.5}{100} = .825$$

$$43\tfrac{1}{2}\% = 43.5\% = \frac{43.5}{100} = .435$$

B. To change a decimal to a percent, write the decimal as a fraction with a denominator of 100. Then change the fraction to a percent.

$$.68 = \frac{68}{100} = 68\%$$

$$.09 = \frac{9}{100} = 9\%$$

$$.4 = \frac{4}{10} = \frac{40}{100} = 40\%$$

Write each percent as a decimal.

1. 5%
2. 42%
3. 1%
4. 62.5%
5. 39%
6. 18%
7. 70%
8. 25%
9. 4%
10. 87.5%
11. 90%
12. 100%

Write each decimal as a percent.

13. .36
14. .11
15. .24
16. .01
17. .37
18. .05
19. .60
20. .79
21. .53
22. .1
23. .8
24. .80

**More practice
Set D, page 318**

Fractions, Decimals, and Percents

$$16\frac{2}{3}\% = \frac{1}{6}$$

To change $16\frac{2}{3}\%$ to a decimal, change $\frac{1}{6}$ to a decimal. Divide 1 by 6 and round the quotient to the nearest thousandth.

$$
\begin{array}{r}
.1666 \\
6\overline{)1.0000} \\
\underline{-6} \\
40 \\
\underline{-36} \\
40 \\
\underline{-36} \\
40 \\
\underline{-36} \\
4
\end{array}
$$

The quotient is .167 to the nearest thousandth.

$$16\frac{2}{3}\% \approx .167$$

Use the fraction to find the decimal for each percent. Round to the nearest thousandth.

1. $\frac{1}{3} = 33\frac{1}{3}\%$

2. $\frac{5}{6} = 83\frac{1}{3}\%$

3. $\frac{2}{3} = 66\frac{2}{3}\%$

Complete the table. Round the decimals for $\frac{1}{3}, \frac{2}{3}, \frac{1}{6}$, and $\frac{5}{6}$ to the nearest thousandth.

	Fraction in lowest terms	Decimal	Percent
	$\frac{1}{2}$	.5	50%
	$\frac{1}{3}$	.333	$33\frac{1}{3}\%$
4.	$\frac{2}{3}$		$66\frac{2}{3}\%$
5.		.25	25%
6.	$\frac{3}{4}$	.75	
7.	$\frac{1}{5}$		
8.			40%
9.		.6	
10.	$\frac{4}{5}$		
11.	$\frac{1}{6}$		$16\frac{2}{3}\%$
12.	$\frac{5}{6}$	.833	
13.			12.5%
14.	$\frac{3}{8}$		
15.		.625	
16.	$\frac{7}{8}$		
17.	$\frac{3}{10}$		
18.		.7	
19.			90%
20.	$\frac{10}{10}$		

Finding a Percent of a Number

A. About 97% of a watermelon's weight is water. Find the weight of the water in a 6-kilogram watermelon.

Find 97% of 6.

> 97 out of 100 is equal to how much out of 6?

$$\frac{97}{100} = \frac{k}{6}$$

$$97 \times 6 = 100 \times k$$

$$582 = 100k$$

$$5.82 = k$$

The weight of the water is about 5.82 kilograms.

B. Here is another way to find 97% of 6.

Write an equation. $97\% \times 6 = r$

Change the percent to a decimal. $.97 \times 6 = r$

$$5.82 = r$$

The weight of the water is about 5.82 kilograms.

282

Find each missing number.

1. 50% of 8 is k.
2. 10% of 30 is m.
3. 75% of 12 is h.
4. 32% of 50 is d.
5. 30% of 25 is x.
6. 63% of 60 is y.
7. 41% of 90 is t.
8. 8% of 22 is b.
9. 27% of 240 is n.
10. c is 98% of 125.
11. d is 3% of 36.
12. m is 50% of 83.
13. z is 72% of 159.
14. w is 14% of 210.
15. t is 100% of 386.

For exercises 16–20, find the weight of the water in grams. The weights and percents are approximate.

	Item	Weight	Percent that is water
16.	Apple	150 g	80%
17.	Pineapple	1800 g	87%
18.	Tomato	300 g	95%
19.	Lobster	2250 g	79%
20.	Chicken	900 g	74%

Water accounts for much of the weight of a person's body. Carlo weighs 60 kilograms.

21. Carlo's body is about 65% water. What is the weight of the water in his body?

22. Carlo's bones weigh about 11 kilograms. 22% of the bones are water. What is the weight of the water in Carlo's bones?

23. Carlo's muscles weigh about 30 kilograms. 76% of the muscles are water. What is the weight of the water in Carlo's muscles?

24. Carlo's fat tissues weigh about 12 kilograms. 20% of the fat tissues are water. What is the weight of the water in Carlo's fat tissues?

**More practice
Set E, page 319**

Using Percents: Discounts

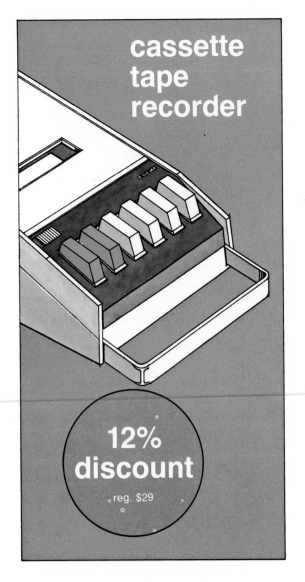

cassette tape recorder

12% discount

reg. $29

Advertisements often tell what percent of the price is subtracted, or *discounted*, during a sale. A discount of 12% tells you that you save 12 cents for every dollar of the regular price.

A. The discount on a cassette recorder is 12%. How much would you save on a recorder that regularly sells for $29?

Find 12% of 29.

$$12\% \times 29 = t$$
$$.12 \times 29 = t$$
$$3.48 = t$$

You would save $3.48.

B. What is the sale price of the recorder?

Subtract the amount of discount from the regular price.

$$\begin{array}{r} \$29.00 \\ -\ 3.48 \\ \hline \$25.52 \end{array}$$

The sale price is $25.52.

Find how much you would save by buying
each item on sale. Then find the sale price.

15% Discount Sale

1. AM Portable Radios   reg. $11
2. AM-FM Portable Radios   reg. $28
3. AM-FM Shortwave Radios   reg. $92
4. 8-Track Portable Stereos   reg. $79
5. Portable Phonographs   reg. $44

20% Discount Sale

6. Hiking Boots   reg. $38
7. Sleeping Bags   reg. $25
8. Tents   reg. $49
9. Cooking Sets   reg. $8
10. Lanterns   reg. $15

One-of-a-Kind Sale

11. Save 40%   Electric Guitar   reg. $58
12. Save 10%   20-watt Amplifier   reg. $51
13. Save 33%   Steel String Guitar   reg. $22
14. Save 25%   18 Speaker PA System   reg. $452
15. Save 5%   Electric Guitar Cord   reg. $4

Finding Percents

A. A $15 discount is given on all bicycles. The regular price of a Targa Racer is $120. What is the percent of discount?

Find what percent 15 is of 120.

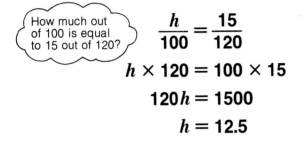
How much out of 100 is equal to 15 out of 120?

$$\frac{h}{100} = \frac{15}{120}$$

$$h \times 120 = 100 \times 15$$

$$120h = 1500$$

$$h = 12.5$$

The discount is 12.5%.

B. The regular price of a deluxe bicycle lock is $12. The sale price is $8. What is the percent of discount?

Subtract the sale price from the regular price to find how much is saved.

$$\begin{array}{r} \$12 \\ -\ \ 8 \\ \hline \$\ 4 \end{array}$$

Now find what percent $4 is of $12.

$$\frac{c}{100} = \frac{4}{12}$$

$$c = 33\frac{1}{3}$$

The discount is $33\frac{1}{3}$%.

Find each percent.

1. 3 is what percent of 4?

2. 14 is what percent of 25?

3. 6 is what percent of 12?

4. 25 is what percent of 75?

5. 9 is what percent of 60?

6. 21 is what percent of 84?

7. 126 is what percent of 300?

8. What percent of 96 is 12?

9. What percent of 100 is 57?

10. What percent of 60 is 24?

11. What percent of 25 is 8?

12. What percent of 47 is 47?

13. What percent of 45 is 30?

14. What percent of 72 is 27?

15. What percent of 96 is 16?

**More practice
Set F, page 319**

A $15 discount is given on each of these bicycles. Find the percent of discount.

16. Lightweight 10-speed .... reg. $150

17. Hi-rise Mustang.......... reg. $60

18. Elite Fivespeed .... reg. $125

19. Pursuit Tenspeed .... reg. $120

20. Which bicycle offers the greatest percent of saving?

For each item, find the amount of discount. Then find the percent of discount.

21. Light............. reg. $5   SALE $4

22. Odometer .... reg. $10 SALE $7

23. Car carrier .... reg. $36 SALE $24

24. Bugle horn .... reg. 80¢ SALE 70¢

25. Reflector .... reg. 38¢ SALE 19¢

time out

A used-car dealer bought a camper for $600. He marked the price up 50% from what he paid. The camper did not sell, so two months later the dealer marked it down 40%. Then the camper sold.

Did the dealer make a profit or lose money? How much?

Finding a Number When a Percent Is Known

The area of Asia is about 45 million square kilometers. This is about 30% of the earth's land area. Find the earth's land area in millions of square kilometers.

45 is 30% of what number?

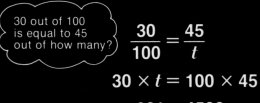

30 out of 100 is equal to 45 out of how many?

$$\frac{30}{100} = \frac{45}{t}$$

$$30 \times t = 100 \times 45$$

$$30t = 4500$$

$$t = 150$$

The earth's land area is about 150 million square kilometers.

Find each missing number.

1. 20% of a is 18.
2. 75% of c is 21.
3. 10% of m is 43.
4. 18% of t is 9.
5. 40% of r is 14.
6. 36% of h is 180.
7. 5% of s is 14.
8. 15% of h is 6.

9. 98 is 70% of x.
10. 7 is 2% of h.
11. 99 is 33% of s.
12. 31 is 62% of m.
13. 19 is 95% of b.
14. 84 is 50% of w.
15. 60 is 24% of a.
16. 15 is 12% of d.

More practice
Set G, page 319

Find these answers in millions of square kilometers.

17. The area of North America is about 22.5 million square kilometers. This is about 75% of the area of Africa. Find the area of Africa.

18. The area of Antarctica is about 60% of the area of North America. Find the area of Antarctica.

19. The area of Oceania is about 9 million square kilometers. This is about 50% of the area of South America. Find the area of South America.

20. The area of Oceania is about 75% of the area of Europe. Find the area of Europe.

21. The continents are Africa, Antarctica, Asia, Europe, North America, Oceania, and South America. List them in order of size, beginning with the smallest. Give the area of each.

★ 22. The total land area of the earth is about 150 million square kilometers. Each continent is what percent of the earth's land area?

Using Percents: Basketball Records

The tables list data on the performance of the basketball team at Hopkins School.

Find the missing numbers.

Free Throws: Hopkins

	Opponent	Number attempted	Number completed	Percent completed
	Central	16	10	62.5%
	Grove	21	7	$33\frac{1}{3}$%
	Oakton	12	3	25%
1.	Greenleaf	15		40%
2.	Longfellow		6	37.5%
3.	Willow		7	50%
4.	North Bay	10		30%
5.	Taylor	18	12	
6.	Erie	16	12	

A. In the Central game, how many free throws were completed?

$$\frac{62.5}{100} = \frac{c}{16}$$

$$c = 10$$

10 throws completed

B. In the Grove game, what percent of the free throws were completed?

$$\frac{x}{100} = \frac{7}{21}$$

$$x = 33\frac{1}{3}\%$$

$33\frac{1}{3}$% completed

Field Goals: Hopkins

	Opponent	Number attempted	Number completed	Percent completed
7.	Central	36	18	
8.	Grove		13	25%
9.	Oakton	40		45%
10.	Greenleaf	50	16	
11.	Longfellow		10	40%
12.	Willow	32		37.5%
13.	North Bay		30	62.5%
14.	Taylor	39	13	
15.	Erie	50		48%

C. In the Oakton game, how many free throws were attempted?

$$\frac{25}{100} = \frac{3}{m}$$

$$m = 12$$

12 throws attempted

The Hopkins Basketball Boosters sold chocolate bars and salted nuts to help the team go to the tournament.

The Boosters received a *commission* of 12% on their sales. This means that they received 12 cents for every one dollar in sales.

16. $675 was collected from the sale of chocolate bars. How much did the Boosters receive in commission?

Find 12% of $675.

17. $1125 was collected from the sale of nuts. How much did the Boosters receive in commission?

18. The Boosters' total commission was $216. $81 of this came from the sale of chocolate bars. What percent of the total commission was the commission from the sale of chocolate bars?

$81 is what percent of $216?

19. $135 of the total commission came from the sale of nuts. What percent of the total commission was the commission from the sale of nuts?

20. 153 eighth-grade students took part in the sale. This is 68% of the class. How many students are in the class?

68% of what number is 153?

21. 177 seventh-grade students took part in the sale. This is 75% of the class. How many students are in the class?

Real Estate Broker

A real estate broker is paid a commission on each building or piece of land sold.

Suppose that the commission is 7% of the selling price. How much would the commission be on each of the following sales?

1. House: $38,000

2. House: $120,000

3. Apartment building: $170,500

4. Small farm: $95,000

5. Office building: $462,000

Writing percents, fractions, and decimals, pages 276–281

Write each fraction as a percent.

1. $\frac{95}{100}$ 3. $\frac{1}{3}$

2. $\frac{3}{10}$ 4. $\frac{3}{4}$

Write each percent as a fraction in lowest terms.

5. 72%   7. 60%

6. 45%   8. 5%

Write each percent as a decimal.

9. 65%   11. 7%

10. 50%   12. 87.5%

Write each decimal as a percent.

13. .36   15. .2

14. .08   16. .125

Using percents, pages 282–283, 286–289

Find each missing number.

17. 40% of 16 is x.

18. 32% of 75 is m.

19. 10% of k is 6.

20. 64% of t is 16.

Find each percent.

21. 14 is what percent of 28?

22. 69 is what percent of 92?

Problem solving, pages 282–291

23. The human body contains about 10 pints of blood. About 80% of the blood is water. How many pints of water are in the blood?

24. The Valley City volleyball team played 32 games and won 20. What percent of the games played did the team win?

25. Brenda's commission for selling newspapers is 18%. One month she earned $27 in commissions. What were her total sales for that month?

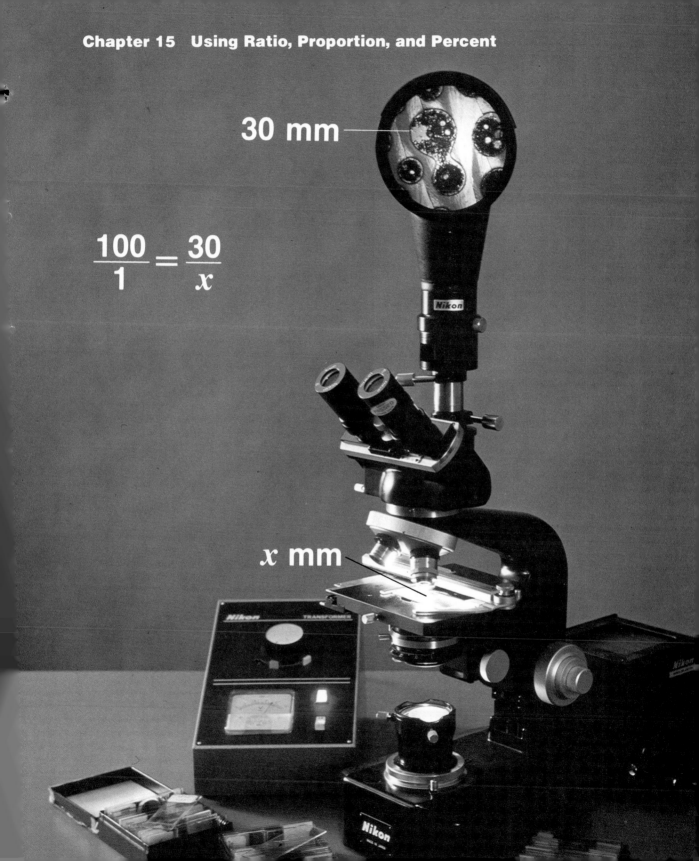

30 mm

$$\frac{100}{1} = \frac{30}{x}$$

x mm

Meteors are masses that enter the earth's atmosphere from outer space. When a stream of meteors enter our atmosphere, they become visible and look like streaks in the sky. Such an occurrence is a meteor shower.

Many meteor showers recur with remarkable regularity. A meteor shower may last from a few hours to several days. Some of the more important annual showers are given in the table on page 295. The normal rate for a meteor shower gives the normal number of meteors seen in the specified time. This rate, however, may increase during a shower.

The normal rate for a Quadrantid shower is $\frac{70}{2}$. This means that during a shower about 70 meteors can be seen every 2 hours.

Suppose that a shower lasts for 6 hours at the normal rate. About how many meteors would be visible?

$$\frac{70}{2} = \frac{n}{6} \begin{matrix} \text{— Meteors} \\ \text{— Hours} \end{matrix}$$

$$n = 210$$

About 210 meteors would be visible.

Complete the table.
Round to the nearest whole number.

	Meteor shower	Normal rate meteors/hours	Number of hours	Number of meteors
	Quadrantids Jan. 3	$\frac{70}{2}$	6	210
1.	Lyrids Apr. 21	$\frac{24}{3}$		40
2.	Aquarids May 6	$\frac{48}{4}$		500
3.	Perseids Aug. 10–14	$\frac{150}{3}$		3900
4.	Orionids Oct. 20–23	$\frac{75}{5}$	63	
5.	Taurids Nov. 3–10	$\frac{20}{2}$	25	
6.	Leonids Nov. 16–17	$\frac{24}{2}$	15	
7.	Geminids Dec. 13–14	$\frac{240}{4}$		4410
8.	Ursids Dec. 22	$\frac{52}{4}$	7	

9. Give the normal rate for each shower as a ratio in which the number of hours is 1.

10. Suppose that the rate for the Perseids increased to 250 meteors every 3 hours and that 10,000 meteors were visible. How many hours would the shower last? How many days?

Mathematics and the Alphabet

Frequency of Letters in Written English					
E	13%	D	4%	G	1.5%
T	9%	L	3.5%	B	1.5%
A	8%	C	3%	V	1%
O	8%	U	3%	K	0.5%
N	7%	M	3%	X	0.5%
R	6.5%	F	2%	J	0.5%
I	6.5%	P	2%	Q	0.3%
S	6%	Y	2%	Z	0.2%
H	6%	W	1.5%		

The table shows the approximate percent of use of each letter in ordinary written English. These percents were calculated by counting the letters in many thousands of sentences.

The letter z occurs only about .2% of the time.

.2% is two-tenths of one percent.

$$.2\% = \frac{2}{1000} = .002$$

About how many z's would you expect in a paragraph of 900 letters?

Find .2% of 900.

$.2\% \times 900 = z$

$.002 \times 900 = z$

$1.8 = z$

You would expect about two z's.

Find about how many times each letter will occur in a paragraph of the given length. Round to the nearest whole number.

1. H in 100 letters

2. C in 100 letters

3. T in 500 letters

4. L in 800 letters

5. P in 1000 letters

6. E in 2500 letters

7. Tell exactly how many times the letter e occurs in the sentence you are reading.

8. The sentence in exercise 7 has 65 letters. What percent of these letters are e's?

9. Write a sentence about yourself without using the letter e.

10. What percent of the letters in the following sentence are z's?

   Zelda Zinzow has a magazine puzzle about zebras in Zanzibar.

★ 11. Write a sentence in which more than 5% of the letters are q's.

Mathematics and Secret Codes

13-5-5-20	13-5	1-20	20-8-5 (H)	4-18-9-14-11-9-14-7 (K)

6-15-21-14-20-1-9-14 (O)	1-20	5-12-5-22-5-14

Cryptography, the science of code writing and code breaking, uses many mathematical ideas.

The message above was written in code. Use the table on page 296 and exercises 1–8 on this page to help you break the code.

1. Copy the coded message. Then list the numerals used and the number of times each occurs.

2. The table on page 296 shows that *E* is the most common letter. The numeral 5 occurs the greatest number of times, so try *E* for 5. Write *E* above each 5.

3. What is the next most common letter according to the table? Look at the fourth word in the message. Does this letter make sense for 20? Write the letter above each 20.

4. What letter will make the first two words sensible? Use it for 13.

5. Look at the third and seventh words. What is a sensible letter for 1?

6. The letter *N* is common. Try *N* for the remaining numeral that occurs the greatest number of times.

7. Another common letter is *I*. What numeral is used for *I*?

8. Guess the remaining letters by trying to make the words make sense.

9. Do you see how the numerals and letters are matched in this code? If you do, write a message in this code.

laboratory activity

You will need one copy of your local newspaper.

1. Find an article in the sports section. For the first 100 words of the article, record the number of words with one, two, three, four, or five syllables. For example, the word *article* has three syllables.

2. Find an article on the editorial page and repeat the activity of exercise 1.

3. Complete this table.

Percent of words with	Sports	Editorial
1 syllable		
2 syllables		
3 syllables		
4 syllables		
5 syllables		
Under 5 syllables		
Under 4 syllables		
Under 3 syllables		

4. Compare and discuss your table with at least one classmate.

5. Use the 200 words from exercises 1 and 2 and fill in this table. The vowels are *a, e, i, o,* and *u.*

Words	Number of vowels	Number of consonants
3-letter words		
4-letter words		
5-letter words		
6-letter words		
7-letter words		
8-letter words		
Over 8 letters		

6. For each entry in the table in exercise 5, give the ratio of vowels to consonants.

Mathematics and Literature

The Lilliputians in *Gulliver's Travels* were tiny people. The ratio of the heights of a Lilliputian and a human was 1 to 12.

The Brobdingnagians were giants. The ratio of the heights of a Brobdingnagian and a human was 12 to 1.

Round your answers to the nearest tenth of a centimeter.

1. If the length of the nose of an average human is 5 centimeters, how long is the nose of an average Lilliputian?

$$\frac{1}{12} = \frac{n}{5}$$ — Lilliputian / — Human

2. How long is the nose of an average Brobdingnagian?

$$\frac{12}{1} = \frac{n}{5}$$ — Brobdingnagian / — Human

3. If the average height of 12-year-old humans is 146 centimeters, what is the average height of a 12-year-old Lilliputian?

4. What is the average height of a 12-year-old Brobdingnagian?

Suppose that a Lilliputian's and a Brobdingnagian's measures were the same as yours, to scale. For each exercise, give three measurements— yours, the Lilliputian's, and the Brobdingnagian's.

5. Foot length
6. Height
7. Thumb length
8. Hand width

9. Ear length
10. Wrist
11. Arm length
12. Head diameter

Mathematics and Woodworking

Making a Birdhouse

1. Cut perch from dowel.
   Cut other pieces from
   1-centimeter plywood.

2. Saw large hole in
   front and drill hole
   for dowel.

3. Nail sides to front
   and back.

4. Nail small roof piece
   in place first. Then
   nail large roof piece
   in place.

5. Push dowel in hole.
   Nail bottom in place.

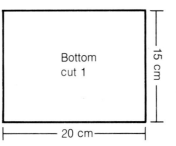

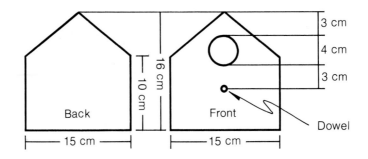

Back

Front

16 cm

10 cm

15 cm

15 cm

3 cm

4 cm

3 cm

Dowel

Dowel perch

7 cm

Side
cut 2

10 cm

20 cm

Roof
cut one 13 cm
cut one 12 cm

13 cm

12 cm

25 cm

Bottom
cut 1

15 cm

20 cm

300

Pat wants to use the directions on page 300 to make a birdhouse, but she wants the sides to be 30 centimeters long instead of 20.

$$\frac{30}{20} = \frac{3}{2}$$

— Pat's birdhouse
— Birdhouse in plan

Pat will have to increase all the dimensions in the plan in the ratio 30 to 20, or 3 to 2.

How wide should the sides be?

$$\frac{3}{2} = \frac{n}{10}$$

— Pat's birdhouse
— Birdhouse in plan

$$n = 15$$

Pat will make the sides of her birdhouse 15 centimeters wide.

Find the dimensions for Pat's birdhouse.

	Piece	Plan	Pat's
	Sides		
	Length	20 cm	30 cm
	Width	10 cm	15 cm
	Front and back		
1.	Height (to roof tip)	16 cm	
2.	Height (to roof edge)	10 cm	
3.	Width	15 cm	
	Front only		
4.	Hole diameter	4 cm	
5.	Hole to roof tip	3 cm	
6.	Hole to perch	3 cm	
	Roof		
7.	Length	25 cm	
8.	Width (small)	12 cm	
9.	Width (large)	13 cm	
	Bottom		
10.	Length	20 cm	
11.	Width	15 cm	
	Dowel perch		
12.	Length	7 cm	

Mathematics and Physiology

The graph on this page shows the percent of each type of tissue in your body.

If, for example, you compute 7% of your weight, you will find about how much the blood tissues in your body weigh.

Joe weighs 50 kilograms. Find the number of kilograms for each of the following tissues in his body. Round to the nearest tenth.

1. Muscle tissues (Find 47% of 50.)

2. Supporting tissues

3. Surface and gland tissues

4. Blood tissues

5. Nervous tissues

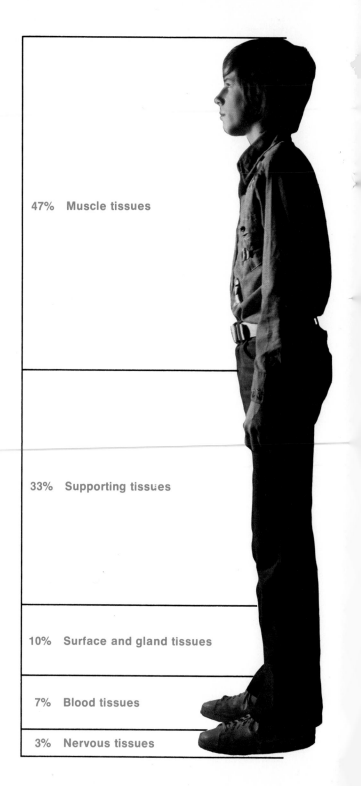

47%   Muscle tissues

33%   Supporting tissues

10%   Surface and gland tissues

7%   Blood tissues

3%   Nervous tissues

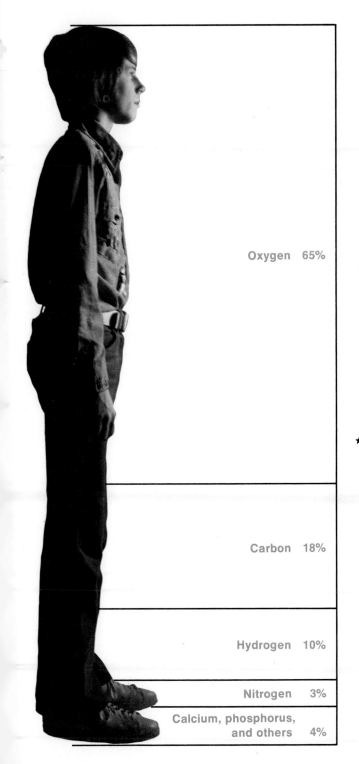

Oxygen 65%

Carbon 18%

Hydrogen 10%

Nitrogen 3%

Calcium, phosphorus, and others 4%

The graph on this page shows the percent of each of the chemical elements in the human body.

Find the number of kilograms of each chemical element in Joe's body. Round to the nearest tenth. Remember, Joe weighs 50 kilograms.

6. Oxygen

7. Carbon

8. Hydrogen

9. Nitrogen

10. Calcium (2%)

11. Phosphorus (1%)

12. Others (1%)

★ 13. The 1% of other elements are listed below. Find the number of kilograms of each in Joe's body.

a. Potassium, .35% (.35% = .0035)

b. Sulphur, .25%

c. Sodium, .15%

d. Chlorine, .15%

e. Miscellaneous, .1%

Mathematics and the Environment

Today, people everywhere are concerned about pollution and its effect on health. These graphs show some of the major sources of pollution in North America.

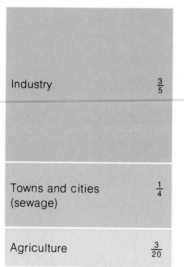

I Sources of Water Pollution

Industry	$\frac{3}{5}$
Towns and cities (sewage)	$\frac{1}{4}$
Agriculture	$\frac{3}{20}$

II Sources of Air Pollution

Transportation	$\frac{21}{50}$
Fuel combustion	$\frac{21}{100}$
Miscellaneous	$\frac{17}{100}$
Industry	$\frac{7}{50}$
Solid waste	$\frac{3}{50}$

1. Use graph I. Express each source of water pollution as a percent.

2. Use graph II. Express each source of air pollution as a percent.

III Sources of Solid Waste

Paper	50%
Ashes, sand, dirt, and grass	16%
Metal	11%
Glass	8%
Garbage	8%
Wood, rags, and plastic	7%

It is estimated that for every person living in North America, about 32 pounds of solid waste is discarded per week.

Graph III shows that 50% of all solid waste is paper.

50% of 32 = .5 × 32 = 16

Therefore, for every North American, about 16 pounds of paper is discarded per week.

16 ÷ 7 ≈ 2.3

This is over 2 pounds of paper per day.

365 × 2.3 = 839.5

Or, about 840 pounds of paper per year.

For every North American, find how many pounds of each type of solid waste is discarded each week, day, and year. Round to the nearest tenth.

3. Ashes, sand, dirt, and grass

4. Metal

5. Glass

6. Garbage (food waste)

7. Wood, rags, and plastic

Mathematics and Physical Fitness

This lesson describes an exercise program for students aged 12 to 18. The fourteen exercises are each to be done the specified number of times and at the recommended per-minute rate.

At a rate of 40 per 60 seconds, how long does it take to run in place at a slow pace 50 times?

$$\frac{40}{60} = \frac{50}{n}$$

$$n = 75$$

It takes 75 seconds.

Find how long it takes to do each exercise the number of times given, at the recommended rate. Round to the nearest second.

1. *Run in place* (slow)
   Number: 50
   Rate: 40 per 60 sec.

2. *Twister*
   Number: 10
   Rate: 15 per 60 sec.

3. *Robot*
   Number: 20
   Rate: 36 per 60 sec.

4. *Windmill*
   Number: 10
   Rate: 30 per 60 sec.

5. *Run in place* (medium)
   Number: 50
   Rate: 50 per 60 sec.

6. *Wingstretcher*
   Number: 15
   Rate: 60 per 60 sec.

7. *Sit-up*
   Number: 15
   Rate: 20 per 60 sec.

8. *Sidewinder*
   Number: 20
   Rate: 50 per 60 sec.

9. *Pushup*
   Number: 10
   Rate: 12 per 60 sec.

10. *Run in place* (fast)
    Number: 50
    Rate: 80 per 60 sec.

11. *Run in place* (slow)
    Number: 50
    Rate: 40 per 60 sec.

12. *Airlift*
    Number: 10
    Rate: 20 per 60 sec.

13. *Propeller*
    Number: 20
    Rate: 60 per 60 sec.

14. *Run in place* (slow)
    Number: 50
    Rate: 40 per 60 sec.

15. The total time for the fourteen exercises is about 600 seconds. Express the time for each exercise as a percent of 600 seconds.

Run in place

Windmill

Pushup

Twister

Wingstretcher

Airlift

Robot

Sit-up

Sidewinder

Propeller

Mathematics and Population

The population of the Saint Louis metropolitan area is about 2.41 million. The population of the United States is about 210 million.

What percent of the population of the United States lives in the Saint Louis area?

$$\frac{2.41}{210} = \frac{m}{100}$$ — St. Louis area
— United States

$$m \approx 1.14$$

About 1.1% of the population of the United States lives in the Saint Louis area.

What percent of the population of the United States lives in each of these metropolitan areas? Round to the nearest tenth of a percent.

1. New York (9.97 million)

2. Los Angeles (7.03 million)

3. Chicago (6.98 million)

4. Philadelphia (4.82 million)

5. Detroit (4.43 million)

6. San Francisco (3.11 million)

7. Washington, D.C. (2.91 million)

8. Boston (2.90 million)

9. Nassau-Suffolk (2.55 million)

10. The areas listed above, along with Saint Louis, are the ten most populous metropolitan areas in the United States. What percent of the total population of the United States lives in these ten areas?

The population of Canada is about 22 million. What percent of the population of Canada lives in each of these metropolitan areas? Round to the nearest tenth of a percent.

11. Montreal (2.74 million)

12. Toronto (2.63 million)

13. Vancouver (1.08 million)

14. Ottawa (.60 million)

15. Winnipeg (.54 million)

16. Hamilton (.50 million)

17. Edmonton (.49 million)

18. Quebec (.48 million)

19. Calgary (.40 million)

20. Saint Catharines (.30 million)

21. The areas listed above are the ten most populous metropolitan areas in Canada. What percent of the total population of Canada lives in these ten areas?

Mathematics and Nutrition

What percent of his daily calcium requirement can a boy get from the hamburger listed in the food-value chart? Round to the nearest tenth of a percent.

Boys need 1.4 grams of calcium per day. A hamburger provides .03 gram of calcium.

Find what percent .03 is of 1.4.

$$\frac{.03}{1.4} = \frac{m}{100}$$

$$2.1 \approx m$$

A boy would get 2.1% of his daily calcium requirement.

Food Values

Food	Protein	Calcium	Iron
Milk (238 ml)	8.3 g	.28 g	.2 mg
Ice cream (78 g)	3.0 g	.13 g	.1 mg
Orange (135 g)	.9 g	.03 g	.4 mg
Peas (70 g)	5.0 g	.02 g	1.4 mg
Bread (28 g)	2.5 g	.02 g	.5 mg
Hamburger (114 g)	18.2 g	.03 g	2.6 mg
Pork chop (142 g)	21.3 g	.02 g	3.2 mg
Chicken (114 g)	22.9 g	.02 g	1.7 mg
Peanut butter (14 g)	5.7 g	.02 g	1.2 mg
Egg (50 g)	3.7 g	.01 g	.3 mg
Chocolate bar (56 g)	5.2 g	.05 g	1.4 mg

Recommended Daily Dietary Allowances

	Protein	Calcium	Iron
Boys (12–15 yr.)	75 g	1.4 g	15 mg
Girls (12–15 yr.)	62 g	1.3 g	15 mg

For exercises 1–7, assume that the amount of food is the same as given in the chart. Round your answers to the nearest tenth of a percent.

1. The milk provides what percent of these daily requirements for girls?

   a. Protein

   b. Calcium

   c. Iron

2. Find the percents in exercise 1 for boys.

3. What percent of the daily requirement of iron for girls and boys comes from

   a. the hamburger?

   b. the orange?

   c. the chocolate bar?

4. What percent of a boy's daily requirement of protein comes from

   a. the egg?

   b. the peas?

   c. the chicken?

5. What percent of a girl's daily calcium requirement comes from

   a. the ice cream?

   b. the orange?

   c. the pork chop?

6. How many grams of protein are in

   a. 3 glasses of milk?

   b. 6 oranges?

   c. a 112-gram chocolate bar?

7. How many milligrams of iron are in

   a. 3 slices (84 g) of bread?

   b. 12 eggs?

   c. 42 grams of peanut butter?

311

Mathematics and a Driving Experiment

EDMONTON, ALBERTA—Two driving experiments were reported in a recent issue of *The Alberta Motorist*. In the first experiment two identical cars were fitted with instruments that measured every detail of a trip. The cars were sent on a 1000-mile journey. Driver A was told to avoid risk and move as safely as the traffic flow permitted. Driver B was told to make the fastest time possible.

Here are the results.

	Driver A	Driver B
Distance	1000 mi.	1000 mi.
Time	20.7 hr.	20.2 hr.
Passed	645 cars	2004 cars
Was passed by	142 cars	13 cars
Used brakes	652 times	1339 times

A motor club conducted a second experiment over an 800-mile run. Their results were about the same. In the second experiment, the slower driver made the 800 miles in 17.2 hours. The faster driver took about .4 of an hour less time, but used 10 more gallons of gasoline.

Round these answers to the nearest whole number.

1. For every car that driver A passed, about how many cars did driver B pass?

$$\frac{645}{2004} = \frac{1}{n} \quad \begin{array}{l} \text{— Cars A passed} \\ \text{— Cars B passed} \end{array}$$

2. For every car that passed driver B, about how many cars passed driver A?

$$\frac{13}{142} = \frac{1}{c} \quad \begin{array}{l} \text{— Cars that passed B} \\ \text{— Cars that passed A} \end{array}$$

3. For every time that driver A used brakes, about how many times did driver B use brakes?

4. How many miles per hour did driver A drive?

$$\frac{1000}{20.7} = \frac{n}{1} \quad \begin{array}{l} \text{— Miles} \\ \text{— Hours} \end{array}$$

5. How many miles per hour did driver B drive?

6. In the second experiment, how many miles per hour did the fast driver drive? The slow driver?

7. The slow driver used 46.4 gallons of gasoline. How many miles did the slow driver get per gallon?

$$\frac{46.4}{800} = \frac{1}{t} \quad \begin{array}{l} \text{— Gallons} \\ \text{— Miles} \end{array}$$

8. How many miles did the fast driver get per gallon?

side trip

Puzzling Problems

1. The weights of four brothers total 272 pounds. Their weights are in the following proportions:

   1 to 3 to 5 to 8.

   How much does each brother weigh?

2. A rope is hung from the side of a ship so that 20 feet of the rope is underwater at low tide. If the tide rises 2 feet per hour, how much of the rope is underwater after 3 hours?

3. Four hundred one-legged and two-legged monsters live on a certain island. Seven percent are one-legged, and half the rest go barefoot. What is the least number of shoes needed?

4. If the population of the island were 600 monsters, if two percent were one-legged, and if half the rest went barefoot, what would be the least number of shoes needed?

5. If one boy can see 5 miles from the top of a building, how many miles can three boys see from the top of the same building?

6. If 6 cats eat 6 rats in 6 minutes, how many cats are needed to eat 100 rats in 100 minutes?

7. Don and Sue planted tulip bulbs for a nursery. They were to be paid $20 and decided they would divide the money according to the amount of work done. There were 12 rows to be planted. Don planted at the rate of 1 row in 40 minutes. It took him another 40 minutes to cover the row of bulbs. Sue planted at a rate of 1 row in 20 minutes, but only covered 2 rows in the time Don covered 3. How should they have divided the $20?

8. Two crews were to pave 7 miles of road. They started at opposite ends of the road. The larger crew started at 8 o'clock, and the smaller crew started at 10 o'clock. At 1 o'clock, the two crews met. The smaller crew of 8 men had paved 2 miles. Assume that the per-hour work of each man in both crews was the same. How many men were in the larger crew?

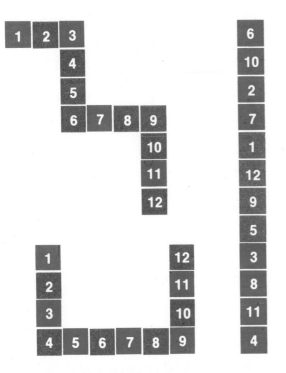

Number of plays	Color choice	Win or lose
1	r	1
2	b	0
3	b	0
4	b	0
5	r	1
6	r	1
7	b	0
8	r	0
9	r	0
10	b	1

Won __4__ points

Played __10__ times

Won __40%__ of the time

Choose-a-Color

Materials

Game board: Each player makes a game board similar to those shown. It must have twelve squares, labeled with the numbers 1 through 12, and colored red or blue. There should be at least four squares of each color.

Score sheet: Each player makes a score sheet like the one shown, but without filling in the columns or blanks.

Dice: One pair of dice is needed. (Or, make twelve cards, two for each of the numbers 1 through 6, and put the cards in a box.)

Rules

1. Each player chooses a number between 8 and 20. Then each player writes the numerals from 1 through the chosen number under "number of plays" on the score sheet. (The number of plays will differ from player to player.)

2. Each player chooses red or blue and writes "r" or "b" next to 1 on the score sheet.

3. One player rolls two dice (or draws two cards) and calls out the sum of the numbers.

4. Each player checks his or her game board. If the sum called is on a square of the chosen color, 1 point is recorded. If not, 0 is recorded.

5. The game continues in this way. Each player stops when reaching his or her chosen number of plays. The game ends when all players have finished.

6. Each player calculates his or her percent of wins. The group decides who was the best chooser.

Rerun

Each player makes a new score sheet and chooses a number between 15 and 30 for the number of plays. Then the game is played again.

Discussion

Did your percent of wins improve in the second game?

Look at your two score sheets. Which color won more often?

These two rectangles are made from 20 toothpicks. Six toothpicks were used for the smaller rectangle, and 14 toothpicks were used for the larger rectangle.

The ratio of the areas of these rectangles is 3 to 1.

Use 20 toothpicks (or lines) to form two polygons. The polygons need not be the same shape.

Use 7 toothpicks for one polygon, and 13 toothpicks for the other. Make the ratio of the areas of these polygons 3 to 1.

Find the answers. If necessary, round your answers to the nearest tenth.

1. At a rate of 25 sit-ups per 60 seconds, how many seconds are required for 20 sit-ups?

2. A model airplane has a wingspan of 12 centimeters. The plane is 9 centimeters long. Carlo wants to make the plane, but he wants it to be 15 centimeters long. What will the wingspan of Carlo's plane be?

3. The population of Texas is about 12 million. About 1.3 million people live in Houston. What percent of the total population of Texas lives in Houston?

4. Suppose that during a meteor shower the normal rate increased to 125 in 3 hours and the shower lasted 9 hours. How many meteors would be visible?

5. What percent of the letters in the following word are *i*'s?

   supercalifragilisticexpialidocious

6. The letter *n* occurs about 7% of the time in an ordinary English paragraph. About how many *n*'s would you expect to occur in a paragraph of 400 letters?

7. Bill weighs 54 kilograms. About 65% of his body weight is oxygen. How many kilograms of oxygen are in Bill's body?

8. Ms. Talcot drives 350 miles per week. Ms. Eng drives 175 miles per week. How many miles does Ms. Talcot drive for every mile Ms. Eng drives?

9. A serving of whitefish contains 26 grams of protein. A girl needs 62 grams of protein a day. What percent of her daily requirement is supplied by the serving of whitefish?

10. A boy needs 75 grams of protein a day. What percent of his daily requirement is supplied by the serving of whitefish?

Unit 5 Test

Ratio and proportion, pages 260–273

Tell whether each pair of ratios forms a proportion.

1. $\frac{9}{12}$ $\frac{15}{20}$ **2.** $\frac{8}{14}$ $\frac{18}{30}$

Solve these proportions.

3. $\frac{5}{8} = \frac{n}{56}$ **5.** $\frac{c}{6} = \frac{15}{45}$

4. $\frac{30}{x} = \frac{9}{12}$ **6.** $\frac{32}{24} = \frac{12}{s}$

Find the answers.

7. In 6 hours, a train travels 1158 kilometers. What is its rate of speed per hour?

8. A 5-kilogram bag of potatoes costs $2.09. What is the price per kilogram to the nearest cent?

9. The scale on a map is 3 centimeters = 1000 kilometers. The actual distance from New York to London is about 5530 kilometers. What is the distance on the map to a tenth of a centimeter?

Percent, pages 276–291

10. Write $\frac{3}{5}$ as a percent.

11. Write 18% as a fraction in lowest terms.

12. Write 9% as a decimal.

13. Write .625 as a percent.

Find each answer.

14. 25% of 32 is x.

15. 60% of t is 54.

16. 18 is what percent of 45?

17. A discount is 15%. How much would Sue save on a television that regularly sells for $160?

18. One day 9 of the 75 students in the choir were absent. What percent of the students were absent?

19. Eduardo saved 35% of his earnings. He saved $63. How much did he earn?

Using ratio, proportion, and percent, pages 294–315

Find each answer.

20. A model of a hotel is 15 centimeters long and 25 centimeters high. The actual building will be 36 meters long. What will be the height?

21. At 190 words per minute, how many minutes will it take to read 950 words?

22. There are 154 calories in 25 grams of milk chocolate. How many calories are there in 100 grams of this chocolate?

23. Canada has about 22 million people. Ontario has about 7 million. What percent of the population of Canada lives in Ontario? Round to the nearest percent.

24. The letter p occurs about 2% of the time. About how many p's would you expect in a paragraph of 1500 letters?

317

More Practice

Set A

Tell whether each pair of ratios forms a proportion.

1. $\dfrac{45}{40}$ $\dfrac{8}{7}$

2. $\dfrac{7}{9}$ $\dfrac{28}{36}$

3. $\dfrac{8}{6}$ $\dfrac{48}{36}$

4. $\dfrac{28}{18}$ $\dfrac{12}{5}$

5. $\dfrac{30}{35}$ $\dfrac{35}{40}$

6. $\dfrac{22}{12}$ $\dfrac{32}{20}$

7. $\dfrac{21}{28}$ $\dfrac{9}{12}$

8. $\dfrac{18}{21}$ $\dfrac{44}{48}$

9. $\dfrac{40}{56}$ $\dfrac{35}{49}$

10. $\dfrac{12}{8}$ $\dfrac{18}{12}$

11. $\dfrac{6}{27}$ $\dfrac{10}{45}$

Set B

Find each missing number.

1. $\dfrac{15}{k} = \dfrac{12}{4}$

2. $\dfrac{9}{24} = \dfrac{15}{c}$

3. $\dfrac{m}{25} = \dfrac{7}{35}$

4. $\dfrac{27}{d} = \dfrac{18}{8}$

5. $\dfrac{18}{42} = \dfrac{h}{49}$

6. $\dfrac{a}{30} = \dfrac{2}{12}$

7. $\dfrac{14}{12} = \dfrac{m}{24}$

8. $\dfrac{28}{e} = \dfrac{21}{27}$

9. $\dfrac{42}{12} = \dfrac{x}{8}$

10. $\dfrac{25}{40} = \dfrac{30}{n}$

11. $\dfrac{b}{35} = \dfrac{16}{14}$

Set C

Write each fraction as a percent.

1. $\dfrac{3}{8}$ 6. $\dfrac{23}{50}$

2. $\dfrac{19}{25}$ 7. $\dfrac{3}{5}$

3. $\dfrac{1}{4}$ 8. $\dfrac{4}{9}$

4. $\dfrac{9}{16}$ 9. $\dfrac{13}{20}$

5. $\dfrac{7}{10}$ 10. $\dfrac{5}{8}$

Write each percent as a fraction in lowest terms.

11. 20%

12. 28%

13. 50%

14. 35%

15. 23%

16. 40%

17. 52%

18. 37.5%

19. 18%

Set D

Write each percent as a decimal.

1. 7%

2. 27%

3. 14.5%

4. 73%

5. 3%

6. 98%

7. 43%

8. 11%

9. 58%

10. 20.5%

Write each decimal as a percent.

11. .30

12. .43

13. .02

14. .67

15. .15

16. .3

17. .08

18. .52

19. .2

20. .86

More Practice

Set E

Find each missing number.

1. 25% of 16 is x.
2. 81% of 70 is m.
3. 35% of 14 is a.
4. 88% of 95 is s.
5. 57% of 50 is n.
6. 40% of 6 is e.
7. 95% of 78 is w.
8. 73% of 20 is h.
9. 44% of 100 is c.
10. g is 99% of 80.
11. b is 4% of 28.
12. k is 84% of 45.
13. t is 62% of 150.
14. d is 68% of 40.
15. r is 20% of 300.

Set F

Find each percent.

1. 4 is ▦ percent of 5.
2. 11 is ▦ percent of 20.
3. 4 is ▦ percent of 28.
4. 7 is ▦ percent of 21.
5. 16 is ▦ percent of 40.
6. 8 is ▦ percent of 50.
7. 32 is ▦ percent of 80.
8. ▦ percent of 25 is 7.
9. ▦ percent of 26 is 13.
10. ▦ percent of 12 is 3.
11. ▦ percent of 100 is 68.
12. ▦ percent of 54 is 36.
13. ▦ percent of 200 is 98.
14. ▦ percent of 70 is 14.
15. ▦ percent of 90 is 18.

Set G

Find each missing number.

1. 30% of m is 18.
2. 65% of b is 78.
3. 8% of y is 2.
4. 14% of w is 35.
5. 25% of d is 9.
6. 12% of r is 9.
7. 85% of h is 68.
8. 3% of e is 6.
9. 9 is 20% of c.
10. 21 is 15% of s.
11. 28 is 28% of k.
12. 57 is 10% of a.
13. 14 is 35% of n.
14. 28 is 16% of g.
15. 12 is 24% of t.

Individualized Skills Maintenance

Diagnosis

A. $\frac{3}{4} + \frac{1}{2}$

$\frac{2}{3} + \frac{3}{8}$

$2\frac{3}{10} + 3\frac{2}{5}$

$1\frac{5}{6} + 2\frac{1}{4}$

B. $\frac{7}{8} - \frac{1}{2}$

$\frac{9}{10} - \frac{2}{3}$

$3\frac{1}{2} - 1\frac{1}{8}$

$4\frac{2}{5} - 3\frac{3}{4}$

C. $3\frac{2}{3} \times 2\frac{1}{4}$

$2\frac{3}{8} \times 4\frac{7}{12}$

$1\frac{5}{6} \times 3\frac{3}{5}$

D. $2\frac{3}{10} \div 1\frac{5}{6}$

$3\frac{1}{2} \div 2\frac{11}{12}$

$1\frac{3}{4} \div 3\frac{2}{3}$

Practice

Set A (pp. 226–229)

1. $\frac{5}{8} + \frac{2}{3}$
2. $\frac{1}{5} + \frac{1}{6}$
3. $\frac{4}{5} + \frac{3}{4}$
4. $\frac{1}{2} + \frac{2}{9}$
5. $\frac{5}{6} + \frac{2}{5}$
6. $\frac{3}{8} + \frac{1}{3}$
7. $\frac{3}{5} + \frac{1}{8}$
8. $\frac{1}{4} + \frac{5}{9}$
9. $3\frac{1}{5} + 2$
10. $4\frac{2}{7} + 7\frac{3}{4}$
11. $6\frac{1}{2} + 2\frac{4}{5}$
12. $5\frac{3}{7} + 3\frac{1}{6}$
13. $2\frac{1}{4} + 8\frac{2}{3}$
14. $1\frac{3}{5} + 3\frac{5}{6}$
15. $9\frac{5}{8} + 5\frac{1}{7}$
16. $7\frac{1}{3} + 4\frac{3}{8}$
17. $6\frac{4}{7} + 1\frac{2}{5}$

Set B (pp. 230–233)

1. $\frac{5}{7} - \frac{1}{4}$
2. $\frac{3}{4} - \frac{2}{7}$
3. $\frac{5}{8} - \frac{1}{2}$
4. $\frac{7}{9} - \frac{2}{5}$
5. $\frac{2}{3} - \frac{3}{8}$
6. $\frac{3}{5} - \frac{2}{9}$
7. $\frac{7}{8} - \frac{1}{3}$
8. $\frac{4}{7} - \frac{1}{5}$
9. $4\frac{2}{3} - 2\frac{3}{4}$
10. $8\frac{3}{5} - 6\frac{2}{3}$
11. $2\frac{1}{2} - 1\frac{3}{5}$
12. $6\frac{1}{5} - 4\frac{3}{7}$
13. $4\frac{1}{4} - 1\frac{2}{5}$
14. $3\frac{4}{5} - 2\frac{6}{7}$
15. $7\frac{1}{3} - 5\frac{5}{6}$
16. $2\frac{2}{5} - 2\frac{2}{7}$
17. $5\frac{3}{4} - 4\frac{7}{8}$

Set C (pp. 242–243)

1. $3\frac{3}{7} \times 3\frac{1}{2}$
2. $3\frac{3}{5} \times 3\frac{3}{4}$
3. $4\frac{3}{8} \times 2\frac{2}{7}$
4. $4\frac{2}{3} \times 2\frac{4}{7}$
5. $1\frac{9}{11} \times 6\frac{3}{5}$
6. $7\frac{1}{3} \times 4\frac{1}{2}$
7. $4\frac{1}{6} \times 2\frac{2}{5}$
8. $6\frac{3}{4} \times 3\frac{5}{9}$

Set D (pp. 248–249)

1. $3\frac{3}{4} \div 7\frac{1}{2}$
2. $5\frac{1}{3} \div 3\frac{5}{9}$
3. $2\frac{4}{7} \div 3\frac{3}{4}$
4. $6\frac{2}{5} \div 3\frac{1}{3}$
5. $4\frac{1}{6} \div 2\frac{2}{9}$
6. $3\frac{1}{9} \div 2\frac{4}{5}$
7. $4\frac{1}{8} \div 3\frac{1}{7}$
8. $8\frac{3}{4} \div 4\frac{1}{6}$

Unit 6

Probability, Statistics, and Integers

Predicting Outcomes

Carol and Pete are playing the spinner game. A game is 30 spins. Each player chooses a different color.

Carol chose red. Pete chose blue. One player twirled the spinner. It stopped on red. Carol won a point.

Whoever has the most points after 30 spins will win the game. Which player do you think will win the game?

What fraction of the times would you expect the spinner to stop on red? Blue? Yellow? Green? Red or blue?

In 30 spins, about how many times would you expect the spinner to stop on red? Blue? Yellow? Green? Red or blue? Blue or yellow? Blue or yellow or red?

You can make a spinner and play this game. Which color will you choose if you can choose first?

Imagine rolling a die a great many times. Each roll can result in any of six different numbers. Each *outcome* is shown below.

What fraction of the rolls would you expect to result in

1. a two?

$\frac{1}{6}$ $\frac{1}{2}$ $\frac{1}{3}$ $\frac{2}{3}$

2. a four?

$\frac{1}{6}$ $\frac{1}{2}$ $\frac{1}{3}$ $\frac{2}{3}$

3. a two or a four?

$\frac{1}{6}$ $\frac{1}{2}$ $\frac{1}{3}$ $\frac{2}{3}$

4. an odd number?

$\frac{1}{6}$ $\frac{1}{2}$ $\frac{1}{3}$ $\frac{2}{3}$

In 60 rolls, about how many times would you expect a roll to result in

5. a two? (Find $\frac{1}{6}$ of 60.)

6. a four?

7. a six?

8. a two or a four?

9. an odd number?

10. an even number?

Rafael decided to experiment. He rolled a die 60 times and recorded his results.

Outcome	One	Two	Three	Four	Five	Six
Tally	llll llll	llll llll	llll llll	llll llll ll	llll lll	llll llll l

Tell how many rolls resulted in

11. a two.

12. a four.

13. a six.

14. an odd number.

Tell what fraction of the rolls resulted in

15. a two.

$\frac{\text{⸬⸬⸬⸬} — \text{Number of twos}}{60 — \text{Number of tosses}}$

16. a four.

17. a six.

18. an odd number.

● **Discuss** On the next roll, do you think an odd number is more likely to occur than a four?

Finding Probabilities

A. If you roll a die, what fraction of the times do you expect the roll to show a four?

The die may land in any of 6 ways. All are equally likely to occur. There are 6 possible outcomes. Four is 1 of the 6 possible outcomes. We say the *probability* that the die will show a four is $\frac{1}{6}$.

$\frac{1}{6}$ —— Number of favorable outcomes
—— Number of possible outcomes

B. If you roll a die, what fraction of the times do you expect the roll to show a two or a five?

There are 6 possible outcomes. All are equally likely to occur. Two is 1 of the possible outcomes. Five is another. Therefore, there are 2 favorable outcomes. The probability that the die will show a two or a five is $\frac{2}{6}$, or $\frac{1}{3}$.

You can use this formula to find the probability of certain outcomes when all outcomes are equally likely:

$$\text{probability} = \frac{\text{number of favorable outcomes}}{\text{number of possible outcomes}}$$

1. If you toss a penny, what is the probability that the coin will show tails?

▓▓▓ —— Favorable outcomes
2 —— Possible outcomes

2. If you roll a die, what is the probability that the roll will show

a. two?

b. five?

c. six?

d. two or six?

e. two or five?

f. two, five, or six?

3. The Elm School Glee Club sold 100 raffle tickets. There are 8 winning tickets. If you buy a ticket, what is the probability that you will buy a winning ticket?

4. Mr. Montoya put the names of 25 students in a hat. 10 were boys. 15 were girls. Kazuo will draw a name at random. What is the probability that he will draw a boy's name? A girl's name?

Ms. Altemeyer is driving to town. Two of the three roads lead to town. One road leads to the lake.

5. What is the probability that the road Ms. Altemeyer chooses will lead to the lake?

6. What is the probability that the road she chooses will lead to town?

Ms. Altemeyer has 7 loose keys in her purse. She picks a key at random.

7. One of the 7 keys is a car key. What is the probability that she will pick the car key?

8. Two of the 7 keys are house keys. What is the probability that she will pick a house key?

9. What is the probability that she will pick a house key or the car key?

10. What is the probability that she will pick neither a house key nor the car key?

Computing Probabilities

What is the probability that the wheel will stop on blue or green?

There are 8 equal parts. Two parts are blue. One part is green. Therefore, there are 3 favorable outcomes.

The probability that the wheel will stop on blue or green is $\frac{3}{8}$.

What is the probability that the wheel will stop on

1. green?
2. blue?
3. black?
4. gold or green?
5. black or white?
6. blue or gold?
7. red, white, or blue?
8. gold, blue, or green?
9. black, white, or red?

  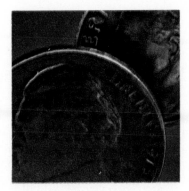

Jean will roll a die.
Give the probability that
the roll will result in

10. five.

11. six.

12. five or six.

13. three, four, or six.

14. an odd number.

15. an even number.

16. an odd or an even
number.

17. a number greater
than two.

18. a number less than
six.

★ **19.** one or an even
number.

★ **20.** a prime number.

Marilyn will pick a card
at random. What is the
probability that she will
pick

21. four?

22. five?

23. an odd number?

24. an even number?

25. seven or nine?

26. ten, two, or four?

27. a number greater
than ten?

★ **28.** a prime number?

● **Discuss** When is the
probability of an outcome
equal to 0? When is the
probability equal to 1?
Can a probability ever
be greater than 1?

Alex will toss a nickel
and a dime.

29. Complete his table
to show the
different outcomes
he can get.

Nickel	Dime
Heads	Heads
Heads	Tails
Tails	
Tails	

What is the probability
of getting these results?

30. Both coins show
heads.

31. The nickel shows
heads, and the dime
shows tails.

32. One coin shows
heads, and the other
shows tails.

laboratory activity

Activity 1

Toss two pennies
50 times. Complete
the table.

Outcomes	Tally	Fraction
2 heads		$\frac{}{50}$
1 head 1 tail		$\frac{}{50}$
2 tails		$\frac{}{50}$

Here are the
probabilities of
getting these outcomes.

Two heads: $\frac{1}{4}$

One head and one tail: $\frac{1}{2}$

Two tails: $\frac{1}{4}$

Compare your fractions
with these probabilities.

Activity 2

Toss three coins
40 times. Complete
the table.

Outcomes	Tally	Fraction
3 heads		$\frac{}{40}$
2 heads 1 tail		
1 head 2 tails		
3 tails		

Here are the
probabilities of getting
these outcomes.

Three heads: $\frac{1}{8}$

Two heads and one tail: $\frac{3}{8}$

One head and two tails: $\frac{3}{8}$

Three tails: $\frac{1}{8}$

Compare your fractions
with these probabilities.

Activity 3

Put cards like these
in a box.

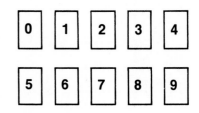

Shake the box.
Draw one card at random.
Record the number.
Return card to the box.
Draw another card.
Add the two numbers.
Record whether the sum
is even or odd.

Outcomes	Tally	Fraction
Even sum		
Odd sum		

Return card to the box.
Repeat these steps
19 times.

Here are the probabilities
of getting these outcomes.

Even sum: $\frac{1}{2}$

Odd sum: $\frac{1}{2}$

Compare your fractions
with these probabilities.

time out

Activity 4

Repeat Activity 3 with the following exception. Find the product of the numbers you draw, instead of the sum.

Outcomes	Tally	Fraction
Even product		
Odd product		

Here are the probabilities of getting these outcomes.

Even product: $\frac{3}{4}$

Odd product: $\frac{1}{4}$

Compare your fractions with these probabilities.

These numbers might be called "stilish" numbers. (A stile is a set of steps going over a wall or fence.) They have a special property.

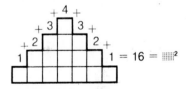

$= 16 = \blacksquare^2$

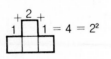

$= 4 = 2^2$

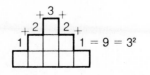

$= 9 = 3^2$

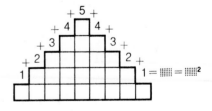

$1 = \blacksquare = \blacksquare^2$

Add three more sets of stilish numbers. Do you think the sum of every set of stilish numbers is a square number?

Counting Choices: Listing

Martin is going to toss three coins. To find the probability of getting two heads and one tail, he first made a list of all possible outcomes.

Coin 1   Coin 2   Coin 3

Possible Outcomes			
H	H	H	
H	H	T	✓
H	T	H	✓
H	T	T	
T	H	H	✓
T	H	T	
T	T	H	
T	T	T	

1. Complete the list to find all possible outcomes for tossing a coin and a die.

   Coin   Die

H	1
H	2
H	3
(?)	4
(?)	(?)
(?)	(?)
T	1
T	(?)
(?)	(?)
(?)	(?)
(?)	(?)
(?)	(?)

2. Give the probability of getting

   a. a tail and an odd number.

   b. a head and an even number.

   c. a head and a number greater than two.

   d. a tail and a number greater than three.

   ★ e. a head and a prime number.

There are 8 possible outcomes. There are 3 outcomes that show two heads and one tail.
Remember, if outcomes are equally likely:

$$\text{probability} = \frac{\text{number of favorable outcomes}}{\text{number of possible outcomes}}$$

Therefore, the probability that Martin will toss two heads and one tail is $\frac{3}{8}$.

(6, 2)

Kimberly will pick one marble from each jar.

3. Complete the list to find all possible outcomes.

red, red
red, (?)
red, (?)
white, red
white, (?)
(?), (?)
blue, red
(?), (?)
(?), (?)

4. Give the probability that Kimberly will pick

  a. a red marble and a blue marble.

  b. a red marble and a white marble.

  c. a blue marble and a white marble.

  d. two red marbles.

  e. two blue marbles.

5. Give the probability that one or more of the marbles she picks will be red.

Jeanne rolled two dice. She used number pairs to list the outcomes.

6. Complete her list to find all possible outcomes.

(1, 1)	(1, 2)	(1, 3)	(▦, ▦)	(▦, ▦)	(1, 6)
(2, 1)	(2, 2)	(▦, ▦)	(▦, ▦)	(▦, ▦)	(2, 6)
(▦, ▦)	(▦, ▦)	(▦, ▦)	(3, 4)	(▦, ▦)	(▦, ▦)
(4, 1)	(▦, ▦)	(▦, ▦)	(▦, ▦)	(4, 5)	(▦, ▦)
(▦, ▦)	(▦, ▦)	(5, 3)	(5, 4)	(▦, ▦)	(▦, ▦)
(▦, ▦)	(6, 2)	(▦, ▦)	(▦, ▦)	(6, 5)	(▦, ▦)

7. Give the probability that on her next roll, she will get

  a. a six on one or both of the dice.

  b. two numbers that are the same.

  c. two numbers that are even.

  d. two numbers that add up to five.

  e. two numbers that add up to seven.

  f. one number that is greater than the other.

Counting Choices: Tree Diagrams

Ruth is going to toss two coins. She asked
Rex and Marsha to find all possible outcomes.

Rex made a list.

Nickel   Dime

H	H
H	T
T	H
T	T

Marsha made a tree diagram.

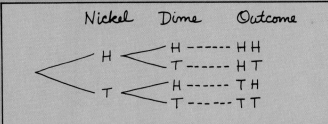

Nickel   Dime   Outcome

- H
  - H ------ H H
  - T ------ H T
- T
  - H ------ T H
  - T ------ T T

There are 4 possible outcomes.
There are 3 outcomes showing at least one head.
The probability that at least one head will show is $\frac{3}{4}$.

Ron is going to toss three coins.

1. Complete his tree diagram to find
all possible outcomes.

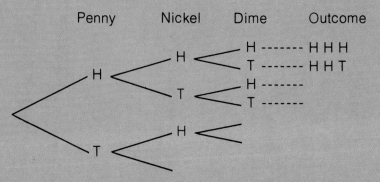

Penny	Nickel	Dime	Outcome
H	H	H ------- H H H	
		T ------- H H T	
	T	H -------	
		T -------	
T	H		

2. Give the probability
of getting

- **a.** 3 heads.
- **b.** 2 heads and 1 tail.
- **c.** 1 head and 2 tails.
- **d.** 3 tails.

3. Complete the tree diagram to show all the ways you can choose answers in a true-false test with three questions.

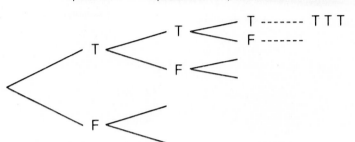

First question Second question Third question Outcome

T ——————— T T T
F ———————

4. Each outcome in the tree diagram is a set of three answers. How many possible outcomes?

5. One outcome gives the right set of answers for the test. What is the probability of guessing the right set of answers?

6. Make a tree diagram to show all the ways you can choose answers in a true-false test with four questions.

7. How many possible outcomes?

8. What is the probability of guessing the right set of answers to all four questions?

9. Make a tree diagram to show all the ways you can choose answers in a multiple-choice test with three questions. The first and second questions have three choices: *a*, *b*, and *c*. The third has two choices: *a* and *b*.

10. How many possible outcomes?

11. What is the probability of guessing the right set of answers to all three questions in the multiple-choice test?

PEANUTS

LET'S SEE NOW... IN A TRUE OR FALSE TEST, THE FIRST QUESTION IS ALMOST ALWAYS 'TRUE'...

THAT MEANS THE NEXT ONE WILL BE FALSE TO SORT OF BALANCE THE TRUE ONE.. THE NEXT ONE WILL ALSO BE FALSE TO BREAK THE PATTERN..

THEN ANOTHER TRUE AND THEN TWO MORE FALSE ONES AND THEN THREE TRUES IN A ROW...THEY ALWAYS HAVE THREE TRUES IN A ROW SOME PLACE...THEN ANOTHER FALSE AND ANOTHER TRUE...

IF YOU'RE SMART, YOU CAN PASS A TRUE OR FALSE TEST WITHOUT BEING SMART!

Counting Choices: Multiplication

Instead of making a list or a tree diagram, you can sometimes multiply to find all possible outcomes. When two coins are tossed, there are four possible outcomes.

Number of ways nickel can land	Number of ways dime can land	Number of possible outcomes
2	**×** **2**	**=** **4**

Multiply to find the answers.

1. How many possible outcomes are there if three coins are tossed?

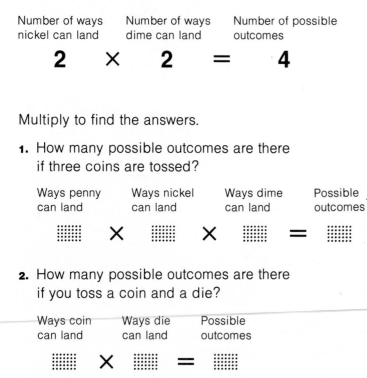

Ways penny can land		Ways nickel can land		Ways dime can land		Possible outcomes
▦	×	▦	×	▦	=	▦

2. How many possible outcomes are there if you toss a coin and a die?

Ways coin can land		Ways die can land		Possible outcomes
▦	×	▦	=	▦

3. How many possible outcomes are there if you toss a coin and two dice?

Ways coin can land		Ways first die can land		Ways second die can land		Possible outcomes
▦	×	▦	×	▦	=	▦

How many possible outcomes would there be if you tossed

4. four coins?

5. five coins?

6. six coins?

7. seven coins?

8. two dice?

9. three dice?

10. two coins and one die?

11. two coins and two dice?

12. three coins and three dice?

time out

If you choose each digit at random, how many different ways can you choose each number? Remember, the digits are the numbers 0 through 9.

In each of these pictures, the scales balance. Can you tell how many boxes of popcorn one bottle of pop weighs? You will need to use all the pictures.

13. A two-digit code number

Ways to choose first digit	Ways to choose second digit	Possible outcomes
10	× 10	= ▦

14. A three-digit identification-card number

15. A four-digit bicycle-lock number

16. A five-digit Zip Code number

17. A six-digit license-plate number

For the following exercises, use your answers to exercises 13–17 to help you.

What is the probability that you would choose

18. 09 for the code number? ($\frac{▦}{100}$)

19. 677 for the identification-card number?

20. 5802 for the bicycle-lock number?

21. 31416 for the Zip Code number?

22. 358460 for the license-plate number?

★ **23.** a two-digit code number whose first digit is 5?

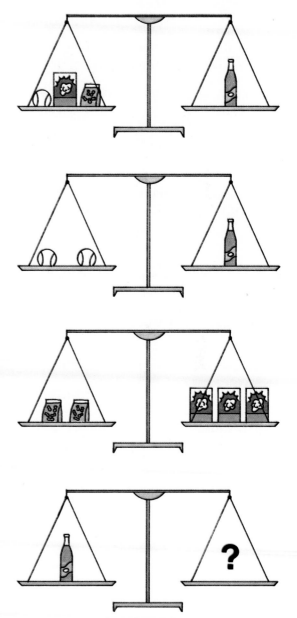

Using Multiplication to Find Probabilities

Sometimes you can multiply to find favorable outcomes as well as possible outcomes.

If Angela rolls a pair of dice, what is the probability that both dice will come up even numbers?

She multiplied to find the number of possible outcomes.

Ways first die can land		Ways second die can land		Possible outcomes
6	**×**	**6**	**=**	**36**

Then she multiplied to find the number of favorable outcomes.

Even numbers on first die		Even numbers on second die		Favorable outcomes
3	**×**	**3**	**=**	**9**

The probability that both dice will come up even is $\frac{9}{36}$, or $\frac{1}{4}$.

Warren is going to twirl both spinners. He wants each spinner to stop on a number greater than three.

1. How many possible outcomes?

Ways first spinner can land		Ways second spinner can land		Possible outcomes
▦	×	▦	=	▦

2. How many favorable outcomes?

Numbers greater than 3 on first spinner		Numbers greater than 3 on second spinner		Favorable outcomes
▦	×	▦	=	▦

3. What is the probability that each spinner will stop on a number greater than three?

Opal is going to twirl both spinners. What is the probability that the number on each spinner will be

4. odd?

5. even?

6. greater than 1?

7. less than 4?

8. less than 3?

9. less than 2?

Using Multiplication and Listing to Find Probabilities

Sometimes you need to use both lists and multiplication to find probability.

If Hal rolls a pair of dice, what is the probability that the sum of the numbers on the dice for a single roll will be 3 or 7?

He multiplied to find the number of possible outcomes.

Ways first die can land	Ways second die can land	Possible outcomes
6 ×	**6** =	**36**

Then he made a list to find the number of favorable outcomes.

Sums of 3	Sums of 7
1 + 2	1 + 6
2 + 1	6 + 1
	2 + 5
	5 + 2
	3 + 4
	4 + 3

There are 8 favorable outcomes. The probability that the sum of the numbers on the dice for a single roll will be 3 or 7 is $\frac{8}{36}$, or $\frac{2}{9}$.

If Mark rolls a pair of dice, what is the probability that the numbers will have a

1. sum of 3 or 12?

2. sum of 3, 7, or 12?

3. sum greater than 9?

4. sum greater than 8?

★ 5. sum that is prime?

Melvin is going to roll three dice. He wants the sum of the numbers to be 5.

6. Multiply to find the number of possible outcomes.

7. Complete the list to find the number of favorable outcomes.

1 + 1 + 3	2 + 2 + ▦
1 + ▦ + 1	2 + ▦ + 2
▦ + 1 + 1	▦ + 2 + 2

8. What is the probability that the sum of the numbers will be 5?

If Betty rolls three dice, what is the probability that the numbers will have a

9. sum of 3?

10. sum of 6?

11. sum less than 5?

12. sum greater than 15?

13. sum greater than 14?

Using Experiments to Predict Probabilities

If you toss thumbtacks, the outcomes are *not* equally likely. You have to experiment to predict a probability.

A. Keith tossed a tack 30 times. He recorded his results.

Outcome		Tally
	Point up	ЦНТ |||
	Point down	ЦНТ ЦНТ ЦНТ ЦНТ ||

He wondered about the probability that the tack would land point up on the next toss. To help him predict the probability, he used this fraction:

number of favorable outcomes
─────────────────────────────
number of experimental tosses

Using the results of his experiment, Keith predicted that the probability the tack would land point up on the next toss would be $\frac{8}{30}$, or $\frac{4}{15}$.

B. Ray tossed the same tack. He recorded his results for 60 tosses.

Outcome		Tally
	Point up	ЦНТ ЦНТ ЦНТ |||
	Point down	ЦНТ ЦНТ ЦНТ ЦНТ ЦНТ ЦНТ ЦНТ ЦНТ ||

He predicted that the probability the tack would land point up on the next toss would be $\frac{18}{60}$, or $\frac{3}{10}$.

Is Ray's prediction the same as Keith's prediction? Ray's prediction was based on a greater number of tosses than was Keith's. What could Ray do to make an even better prediction?

1. Ellen tossed a tack 30 times. It landed point up 14 times, and point down 16 times.

   Use the results of Ellen's experiment to predict the probability that, on the next toss, the tack would land point up. Point down.

2. Marlene tossed a tack 60 times. It landed point up 45 times, and point down 15 times.

   Use the results of Marlene's experiment to predict the probability that, on the next toss, the tack would land point up. Point down.

3. Toss a tack of your own 60 times. Record your results. Use your results to predict the probability that, on the next toss, the tack will land point up. Point down.

4. Nora tossed a paper cup 30 times. She recorded her results.

Outcome		Tally
	Top up	I
	Top down	$\cancel{IIII}$
	Side	$\cancel{IIII}$ $\cancel{IIII}$ $\cancel{IIII}$ $\cancel{IIII}$ IIII

Use the results of Nora's experiment to predict the probability that the paper cup will land

a. top up.

b. top down.

c. on its side.

d. top down or on its side.

e. top up, top down, or on its side.

5. Toss a paper cup 90 times. Record your results. Use your results to predict the probability that the cup will land top up. Top down. On its side.

Finding probability, pages 324–329

1. If you toss a nickel, what is the probability that it will show heads?

2. If you roll a die, what is the probability that it will show four or six?

Finding probability by counting choices, pages 332–339

3. Complete the list to find all possible outcomes for tossing two coins. How many are there?

Penny	Dime
H	H
H	T
T	(?)
(?)	(?)

4. What is the probability of getting two tails?

5. Complete the tree diagram to find all possible outcomes for tossing three coins. How many are there?

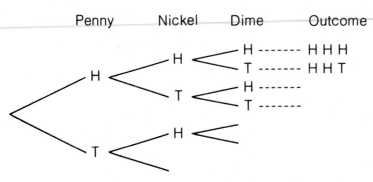

6. What is the probability of getting three tails?

7. What is the probability of getting one head and two tails?

8. How many different ways can you choose a three-digit bicycle-lock number?

9. What is the probability that the bicycle-lock number you choose will be 009?

Jane is going to roll a pair of dice.

10. How many possible outcomes are there?

11. What is the probability that both dice will come up odd numbers?

12. What is the probability that the numbers will show a sum of 2 or 10?

Predicting probability by using experiments, pages 340–341

Bart tossed a paper cup 36 times. He recorded his results.

Outcome	Tally
Top up	JHT I
Top down	JHT JHT III
Side	JHT JHT JHT II

13. Use the results of Bart's experiment to predict the probability that the cup will land top up on the next toss.

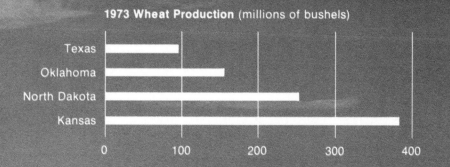

1973 Wheat Production (millions of bushels)

Using Data: A Small Business

Pete saves the sales slip for each customer. He uses the *data* on the sales slips to make a weekly sales record.

Pete analyzes the *statistics* to help him estimate future sales and decide how much food to order.

Pizza Sales for One Week Beginning April 6

Day	Number of small pizzas	Number of medium pizzas	Number of large pizzas
Sunday	86	61	93
Monday	41	29	50
Tuesday	28	16	31
Wednesday	53	32	56
Thursday	32	14	35
Friday	75	59	90
Saturday	112	93	126

On which day did Pete sell the fewest

1. small pizzas?
2. medium pizzas?
3. large pizzas?

During the week, Pete sold how many

4. small pizzas?
5. medium pizzas?
6. large pizzas?

Find the total number of pizzas
Pete sold each day.

7. Sunday

8. Monday

9. Tuesday

10. Wednesday

11. Thursday

12. Friday

13. Saturday

Pete's records show that he sells
about a liter of milk for every six
pizzas sold. About how much milk
should he order for

14. Sunday? (Find 240 ÷ 6.)

15. Monday?

16. Tuesday and Wednesday?

17. Thursday, Friday, and Saturday?

His records show that he sells about
one case of cola for every twelve
pizzas sold. About how many cases
should he order for

18. Sunday?

19. Monday?

20. Tuesday and Wednesday?

21. Thursday, Friday, and Saturday?

Picturing Data: Bar Graphs

Statistical data can be displayed in many ways.
Pete made a *bar graph* so that he could compare daily
sales more easily.

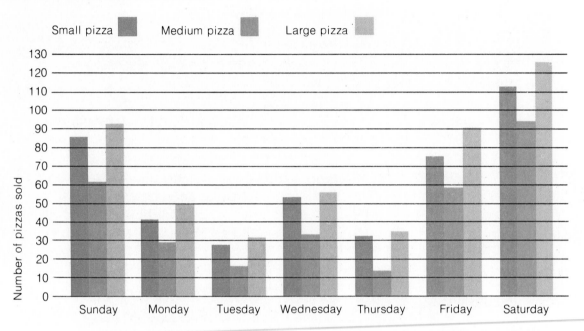

On how many days did
Pete sell more than

1. 50 small pizzas?

2. 40 medium pizzas?

3. 90 large pizzas?

On how many days did
Pete sell fewer than

4. 60 small pizzas?

5. 20 medium pizzas?

6. 50 large pizzas?

On which day did Pete
sell more medium pizzas?

7. Monday or Wednesday

8. Sunday or Friday

9. Tuesday or Thursday

On which day did Pete
sell more small pizzas?

10. Sunday or Saturday

11. Monday or Friday

12. Tuesday or Thursday

13. Make a bar graph
    to show the number
    of pizzas sold each
    day for the week
    beginning May 4.

Sunday	230
Monday	120
Tuesday	90
Wednesday	150
Thursday	100
Friday	190
Saturday	260

Picturing Data: Pictographs

Pete made a *pictograph* to show about how much money he received each day. Each circle represents $100 in sales.

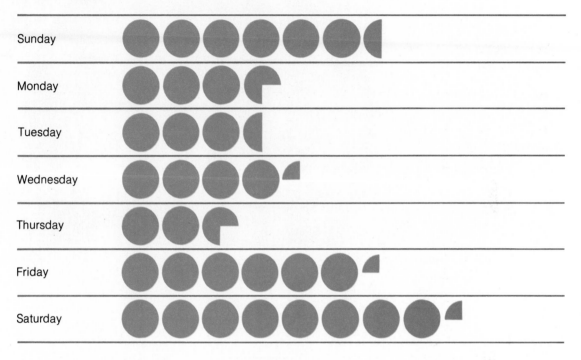

Sunday	
Monday	
Tuesday	
Wednesday	
Thursday	
Friday	
Saturday	

About how much money did Pete receive for

1. Sunday?
2. Monday?
3. Tuesday?
4. Wednesday?
5. Thursday?
6. Friday?
7. Saturday?
8. the entire week?

On which day did Pete receive more money? About how much more?

9. Sunday or Monday
10. Monday or Tuesday
11. Tuesday or Wednesday
12. Friday or Saturday
13. Sunday or Friday
14. Sunday or Saturday
15. Wednesday or Friday

16. Make a pictograph to show the number of cases of cola Pete sold. Use ◇ to represent four cases of cola.

Sunday	20 cases
Monday	10 cases
Tuesday	6 cases
Wednesday	12 cases
Thursday	8 cases
Friday	18 cases
Saturday	28 cases

Picturing Data: Circle Graphs

On school days, Sandy never had enough time for hobbies. So she decided to make a time budget.

Activity	Time
Sleeping	9 hours
Eating	2 hours
Classes	6 hours
Homework	1 hour
Travel	2 hours
Grooming	1 hour
Telephone	1 hour
Hobbies	2 hours

Then she made a *circle graph* of her time budget.

To make the circle graph, Sandy started by finding what fraction of a 24-hour school day she plans to spend on each activity. Complete her table.

	Activity	Time in hours	Fraction of a day
	Sleeping	9	$\frac{9}{24}$, or $\frac{3}{8}$
1.	Eating		
2.	Classes		
3.	Homework		
4.	Travel		
5.	Grooming		
6.	Telephone		
7.	Hobbies		

8. Next, Sandy used the fractions to compute the size of the central angle for each activity. She multiplied to find the central angle for sleeping.

$$\frac{3}{8} \times 360° = 135°$$

Find the number of degrees in each central angle for the rest of Sandy's activities.

9. Make a circle graph to show how you usually spend a typical 24-hour school day.

Make a circle graph to show each set of data.

10. Sources of water pollution

Industry	$\frac{3}{5}$,	or 60%
Urban sewage	$\frac{1}{4}$,	or 25%
Agriculture	$\frac{3}{20}$,	or 15%

★ 11. Sources of air pollution

Transportation	42%
Fuel combustion	21%
Industry	14%
Solid waste	6%
Miscellaneous	17%

time out

$1 + 2 = 3$
$1^3 + 2^3$
$1 + 8 = 9$

$1 + 2 + 3 = 6$
$1^3 + 2^3 + 3^3$
$1 + 8 + 27 = 36$

$1 + 2 + 3 + 4 = 10$
$1^3 + 2^3 + 3^3 + 4^3$
$1 + 8 + 27 + 64 = 100$

Notice that the blue number in each example is the square of the red number. Use this idea to help you find these sums.

$1^3 + 2^3 + 3^3 + 4^3 + 5^3$

$1^3 + 2^3 + 3^3 + 4^3 + 5^3 + 6^3$

$1^3 + 2^3 + 3^3 + 4^3 + 5^3 + 6^3 + 7^3$

Picturing Data: Line Graphs

Line graphs can show trends, or changes, in data over a period of time. You may compute the *range* from a line graph. The range is the difference between the largest and the smallest numbers in the data.

This graph shows a decrease in the number of milk cows on farms in the United States from 1965 to 1972.

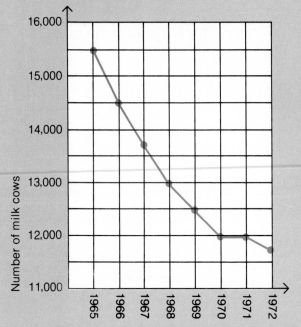

This graph shows an increase in the number of tons of peanuts produced in the United States from 1965 to 1972.

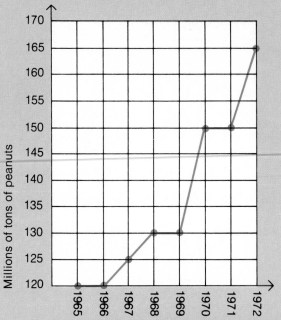

1. For each year, give the number of milk cows on farms in the United States.

2. Compute the range.
   (Find 15,500 − 11,750.)

3. For each year, give the number of millions of tons of peanuts produced in the United States.

4. Compute the range.

This graph shows a fluctuation in the number of tons of pecans produced in the United States from 1965 to 1972.

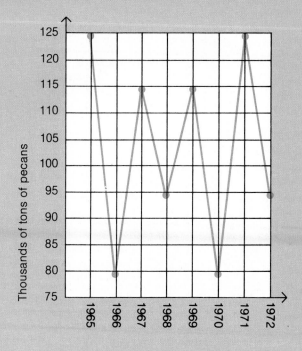

7. Make a line graph to show the number of tons of filberts produced in the United States from 1965 to 1972.

Year	Number of tons
1965	8,000
1966	12,000
1967	8,000
1968	8,000
1969	8,000
1970	9,000
1971	11,000
1972	10,000

8. Compute the range.

● **Discuss** Does your graph show that the production of filberts increased, decreased, or fluctuated during this period of time?

5. For each year, give the number of thousands of tons of pecans produced in the United States.

6. Compute the range.

A Statistical Measure: The Mean

In statistics, the average of a set
of data is called the *mean*.
Find the mean height of these
13-year-old girls.

Add the data.

Divide by the
number of data.

$$\frac{142 + 152 + 163 + 170}{4} = \frac{627}{4} = 156.75$$

The mean height of the four girls
is 156.75 centimeters.

170 cm

163 cm

152 cm

142 cm

1. Find the mean weight of the four girls.

Jane	44 kg
Nicole	45 kg
Mary	56 kg
Pam	53 kg

2. Find the mean distance of the standing broad jumps made by these eight students.

Michael	107 cm
Naomi	116 cm
David	95 cm
Rachel	99 cm
Rhonda	109 cm
Manuel	122 cm
Doris	101 cm
Lisa	115 cm

3. Find the mean test score of the twelve math students in Mr. Rivera's class.

Harold	74
Marie	62
Betty	96
Linda	85
Carlos	75
Dennis	52
Jerry	43
Sandy	89
Ricardo	100
Norman	89
Kinuko	89
Beverly	76

4. Find the mean number of points scored by the leading scorers in the North American Soccer League in 1973. Round your answer to the nearest whole number.

Kyle Rote, Jr. (Dallas)	30
Warren Archibald (Miami)	29
Andy Provan (Philadelphia)	28
Gene Gelmer (St. Louis)	25
Ilija Mitic (Dallas)	25
Randy Horton (New York)	23
Joe Fink (New York)	22
Richard Reynolds (Dallas)	22
Miguel Perrichon (Toronto)	22
Willie Roy (St. Louis)	18
Tom Ord (Montreal)	18
Bruno Pilas (Toronto)	18

5. Find the mean height of these North American mountain peaks. Round your answer to the nearest meter.

McKinley (Alaska)	6194 m
Logan (Canada)	6050 m
Citlaltépetl (Mexico)	5700 m
St. Elias (Alaska-Canada)	5489 m
Popocatépetl (Mexico)	5452 m
Foraker (Alaska)	5304 m
Iztaccíhuatl (Mexico)	5286 m

★ 6. For each country, find the mean value of the gold produced for this period of time. Round your answer to the nearest hundred thousand.

United States		Canada	
1966	$63,100,000	1966	$114,600,000
1967	53,400,000	1967	103,700,000
1968	53,900,000	1968	94,100,000
1969	60,100,000	1969	89,100,000
1970	63,500,000	1970	84,300,000

More practice
Set A, page 382

Statistical Measures: The Median and the Mode

Melanie compiled these statistics on the inaugural ages and the death ages of seven United States Presidents.

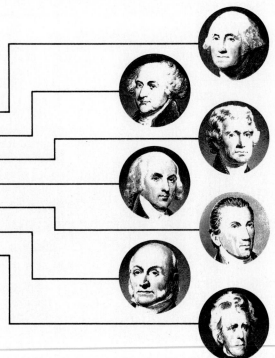

President	Inaugural age	Death age
George Washington	57	67
John Adams	61	90
Thomas Jefferson	57	83
James Madison	57	85
James Monroe	58	73
John Quincy Adams	57	80
Andrew Jackson	61	78

Sometimes statisticians describe data by using the *median* or the *mode*.

A. To find the median of the death ages of the seven Presidents, first arrange the ages in order.

90
85
83
80 ——— 80 is the median.
78
73
67

The median has as many numbers above it as below it. The median is 80 years.

B. To find the mode of the inaugural ages of the seven Presidents, first arrange the ages in order.

61
61
58
57 ⎫
57 ⎬ ——— 57 is the mode.
57 ⎪
57 ⎭

The mode is the number appearing most often. The mode is 57 years.

The students in Ms. Massena's math class made these scores on a test.

74, 62, 96, 74, 51, 43, 89, 89, 76, 89, 95, 76, 100

1. Find the median.

2. Find the mode.

3. Compute the mean.

4. Compute the range.

Mr. Rodriguez recorded the daily attendance at Blake Junior High for a two-week period.

407, 425, 417, 417, 425, 413, 441, 425, 396, 414

5. Find the median.

6. Find the mode.

7. Compute the mean.

8. Compute the range.

In July, Sarah recorded the highest temperature every day for three weeks.

81, 84, 87, 69, 79, 81, 80
78, 81, 79, 81, 79, 96, 90
88, 82, 79, 85, 83, 80, 80

9. Find the median.

10. Find the two modes.

11. Compute the mean.

12. Compute the range.

**More practice
Set B, page 382**

```
        M     N
        O     A
      MODE    E
        EDOMODE
              E
        S     D
      STATISTICS
  M     M       A
  O     P       N
  D     L
  EDOMEDIAN
      E
      NAEMODE
      N   O
          D
          E
```

1. Record the number of times you find these words in the puzzle. You may read forward, backward, up, or down.

Mean	Statistics
Median	Sample
Mode	

2. Which of these words occurs the median number of times? The mean number of times? The mode number of times?

3. Fifty-eight letters were used in this puzzle. Use the same words the same number of times to make up another puzzle with fewer than 58 letters.

Misuses of Statistics

Sometimes people misuse statistics because of ignorance. Sometimes they misuse statistics on purpose.

Bobby Bridges misuses percents because of ignorance. He read a table giving the percent of 15-year-old girls who have protein, calcium, or iron deficiencies.

Protein   10%
Calcium   45%
Iron   35%

He added the percents and concluded that 90% of all 15-year-old girls have one of these diet deficiencies.

1. Can more than 90% of all 15-year-old girls have one of these deficiencies?

2. Can fewer than 45% have a deficiency?

● **Discuss**   Using these data, can Bobby Bridges give an exact percent of 15-year-old girls who have only one of these diet deficiencies?

Silas Scrooge misuses the mean on purpose. He told a prospective employee that the mean yearly salary of his fifteen employees is $15,000. Here is the list of salaries.

$61,500
 50,000
 12,000
 10,000
  9,800
  9,700
  9,000
  9,000
  9,000
  8,000
  8,000
  8,000
  8,000
  7,000
  6,000

3. What is the mode?

4. What is the median?

● **Discuss**   Is the mean a good way to describe these data? The median? The mode?

Manny Manovis misuses the median on purpose. He claims that his basketball team is tall and quotes the median height of his five starting players as 6 feet 1 inch. Here is a list of the players' heights.

6 ft. 2 in.   (74 in.)
6 ft. 2 in.   (74 in.)
6 ft. 1 in.   (73 in.)
5 ft. 3 in.   (63 in.)
5 ft. 1 in.   (61 in.)

5. What is the mode?

6. What is the mean?

● **Discuss**   Is the mean a good way to describe these data? The median? The mode?

A national magazine used this form of pictograph to help readers compare visually the 1974 defense budget with the 1954 defense budget.

7. What percent of the gross national product was allocated to defense in 1954?

8. What percent of the gross national product was allocated to defense in 1974?

9. Is the percent of the gross national product spent on defense in 1974 about half as much as the percent spent in 1954?

10. Is the small soldier about half as tall as the large soldier?

11. Is the small soldier about half as wide as the large soldier?

12. Is the area of the small soldier less than half of the area of the large soldier?

Defense Budget
Percent of Gross National Product

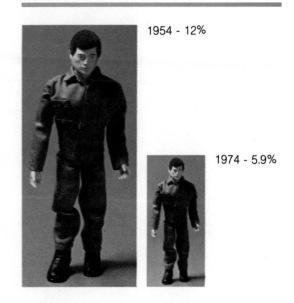

1954 - 12%

1974 - 5.9%

Insurance Agent

Barbara sells automobile insurance. She often sells insurance to students whose parents' cars are insured with her company.

She wrote a policy for Art and one for Carl. Before she could write either policy, however, she needed to know where each student lived, his age, his grades, and the car make and model. All these factors influence the amount of the premium.

She computed the rates by checking tables of data prepared by an actuary who studies these factors.

Art lives in a suburb of Chicago. He bought a 1968 Ford Galaxie. He is 16 and has a "B" grade average. Barbara wrote this policy to cover Art's car for six months.

Liability Coverage 　Bodily Injury Limits ($50,000/$100,000) 　Property Damage Limits ($25,000)	$110.50
Medical Payments Coverage 　($5000 limit per person)	8.50
Comprehensive Coverage	15.50
Collision ($100 deductible)	43.94
Uninsured Motorist Coverage	3.00

1. What is Art's total premium for six months?

2. How much would he pay for one year?

3. If Art pays the yearly premium in four equal payments, he must pay an additional $4 per year. How much would each quarterly payment be?

4. If Art pays the yearly premium in twelve equal payments, he must pay an additional $15 per year. How much would each monthly payment be?

5. If Art had a "C" grade average, his six-month premium would be $224.89. How much more would he pay on his insurance for six months?

Carl also lives in a suburb of Chicago. He owns a 1970 Corvette. He is 17 and has a "C" grade average. Barbara wrote this policy to cover Carl's car for six months.

Liability Coverage 　Bodily Injury Limits ($50,000/$100,000) 　Property Damage Limits ($25,000)	$148.07
Medical Payments Coverage 　($5000 limit per person)	11.39
Comprehensive Coverage	40.20
Collision ($100 deductible)	108.54
Performance Surcharge	77.00
Uninsured Motorist Coverage	3.00

6. What is Carl's total premium for six months? For one year?

7. If Carl pays the yearly premium in four equal payments, he must pay an additional $4 per year. How much would each quarterly payment be?

8. If Carl had a "B" grade average, his six-month premium would be $294.95. How much would he save on his insurance for six months?

9. Carl had a collision. He got two estimates of the damage to his car. Find the difference.

First estimate　　$1035
Second estimate　　1180

10. The insurance company accepted the estimate of $1035. Carl paid $100. How much did the insurance company pay?

Pictured data, pages 344–351

This bar graph shows sandwich sales in the school cafeteria.

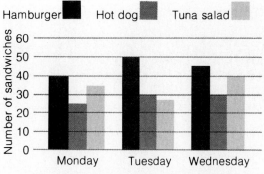

Hamburger ■   Hot dog ■   Tuna salad ■

1. On how many days were fewer than 30 hot dogs sold?

2. On how many days were more than 40 hamburgers sold?

3. Were more tuna salad sandwiches sold on Monday or on Wednesday?

This pictograph shows how much money the cafeteria received from the sale of sandwiches. Each circle represents $10 in sales.

4. How much money did the cafeteria receive on Monday?

5. How much on Tuesday?

6. The human body is made up of these materials. In a circle graph, how many degrees would be in the central angle for "fat"?

Muscle $\frac{1}{2}$, or 50%

Fat $\frac{1}{5}$, or 20%

Bone $\frac{9}{50}$, or 18%

Other $\frac{3}{25}$, or 12%

This graph shows the number of tons of almonds produced in the United States. How many tons were produced in

7. the year 1970?

8. the year 1972?

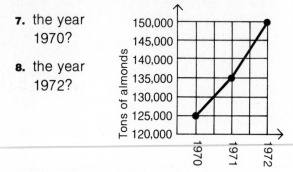

Finding range, mean, median, and mode, pages 350–357

The students in Mrs. Wong's science class made these scores on a test.

73 84 98 44 60 78 95 87
87 85 87 75 87

9. Compute the range.

10. Compute the mean.

11. Find the median.

12. Find the mode.

Positive and Negative Numbers

Positive numbers and *negative numbers* are useful for describing such "opposite" quantities as gains and losses or temperatures above and below zero. For example, you could use ⁺7 to mean a gain of 7 grams, and ⁻7 to mean a loss of 7 grams.

Write the missing numbers.

Here's how

390 meters below sea level, ⁻390
8850 meters above sea level, ▦ **⁺8850**

1. Gain of 6 yards, ⁺6
   Loss of 8 yards, ▦

2. 5°C below zero, ⁻5
   14°C above zero, ▦

3. Loss of $30, ⁻30
   Profit of $50, ▦

4. Deposit of $160, ⁺160
   Withdrawal of $45, ▦

5. Six strokes over par, ⁺6
   Four strokes under par, ▦

6. 20 kilometers south, ⁻20
   10 kilometers north, ▦

7. 500 feet above sea level, ⁺500
   5 feet below sea level, ▦

8. Three days before Thanksgiving, ⁻3
   Two days after Thanksgiving, ▦

9. Price increase of 14 cents, ⁺14
   Price decrease of 9 cents, ▦

10. 20 meters forward, ⁺20
    15 meters back, ▦

+10 —— Positive 10
+9
+8
+7
+6
+5
+4
+3
+2
+1
0
−1
−2
−3
−4
−5
−6
−7
−8
−9
−10 —— Negative 10

Positive numbers

Negative numbers

Zero is neither positive nor negative.

Integers

The numbers in this list are *integers:*

$$\ldots, \ ^-6, \ ^-5, \ ^-4, \ ^-3, \ ^-2, \ ^-1, \ 0, \ ^+1, \ ^+2, \ ^+3, \ ^+4, \ ^+5, \ ^+6, \ldots$$

In the table, the positive integers mean temperatures above zero. The negative integers mean temperatures below zero.

Extreme Temperatures over a 30-Year Period (°F)

State or province	City	Highest	Lowest
California	Los Angeles	$^+110$	$^+28$
Louisiana	Baton Rouge	$^+110$	$^+2$
Montana	Helena	$^+105$	$^-42$
New York	New York	$^+106$	$^-15$
Ontario	Toronto	$^+105$	$^-26$
Quebec	Montreal	$^+97$	$^-29$
South Dakota	Huron	$^+112$	$^-43$
Wyoming	Cheyenne	$^+100$	$^-38$

Use the table to answer these questions.

1. In which cities was the temperature always above zero?

2. Which city had the highest recorded temperature? The lowest?

Compare the highest temperatures.
Which city was warmer?

3. New York or Cheyenne

4. Toronto or Helena

5. Los Angeles or Huron

Compare the lowest temperatures.
Which city was colder?

6. Baton Rouge or New York

7. Toronto or Montreal

8. Helena or Huron

★ 9. Using the lowest temperatures, list the cities and their temperatures in order from warmest to coldest.

Comparing Integers

You can use a number line
to compare integers.

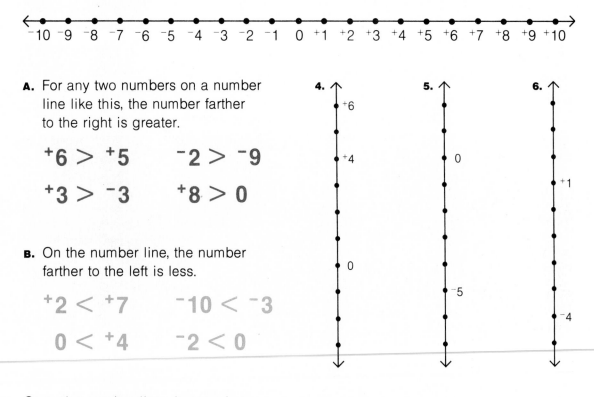

A. For any two numbers on a number
line like this, the number farther
to the right is greater.

$$^+6 > {}^+5 \qquad ^-2 > {}^-9$$

$$^+3 > {}^-3 \qquad ^+8 > 0$$

B. On the number line, the number
farther to the left is less.

$$^+2 < {}^+7 \qquad ^-10 < {}^-3$$

$$0 < {}^+4 \qquad ^-2 < 0$$

4.

5.

6.

Copy the number lines in exercises
1–6. Use an integer to label each
point shown.

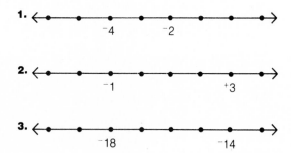

1.

2.

3.

Compare the integers in each exercise.
Use > or <.

7. $^+5$ ⬤ $^+3$

8. $^-1$ ⬤ 0

9. $^-2$ ⬤ $^-1$

10. $^-6$ ⬤ $^+13$

11. $^+8$ ⬤ $^-13$

12. $^+5$ ⬤ $^+12$

13. $^+18$ ⬤ $^-16$

14. $^-9$ ⬤ $^-3$

15. $^+2$ ⬤ $^-2$

16. $^-34$ ⬤ $^+34$

For each exercise, arrange the integers in order from least to greatest.

17. $^+1$, $^-1$, $^+2$, $^-2$

18. $^-7$, $^-8$, $^-9$, $^+8$, 0

19. $^-6$, $^+7$, $^-8$, $^+9$, $^-10$

20. $^+5$, 0, $^-4$, $^+6$, $^-2$

21. $^+1$, $^+5$, $^+7$, $^-1$, $^-5$, $^-7$

22. $^+8$, $^+16$, $^-8$, $^-1$, $^-12$

23. $^-12$, 0, $^-4$, $^+8$, $^-1$

24. $^-15$, $^+15$, $^-16$, $^+16$, $^-17$, $^+17$

What integers correspond to the lettered points? In exercises 25–27, match each integer with its letter. Then write the letters.

A J B K C L D M E N F O G P H R I
$^-8$ $^-5$ 0 $^+2$ $^+7$

25. $^+6$, $^-1$, $^-9$, $^-4$ 0, $^+7$, $^-5$, $^-1$

26. $^+3$, $^+2$ $^-7$, $^-9$, $^-5$, $^-6$

27. $^-9$ $^-5$, $^-4$, $^-1$, $^-9$, 0 $^-8$, $^+2$, $^-7$

● **Discuss**   Imagine continuing a number line on and on in both directions. Is there a greatest integer? Is there a least integer?

What kind of integers are greater than zero? Less than zero?

In ten moves or fewer, rearrange the tiles to form a well-known saying.

You can slide the tiles in the box, but you must not remove any and replace them.

Cut eight squares of paper or cardboard, write a word on each, then slide them around to get the saying.

Adding Integers

A number line can help you add integers.

A. $^+6 + ^+3 = ^+9$

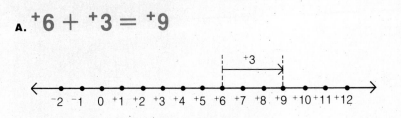

One addend is $^+6$. Find $^+6$ on the number line. The other addend is $^+3$, a positive integer. Move 3 units to the right. The sum is $^+9$.

B. $^-3 + ^-4 = ^-7$

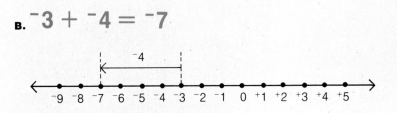

Find $^-3$ on the number line. Since $^-4$ is negative, move 4 units to the left. The sum is $^-7$.

C. $^+5 + ^-2 = ^+3$

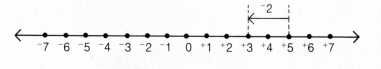

D. $^+2 + ^-6 = ^-4$

Use a number line to find each sum.

1. $^+3 + ^+4$

2. $^-5 + ^-2$

3. $^+4 + ^-5$

4. $^-6 + ^+8$

5. $^+6 + ^-10$

6. $^-7 + ^+7$

Find each sum. Use a number line if necessary.

7. $^+8 + ^+9$

8. $^+3 + ^+7$

9. $^+16 + ^+2$

10. $^+20 + ^+25$

11. Is the sum of two positive integers positive, or is it negative?

12. $^-2 + ^-2$

13. $^-4 + ^-8$

14. $^-10 + ^-15$

15. $^-9 + ^-13$

16. Is the sum of two negative integers positive, or is it negative?

17. a. $^-9 + {}^+5 = $ ▦

Which addend, $^-9$ or $^+5$, is farther from zero on the number line? Is this addend positive, or is it negative?

b. Is the sum of $^-9$ and $^+5$ positive or negative?

18. a. $^-5 + {}^+7 = $ ▦

Which addend is farther from zero on the number line? Is this addend positive, or is it negative?

b. Is the sum positive or negative?

19. a. $^+3 + {}^-3 = $ ▦

Which addend is farther from zero on the number line?

b. What do you notice about the sum of $^+3$ and $^-3$?

Find each sum. Use a number line if necessary.

20. $^+4 + {}^-9$	**25.** $^+13 + {}^-10$
21. $^-5 + {}^+7$	**26.** $^-14 + {}^+8$
22. $^-16 + {}^+9$	★ **27.** $^+3 + {}^-4 + {}^+5$
23. $^+8 + {}^-8$	★ **28.** $^-5 + {}^-9 + {}^+6$
24. $^-6 + {}^+10$	

**More practice
Set C, page 382**

Trace a path through the diagram from Start to Finish. Move from one square to the next, adding the integers as you go along. The number opposite Finish is the final sum. Move only horizontally or vertically.

Here's how

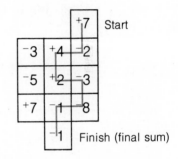

★ **29.**

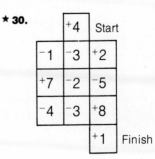

★ **30.**

Using Integers: Magic Squares

In a magic square, the sum of the numbers in each row, each column, and each diagonal is the same.

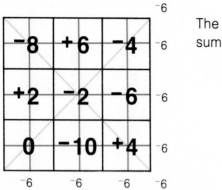

	⁻6	
⁻8	+6	⁻4	⁻6
+2	⁻2	⁻6	⁻6
0	⁻10	+4	⁻6

⁻6   ⁻6   ⁻6   ⁻6

The magic sum is ⁻6.

Tell which of these are magic squares. What is the magic sum?

1.

+4	⁻3	+2
⁻1	+1	+3
0	+5	⁻2

3.

+8	⁻13	+2
⁻7	⁻1	+5
⁻4	+11	⁻10

2.

⁻5	+8	⁻1
+5	+1	⁻3
+3	⁻7	+7

time out

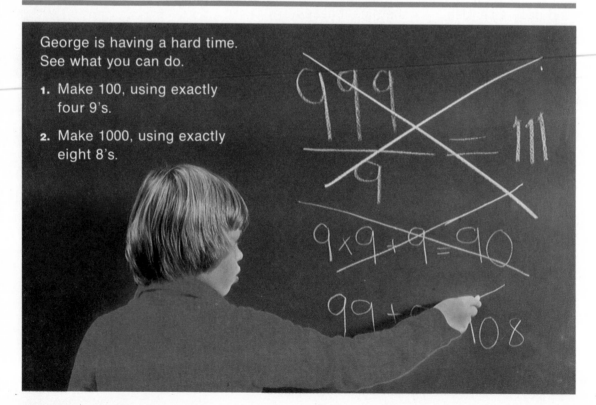

George is having a hard time. See what you can do.

1. Make 100, using exactly four 9's.

2. Make 1000, using exactly eight 8's.

An Integer and Its Opposite

A. For each integer there is an opposite integer. On a number line, an integer and its opposite are equally distant from zero.

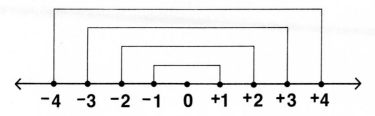

The opposite of $^+1$ is $^-1$. What is the opposite of $^+2$? Of $^-3$? Of $^-4$?

Zero is its own opposite.

B. The nomograph illustrates the sum of an integer and its opposite. The sum of $^+1$ and $^-1$ is 0. The sum of $^-2$ and $^+2$ is ▦.

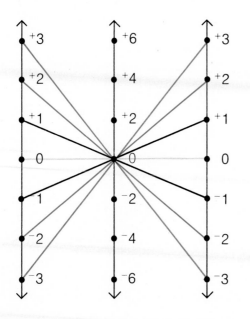

■ *The sum of an integer and its opposite is zero.*

Name the opposite of each of the following integers.

1. $^-7$ **6.** $^+23$

2. $^+8$ **7.** $^-80$

3. $^-5$ **8.** $^-365$

4. 0   **9.** $^+340$

5. $^+12$ **10.** $^-500$

Find n.

11. $^-12 + {}^+12 = n$

12. $^+39 + {}^-39 = n$

13. $n + {}^+7 = 0$

14. $^-15 + n = 0$

15. $n + {}^-75 = 0$

Find each sum.

16. $^+8 + {}^-8 + {}^+6$

17. $^-9 + {}^+9 + {}^-4$

18. $^+5 + {}^-13 + {}^-5$

19. $^-27 + {}^+52 + {}^+27$

20. $^+350 + {}^-350 + {}^-300$

Subtracting Integers

A. Aram wanted to find $^+5 - {}^-1$.
He said to himself:

"I know how to find $^+5 - {}^+2$ and
$^+5 - {}^+1$ and $^+5 - 0$. But how do I
subtract a negative number?

"It looks as if the answer is $^+6$.
Can that be right?

"If I'm right, the answer
to $^+5 - {}^-2$ must be $^+7$.
And the answer to $^+5 - {}^-3$ is $^+8$."

Aram checked his answers by
adding. They all checked.

$$^+5 - {}^+2 = {}^+3$$
$$^+5 - {}^+1 = {}^+4$$
$$^+5 - 0 = {}^+5$$
$$^+5 - {}^-1 = {}^+6$$
$$^+5 - {}^-2 = {}^+7$$
$$^+5 - {}^-3 = {}^+8$$

Check

$$^+2 + {}^+3 = {}^+5$$
$$^+1 + {}^+4 = {}^+5$$
$$0 + {}^+5 = {}^+5$$
$$^-1 + {}^+6 = {}^+5$$
$$^-2 + {}^+7 = {}^+5$$
$$^-3 + {}^+8 = {}^+5$$

B. Study the pattern.

Check

$$^+5 - {}^+3 = {}^+2 \qquad {}^+3 + {}^+2 = {}^+5$$
$$^+4 - {}^+3 = {}^+1 \qquad {}^+3 + {}^+1 = {}^+4$$
$$^+3 - {}^+3 = 0 \qquad {}^+3 + 0 = {}^+3$$
$$^+2 - {}^+3 = {}^-1 \qquad {}^+3 + {}^-1 = {}^+2$$
$$^+1 - {}^+3 = {}^-2 \qquad {}^+3 + {}^-2 = {}^+1$$
$$0 - {}^+3 = {}^-3 \qquad {}^+3 + {}^-3 = 0$$
$$^-1 - {}^+3 = {}^-4 \qquad {}^+3 + {}^-4 = {}^-1$$

C. Complete the pattern.

$$^+2 - {}^-2 = {}^+4$$
$$^+1 - {}^-2 = \text{▨}$$
$$0 - {}^-2 = {}^+2$$
$$^-1 - {}^-2 = \text{▨}$$
$$^-2 - {}^-2 = 0$$
$$^-3 - {}^-2 = {}^-1$$
$$^-4 - {}^-2 = {}^-2$$
$$^-5 - {}^-2 = \text{▨}$$

D. Study these pairs of equations.

$$^+6 - {}^+4 = {}^+2 \qquad {}^-8 - {}^-2 = {}^-6$$
$$^+6 + {}^-4 = {}^+2 \qquad {}^-8 + {}^+2 = {}^-6$$

$$^+4 - {}^-1 = {}^+5 \qquad {}^-3 - {}^+4 = {}^-7$$
$$^+4 + {}^+1 = {}^+5 \qquad {}^-3 + {}^-4 = {}^-7$$

You get the same answer whether you subtract a number or add its opposite.

■ *To subtract a number, add its opposite.*

$$^-5 - {}^-7 = \text{▨} \qquad\qquad {}^-5 + {}^+7 = {}^+2$$

Change each subtraction problem to an addition problem.

Here's how

$$^+5 - {}^+7 \quad {}^+5 + {}^-7$$

1. $^-4 - {}^-1$
2. $^+6 - {}^-3$
3. $^-3 - {}^+7$
4. $^-6 - {}^+3$
5. $^+10 - {}^-5$

6. $^+4 - {}^+8$
7. $0 - {}^+12$
8. $^-5 - {}^-12$
9. $0 - {}^-2$
10. $^+14 - {}^+6$

Subtract.

11. $^+9 - {}^+6$
12. $^+5 - {}^-6$
13. $^-4 - {}^+2$
14. $^-10 - {}^-9$
15. $^+6 - {}^+9$
16. $^+12 - {}^+8$
17. $^+2 - {}^-8$
18. $^-7 - {}^-16$
19. $^+5 - {}^+13$
20. $^+7 - {}^-8$

21. $^-3 - {}^+10$
22. $0 - {}^-5$
23. $^-4 - {}^-7$
24. $^-8 - {}^-8$
25. $^+16 - {}^-7$
26. $^-15 - {}^+8$
27. $0 - {}^+20$
28. $^+20 - {}^-4$
29. $^-13 - {}^-6$
30. $^+14 - {}^-12$

**More practice
Set D, page 382**

Multiplying Integers

Complete the patterns.

$^+4 \times {}^+4 = {}^+16$	$^-4 \times {}^+4 = {}^-16$
$^+4 \times {}^+3 = {}^+12$	$^-4 \times {}^+3 = {}^-12$
$^+4 \times {}^+2 = {}^+8$	$^-4 \times {}^+2 = {}^-8$
$^+4 \times {}^+1 = {}^+4$	$^-4 \times {}^+1 = {}^-4$
$\mathbf{^+4 \times 0 = 0}$	$\mathbf{^-4 \times 0 = 0}$
$^+4 \times {}^-1 = {}^-4$	$^-4 \times {}^-1 = {}^+4$
$^+4 \times {}^-2 = {}^-8$	$^-4 \times {}^-2 = \blacksquare$
$^+4 \times {}^-3 = \blacksquare$	$^-4 \times {}^-3 = {}^+12$
$^+4 \times {}^-4 = \blacksquare$	$^-4 \times {}^-4 = \blacksquare$

1. Complete the table.

×	+3	+2	+1	0	-1	-2	-3
+3	+9	+6		0	-3		-9
+2	+6	+4	+2		-2		
+1	+3				-1	-2	
0	0				0		
-1	-3	-2			+1		
-2	-6		-2			+4	+6
-3			-3		+3		

■ *The product of two positive numbers is positive.*

$^+6 \times {}^+4 = {}^+24$ $^+3 \times {}^+6 = {}^+18$

■ *The product of two negative numbers is positive.*

$^-5 \times {}^-2 = {}^+10$ $^-5 \times {}^-5 = {}^+25$

■ *The product of a positive number and a negative number is negative.*

$^+6 \times {}^-6 = {}^-36$ $^-4 \times {}^+5 = {}^-20$

Find the product.

2. $^+5 \times {}^+3 = {}^+\blacksquare$

3. $^+6 \times {}^+7$

4. $^+9 \times {}^+4$

5. $^+2 \times {}^+8$

6. $^-5 \times {}^-4 = {}^+\blacksquare$

7. $^-3 \times {}^-6$

8. $^-9 \times {}^-1$

9. $^-8 \times {}^-5$

10. $^-6 \times {}^+4 = {}^-\blacksquare$

11. $^-7 \times {}^+3$

12. $^-8 \times {}^+7$

13. $^-12 \times {}^+9$

14. $^+4 \times {}^-8 = {}^-\blacksquare$

15. $^+8 \times {}^-7$

16. $^+12 \times {}^-6$

17. $^+10 \times {}^-15$

18. $^+8 \times {}^+6$

19. $^-8 \times {}^+6$

20. $^+8 \times {}^-6$

21. $^-8 \times {}^-6$

**More practice
Set E, page 382**

Dividing Integers

Division is related
to multiplication.

$^+4 \times {}^+2 = {}^+8$

$^+8 \div {}^+2 = {}^+4$

$^+4 \times {}^-2 = {}^-8$

$^-8 \div {}^-2 = {}^+4$

$^-4 \times {}^+2 = {}^-8$

$^-8 \div {}^+2 = {}^-4$

$^-4 \times {}^-2 = {}^+8$

$^+8 \div {}^-2 = {}^-4$

■ *If two numbers are
positive, their quotient
is positive.*

$^+6 \div {}^+3 = {}^+2$
$^+49 \div {}^+7 = {}^+7$

■ *If two numbers are
negative, their quotient
is positive.*

$^-36 \div {}^-4 = {}^+9$
$^-49 \div {}^-7 = {}^+7$

■ *If one number is positive
and the other negative,
their quotient is negative.*

$^+16 \div {}^-2 = {}^-8$
$^-12 \div {}^+3 = {}^-4$

Divide.

1. $^+16 \div {}^+4$

2. $^+18 \div {}^+2$

3. $^+48 \div {}^+6$

4. $^+102 \div {}^+3$

5. $^-12 \div {}^-3$

6. $^-10 \div {}^-5$

7. $^-72 \div {}^-8$

8. $^-56 \div {}^-7$

9. $^+12 \div {}^-3$

10. $^+32 \div {}^-2$

11. $^+56 \div {}^-4$

12. $^+77 \div {}^-11$

13. $^-16 \div {}^+8$

14. $^-28 \div {}^+7$

15. $^-70 \div {}^+10$

16. $^-144 \div {}^+12$

17. $^+78 \div {}^-3$

18. $^-86 \div {}^-43$

19. $^+121 \div {}^+11$

20. $^-75 \div {}^+15$

**More practice
Set F, page 382**

21. What is the magic sum
in this magic square?

$^+16$	$^-40$	0
$^-24$	$^-8$	$^+8$
$^-16$	$^+24$	$^-32$

Divide each number
in the square by $^-8$
to get a new square.
Is it also a magic
square?

22. Divide each number
in this magic square
by $^+9$ to get a new
square. Is your
new square a magic
square?

$^-27$	$^-36$	$^+9$
$^+18$	$^-18$	$^-54$
$^-45$	0	$^-9$

Graphing in Four Quadrants

You can use *ordered pairs* of integers to locate points on a grid.

The ordered pair (+3, +2) gives the location of point A. Start at the *origin*, or (0, 0).

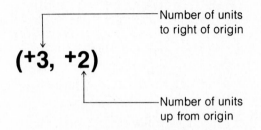

(+3, +2)

Number of units to right of origin

Number of units up from origin

The ordered pair (−4, +6) gives the location of point B.

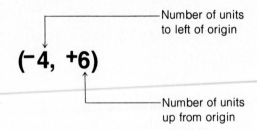

(−4, +6)

Number of units to left of origin

Number of units up from origin

Point C is on the vertical axis. The ordered pair is (0, −3).

Point D is on the horizontal axis. The ordered pair is (+5, 0).

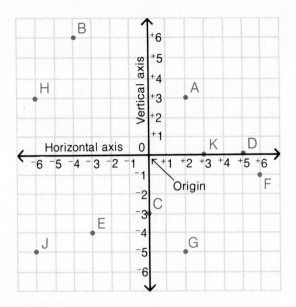

Complete each ordered pair.

1. E (▦, −4)

2. F (+6, ▦)

3. G (▦, −5)

4. H (−6, ▦)

5. Which is the ordered pair for point J, (−6, −5) or (−5, −6)?

6. Which is the ordered pair for point K, (0, +3) or (+3, 0)?

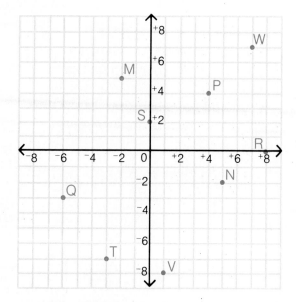

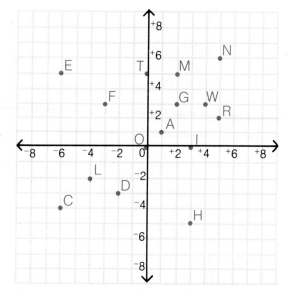

Use the above grid. Give the ordered pair for each point.

7. M

8. N

9. P

10. Q

11. R

12. S

13. T

14. V

15. W

Tell how to locate these points on a grid.

Here's how

($^-$2, $^+$7) **2 units to the left**
      7 units up

16. ($^+$1, $^+$5)

17. ($^+$6, $^-$4)

18. ($^-$3, $^-$3)

19. ($^-$5, $^+$8)

20. ($^+$7, 0)

21. (0, $^+$4)

Use the above grid to find the words spelled by the ordered pairs in each exercise.

Here's how

($^+$4, $^+$3) **W**
($^+$3, 0)   **I**
($^+$5, $^+$6) **N**

22. ($^-$6, $^-$4)
($0, 0$)
($^-$4, $^-$2)
($^-$2, $^-$3)

23. ($^+$4, $^+$3)
($^+$1, $^+$1)
($^+$5, $^+$2)
($^+$2, $^+$5)

24. ($^+$5, $^+$2)
($^+$3, 0)
($^+$2, $^+$3)
($^+$3, $^-$5)
($0, ^+$5)

25. ($^-$4, $^-$2)
($^-$6, $^+$5)
($^-$3, $^+$3)
($0, ^+$5)

Moving Polygons in Four Quadrants

Masumi drew figure ABCD on graph paper. She used the following ordered pairs to locate the vertices.

A	B	C	D
(⁺3, ⁺6)	(⁺8, ⁺3)	(⁺6, ⁺1)	(⁺2, ⁺3)

Then Masumi added ⁻9 to the first number in each ordered pair.

She used the new ordered pairs to draw figure EFGH.

E	F	G	H
(⁻6, ⁺6)	(⁻1, ⁺3)	(⁻3, ⁺1)	(⁻7, ⁺3)

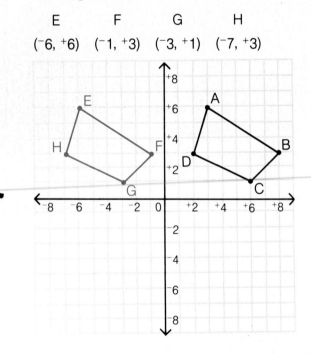

Compare figures ABCD and EFGH. Are they the same shape and size?

In exercises 1 and 2, first list the ordered pairs for the vertices of the polygon. Draw the polygon on graph paper. Then follow the rule to obtain new ordered pairs and draw the new figure. Compare the two figures.

1. *Rule:* Add ⁻5 to the second number in each ordered pair.

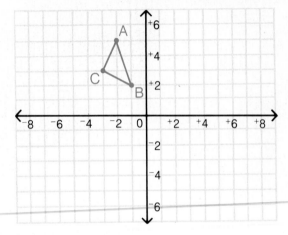

2. *Rule:* Add ⁺6 to both numbers in each ordered pair.

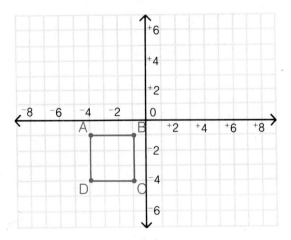

3. List the ordered pairs for the vertices. Then draw rectangle ABCD.

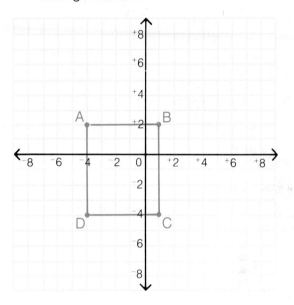

In exercises 6 and 7, list the ordered pairs for the vertices and draw the polygon. Follow the rule to obtain new ordered pairs and draw the new figure.

6. *Rule:* Multiply both numbers in each ordered pair by ⁻3.

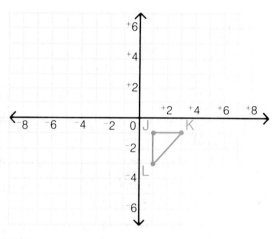

4. Multiply both numbers in each ordered pair by ⁺2. Draw the new figure. Compare the two figures. Are they the same shape? The same size?

★ **5.** Find the area of rectangle ABCD by counting squares on the graph paper. Find the area of the new rectangle. How do the areas compare?

★ **7.** *Rule:* In each ordered pair, multiply the first number by ⁻2. Multiply the second number by ⁺3.

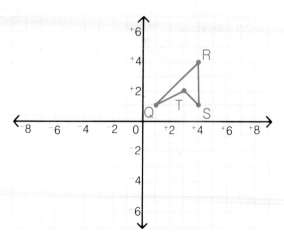

laboratory activity

Draw a horizontal axis and a vertical axis
on a full sheet of graph paper.

Label the units on the horizontal axis from ⁻18
to ⁺18. Label the units on the vertical axis
from ⁺14 to ⁻14.

Working down each column, locate the following
points and connect the dots in order. You will have
a picture of "Boney."

Start

(⁺10, 0)	(⁺10, ⁺11)	(⁻11, ⁻8)	(0, ⁻7)
(⁺9, ⁺4)	(⁺9, ⁺13)	(⁻11, ⁻11)	(⁺3, ⁻7)
(⁺12, ⁺1)	(⁺8, ⁺11)	(⁻7, ⁻11)	(⁺2, ⁻6)
(⁺12, ⁺2)	(⁺4, ⁺4)	(⁻8, ⁻10)	(⁺4, ⁻7)
(⁺13, ⁺1)	(⁺3, ⁺3)	(⁻7, ⁻9)	(⁺3, ⁻9)
(⁺14, ⁺1)	(0, ⁺2)	(⁻6, ⁻10)	(⁺4, ⁻10)
(⁺17, ⁺5)	(⁻7, ⁺2)	(⁻7, ⁻11)	(⁺4, ⁻11)
(⁺16, ⁺7)	(⁻6, ⁺8)	(⁻3, ⁻11)	(⁺8, ⁻11)
(⁺14, ⁺8)	(⁻9, ⁺5)	(⁻4, ⁻10)	(⁺8, ⁻9)
(⁺14, ⁺9)	(⁻8, ⁺2)	(⁻3, ⁻8)	(⁺7, ⁻7)
(⁺13, ⁺10)	(⁻10, ⁻2)	(⁻1, ⁻8)	(⁺9, ⁻6)
(⁺11, ⁺10)	(⁻9, ⁻7)	(⁻2, ⁻7)	(⁺10, ⁻2)
(⁺11, ⁺13)	(⁻10, ⁻8)	(⁺1, ⁻8)	(⁺10, 0)
			Stop

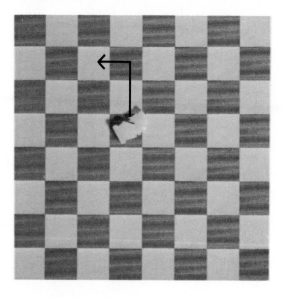

The Knight's Move

The first diagram above shows a legal move for the knight in the game of chess. The knight can move: (1) two squares horizontally and one square vertically, or (2) two squares vertically and one square horizontally.

Suppose that the knight is in the square marked with an X.

The 1's show the squares the knight can reach in one move. The 2's show some of the squares the knight can reach in two moves.

1. Copy the chessboard on grid paper. Complete the 2's for the knight.

2. List the sums for each row and each column.

3. Now write 3 in the remaining squares that can be reached in three moves.

4. Write 4 in the empty squares that can be reached in four moves.

5. Can the knight reach any square on the board in four or fewer moves?

Chapter 18 Test
Integers, Pages 362–379

Writing integers, pages 362, 363

Write the missing number.

1. 40°C above zero, $^+40$
12°C below zero, ▦

2. Price decrease of 15 cents, $^-15$
Price increase of 24 cents, ▦

Comparing integers, pages 364–365

Compare the integers in each exercise. Use > or <.

3. $^-5$ ● $^+1$

4. 0 ● $^-1$

5. $^-15$ ● $^-14$

Adding integers, pages 366–367, 368, 369

Find each sum.

6. $^+4 + {}^-3$

8. $^-6 + {}^-8$

7. $^+8 + {}^+5$

9. $^-10 + {}^+7$

Subtracting integers, pages 370–371

Subtract.

10. $^+3 - {}^+5$

12. $0 - {}^-4$

11. $^-6 - {}^-8$

13. $^-9 - {}^+2$

Multiplying integers, page 372

Find each product.

14. $^+6 \times {}^+5$

16. $^+3 \times {}^-3$

15. $^-7 \times {}^-7$

17. $^-4 \times {}^+8$

Dividing integers, page 373

Find each quotient.

18. $^+25 \div {}^-5$

20. $^-16 \div {}^-4$

19. $^+27 \div {}^+3$

21. $^-40 \div {}^+8$

Graphing in four quadrants, pages 374–378

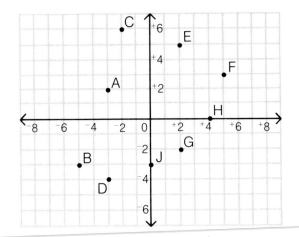

Give the ordered pair for each point.

22. E

25. B

23. A

26. J

24. G

27. F

Name the point for each ordered pair.

28. $(^-2, {}^+6)$

29. $(^+4, 0)$

30. $(^-3, {}^-4)$

Unit 6 Test

Probability, pages 324–341

1. If you toss a penny, what is the probability that it will show tails?

2. If you roll a die, what is the probability that it will show a one or a three?

3. Complete the tree diagram to find all possible outcomes for tossing two coins. How many are there?

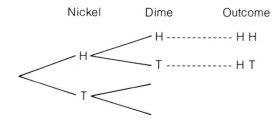

4. If you toss two coins, what is the probability of getting two heads?

5. How many different ways can you choose a three-digit code number?

6. What is the probability that the three-digit code number you choose will be 068?

Statistics, pages 344–359

The students in Mrs. Klein's English class made these scores on a test.

87 89 95 72 48 75
89 79 89 87 78 96

7. Compute the range.

8. Compute the mean.

9. Find the median.

10. Find the mode.

Integers, pages 362–379

Add.

11. $^+6 + ^-2$

12. $^+5 + ^+7$

13. $^-8 + ^-3$

14. $^-9 + ^+4$

Subtract.

15. $^+2 - ^+7$

16. $^-4 - ^-5$

17. $0 - ^-6$

18. $^-8 - ^+1$

Multiply.

19. $^+4 \times ^+9$

20. $^-6 \times ^-6$

21. $^+7 \times ^-2$

22. $^-3 \times ^+8$

Divide.

23. $^+36 \div ^-9$

24. $^+28 \div ^+7$

25. $^-45 \div ^-5$

26. $^-18 \div ^+3$

More Practice

Set A

Find the mean for each set of data.

1. 26   14   28   17   20

2. 10   3   12   7   13

3. 128   144   123   184   136

4. 390   253   439   338   205

5. 14   5   22   8   20   11   4

6. 43   67   60   80   50   74   39

7. 64   91   58   99   64   73   83

8. 40   32   43   33   41   39   31

9. 5   10   3   6   3   15   8   1   3

10. 8   3   10   13   2   10   10   7   9

Set B

Find the mean, the median, and the mode for each set of data.

1. 48   16   28   48   40

2. 15   33   9   24   9

3. 70   60   51   75   60   56

4. 45   35   42   52   35   49   29

5. 88   57   88   77   51   88   69

6. 26   16   23   32   19   29   16

7. 67   61   61   42   61   46   61   73

8. 9   3   15   10   3   2   6   3   12

9. 6   3   5   1   8   2   6   4   10

Set C

1. $^+5 + {}^-7$

2. $^-13 + {}^+5$

3. $^+2 + {}^-2$

4. $^-7 + {}^+3$

5. $^+17 + {}^-8$

6. $^-8 + {}^+1$

7. $^-4 + {}^+7$

8. $^-3 + {}^+4$

9. $^+9 + {}^-6$

10. $^+1 + {}^-12$

11. $^+6 + {}^-2$

Set D

1. $^-7 - {}^-13$

2. $^-3 - {}^-3$

3. $^+10 - {}^-5$

4. $^+6 - {}^+2$

5. $^+8 - {}^+12$

6. $0 - {}^-7$

7. $^-5 - {}^+8$

8. $^+4 - {}^-9$

9. $^-9 - {}^-1$

10. $^-11 - {}^+6$

11. $^+2 - {}^+4$

Set E

1. $^+4 \times {}^+5$

2. $^+8 \times {}^+7$

3. $^-1 \times {}^-6$

4. $^-9 \times {}^+3$

5. $^-5 \times {}^+15$

6. $^+2 \times {}^-8$

7. $^+11 \times {}^+1$

8. $^+6 \times {}^-4$

9. $^-3 \times {}^+9$

10. $^-12 \times {}^-2$

11. $^-7 \times {}^-20$

Set F

1. $^+9 \div {}^+3$

2. $^-15 \div {}^-5$

3. $^-4 \div {}^+4$

4. $^-24 \div {}^-6$

5. $^-10 \div {}^+2$

6. $^-42 \div {}^-3$

7. $^+6 \div {}^-2$

8. $^+55 \div {}^-5$

9. $^+25 \div {}^-5$

10. $^-8 \div {}^+4$

11. $^+36 \div {}^-6$

Individualized Skills Maintenance

Diagnosis

A. $^-6 + ^-3$

$^-12 + ^+4$

$^+6 + ^+5$

B. $^+4 - ^-6$

$^-3 - ^-8$

$^+8 - ^+9$

C. $^-5 \times ^+3$

$^-9 \times ^-9$

$^+6 \times ^+8$

D. $^-42 \div ^+6$

$^-56 \div ^-8$

$^+64 \div ^+8$

E. 25% of 40 is m.

60% of 75 is x.

F. 12 is ▨% of 60.

27 is ▨% of 36.

G. 30% of d is 18.

80% of s is 40.

Practice

Set A (pp. 366–367)

1. $^-9 + ^+23$
2. $^+13 + ^+31$
3. $^-37 + ^-52$
4. $^-7 + ^-45$
5. $^+22 + ^+15$
6. $^+11 + ^+64$
7. $^-14 + ^+8$
8. $^+42 + ^-34$
9. $^+8 + ^-19$
10. $^-12 + ^+29$

Set B (pp. 370–371)

1. $^+7 - ^+29$
2. $^-9 - ^+40$
3. $^+5 - ^-27$
4. $^-2 - ^+55$
5. $^+66 - ^+49$
6. $^-19 - ^-77$
7. $^+33 - ^-19$
8. $^-57 - ^+34$
9. $^+46 - ^-48$
10. $^-22 - ^-18$

Set C (p. 372)

1. $^+8 \times ^+9$
2. $^-4 \times ^+34$
3. $^-31 \times ^-7$
4. $^+12 \times ^-25$
5. $^-16 \times ^+9$
6. $^+35 \times ^-28$
7. $^-17 \times ^+32$
8. $^-9 \times ^-43$
9. $^+22 \times ^+14$
10. $^+7 \times ^-24$

Set D (p. 373)

1. $^+48 \div ^+12$
2. $^-91 \div ^-7$
3. $^-36 \div ^-4$
4. $^+32 \div ^-8$
5. $^-49 \div ^+7$
6. $^+38 \div ^-19$
7. $^-85 \div ^+17$
8. $^-72 \div ^+9$
9. $^+27 \div ^+3$
10. $^+24 \div ^+6$

Individualized Skills Maintenance

Practice *(continued)*

Set E (pp. 282–283)

Find each missing number.

1. 30% of 60 is x.
2. 48% of 50 is c.
3. 45% of 80 is z.
4. 90% of 20 is k.
5. 25% of 48 is p.
6. 36% of 100 is d.
7. 40% of 60 is y.
8. 44% of 50 is r.
9. 75% of 8 is a.
10. 60% of 25 is t.
11. 16% of 75 is m.
12. 12% of 200 is u.
13. 30% of 90 is b.
14. 80% of 240 is v.
15. 60% of 775 is k.
16. 21% of 800 is s.
17. 80% of 245 is q.
18. 90% of 610 is c.
19. 4% of 500 is w.
20. 59% of 800 is n.
21. 81% of 600 is g.

Set F (pp. 286–287)

Find each percent.

1. 4 is ▦% of 8.
2. 15 is ▦% of 20.
3. 42 is ▦% of 70.
4. 9 is ▦% of 45.
5. 20 is ▦% of 25.
6. 27 is ▦% of 36.
7. 5 is ▦% of 25.
8. 35 is ▦% of 175.
9. 21 is ▦% of 60.
10. 12 is ▦% of 15.
11. 16 is ▦% of 80.
12. 30 is ▦% of 375.
13. 6 is ▦% of 150.
14. 24 is ▦% of 80.
15. 36 is ▦% of 225.
16. 14 is ▦% of 56.
17. 28 is ▦% of 140.
18. 8 is ▦% of 160.
19. 40 is ▦% of 200.
20. 25 is ▦% of 625.
21. 18 is ▦% of 45.

Set G (pp. 288–289)

Find each missing number.

1. 10% of t is 5.
2. 96% of d is 24.
3. 51% of n is 153.
4. 6% of s is 12.
5. 64% of g is 48.
6. 42% of j is 21.
7. 84% of q is 42.
8. 53% of b is 212.
9. 11% of m is 77.
10. 88% of e is 66.
11. 43% of u is 258.
12. 82% of h is 205.
13. 29% of x is 87.
14. 77% of y is 154.
15. 37% of p is 148.
16. 19% of a is 57.
17. 7% of r is 35.
18. 56% of z is 42.
19. 93% of k is 372.
20. 62% of c is 155.
21. 13% of v is 78.

Measures and Formulas

Metric System

Length
10 millimeters (mm) = 1 centimeter (cm)
10 centimeters ⎫
100 millimeters ⎭ = 1 decimeter (dm)
10 decimeters ⎫
100 centimeters ⎭ = 1 meter (m)
1000 meters = 1 kilometer (km)

Area
100 square millimeters (mm²) = 1 square centimeter (cm²)
10,000 square centimeters = 1 square meter (m²)
100 square meters = 1 are (a)
10,000 square meters = 1 hectare (ha)

Volume
1000 cubic millimeters (mm³) = 1 cubic centimeter (cm³)
1000 cubic centimeters = 1 cubic decimeter (dm³)
1,000,000 cubic centimeters = 1 cubic meter (m³)

1000 milliliters (ml) = 1 liter (ℓ)
1000 liters = 1 kiloliter (kl)

Mass (weight)
1000 milligrams (mg) = 1 gram (g)
1000 grams = 1 kilogram (kg)
1000 kilograms = 1 metric ton (t)

Time

60 seconds (sec.) = 1 minute (min.)
60 minutes = 1 hour (hr.)
24 hours = 1 day (da.)
7 days = 1 week (wk.)
365 days ⎫
52 weeks ⎬ = 1 year (yr.)
12 months (mo.) ⎭
366 days = 1 leap year

United States Customary System

Length
12 inches (in.) = 1 foot (ft.)
3 feet ⎫
36 inches ⎭ = 1 yard (yd.)
1760 yards ⎫
5280 feet ⎭ = 1 mile (mi.)
6076 feet = 1 nautical mile

Area
144 square inches (sq. in.) = 1 square foot (sq. ft.)
9 square feet = 1 square yard (sq. yd.)
4840 square yards = 1 acre (A.)

Volume
1728 cubic inches (cu. in.) = 1 cubic foot (cu. ft.)
27 cubic feet = 1 cubic yard (cu. yd.)

Weight
16 ounces (oz.) = 1 pound (lb.)
2000 pounds = 1 ton (T.)

Capacity
8 fluid ounces (fl. oz.) = 1 cup (c.)
2 cups = 1 pint (pt.)
2 pints = 1 quart (qt.)
4 quarts = 1 gallon (gal.)

Geometric Formulas

Area

of a circle, p. 166	$A = \pi r^2$
of a parallelogram, p. 244	$A = bh$
of a rectangle, p. 153	$A = bh$
of a trapezoid, p. 158	$A = \frac{1}{2}h(a + b)$
of a triangle, pp. 156, 244	$A = \frac{1}{2}bh$

Circumference

of a circle, p. 164 $\quad C = \pi d$ or
$\quad C = 2\pi r$

Volume

of a cylinder, p. 184 $\quad V = \pi r^2 h$
of a rectangular prism, p. 180 $\quad V = lwh$

Glossary

Acute angle   An angle whose measure is less than 90°.

Adjacent angles   Angles ABC and CBD are adjacent.

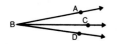

Alternate interior angles   Angles 3 and 5 are alternate interior angles.

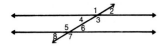

Altitude of a triangle   A segment that extends from one vertex of the triangle to the opposite side and is perpendicular to that side.

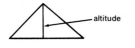

Angle   Two rays with the same endpoint.

Arc   Part of a circle.

Area   A number indicating the region inside a plane figure.

Associative property of addition   The way in which numbers are grouped does not change the sum.
$$(7 + 2) + 4 = 7 + (2 + 4)$$

Associative property of multiplication   The way in which numbers are grouped does not change the product.
$$(7 \times 2) \times 4 = 7 \times (2 \times 4)$$

Average   The quotient obtained by dividing the sum of a set of numbers by the number of addends.

Central angle   An angle whose vertex is the center of a circle.

Chord   A segment whose endpoints are on a circle. A diameter is a special chord.

Circle   A closed curve in a plane, all of whose points are the same distance from a given point called the center.

Circumference   The distance around a circle.

Common denominator   A common multiple of two or more denominators. 12 is a common denominator for $\frac{2}{3}$ and $\frac{1}{4}$.

Commutative property of addition   The order in which numbers are added does not change the sum.
$$4 + 6 = 6 + 4$$

Commutative property of multiplication   The order in which numbers are multiplied does not change the product.
$$4 \times 6 = 6 \times 4$$

Composite number   A whole number greater than zero that has more than two factors.

Concentric circles   Circles in the same plane that have the same center but different radii.

Cone   A space figure shaped like this.

Congruent   Having the same size and shape.

Consecutive angles   In this quadrilateral, angles J and K are consecutive.

Cosine   For a given acute angle in a right triangle, the ratio:
$$\frac{\text{length of adjacent side}}{\text{length of hypotenuse}}$$

Counting principle   If there is a number of successive choices to make, the total number of choices is the product of the number of choices at each stage.

Cross-products   In two fractions or ratios, the products of the first number of one and the second number of the other. For $\frac{3}{4}$ and $\frac{9}{12}$, the cross-products are 3×12 and 4×9.

Cube   A rectangular prism with all square faces.

Cylinder   A space figure shaped like this.

Degree   A unit for measuring angles and arcs.

Diagonal   In a polygon, a segment that connects one vertex to another and that is not a side of the polygon.

Diameter   A segment having its endpoints on a circle and passing through the center.

Distributive property of multiplication over addition   A property that relates addition and multiplication as follows:
$$4(7 + 3) = 4(7) + 4(3)$$

Dividend   In $45 \div 6$, 45 is the dividend.

Divisor   In $45 \div 6$, 6 is the divisor.

Edge   In a space figure, a segment where two faces meet.

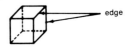

Endpoint The end of a line segment or a ray.

Equilateral triangle A triangle whose three sides are congruent.

Even number A whole number with a factor of 2.

Exponent In 4^3, 3 is the exponent. It tells that 4 is to be used as a factor three times.
$$4^3 = 4 \times 4 \times 4 = 64$$

Face A plane region of a space figure.

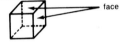

Factor A number used in multiplication. In $3 \times 8 = 24$, 3 and 8 are factors.

Factorial The product of a whole number and every whole number less than itself.
$$4! = 4 \times 3 \times 2 \times 1 = 24$$

Frequency table In statistics, a listing of the data and how many times each item of data occurred.

Grouping property *See* Associative property of addition *and* Associative property of multiplication.

Hexagon A six-sided polygon.

Hypotenuse In a right triangle, the side opposite the right angle.

Improper fraction A fraction whose numerator is equal to or greater than its denominator. Examples are $\frac{4}{4}$, $\frac{15}{2}$, and $\frac{8}{1}$.

Inscribed angle An angle whose vertex is on a circle and whose sides cut off an arc of the circle.

Inscribed polygon A polygon inside a circle, with its vertices on the circle.

Integer A number such as $^-183$, $^-6$, 0, $^+32$, or $^+14{,}029$.

Intersecting lines Two lines with exactly one point in common.

Isosceles triangle A triangle with two congruent sides.

Least common multiple The smallest number that is a common multiple of two given numbers. The least common multiple of 6 and 8 is 24.

Lowest terms A fraction is in lowest terms if the only common factor of the numerator and the denominator is 1.

Mean Another name for "average." The mean of the set 2, 4, 5, 6, 6 is $23 \div 5$, or 4.6.

Median The middle number in a set of numbers when the numbers are in order. The median of the set 2, 4, 5, 6, 6 is 5.

Midpoint The point in a segment that divides it into two equal parts.

Mode The number that occurs most often in a set of numbers. The mode of the set 2, 4, 5, 6, 6 is 6.

Multiple The product of a given number and a whole number. The multiples of 3 are 3, 6, 9, 12, and so on.

Obtuse angle An angle whose measure is greater than 90°.

Octagon An eight-sided polygon.

Odd number A whole number that does not have 2 as a factor.

Opposite angles In this quadrilateral, angles J and L are opposite angles.

Opposites Two numbers whose sum is zero. 5 and $^-5$ are opposites.

Order property *See* Commutative property of addition *and* Commutative property of multiplication.

Origin On a coordinate grid, the point (0, 0) where the two number lines, or axes, intersect.

Parallel lines Lines in the same plane that do not intersect.

Parallelogram A quadrilateral whose opposite sides are parallel.

Pentagon A five-sided polygon.

Percent A fraction whose denominator is 100. $45\% = \frac{45}{100}$

Perimeter The distance around a closed figure.

Permutations The ordered arrangements of a set of objects or numbers. The permutations of the set A, B, C are:
ABC   BAC   CAB
ACB   BCA   CBA

Perpendicular lines Two lines that intersect to form right angles.

Polygon A closed figure made up of segments.

Polyhedron A space figure whose faces are regions shaped like polygons.

Power 2^3 is read "2 to the third power." $2^3 = 2 \times 2 \times 2 = 8$. The third power of 2 is 8. *See also* Exponent.

Precision A property of measurement that depends upon the size of the unit of measure. The smaller the unit, the more precise the measurement.

Prime factor A factor that is a prime number.

Prime number A whole number, such as 17, that has only two factors, itself and 1.

Prism A polyhedron with two parallel faces, called bases, that are congruent.

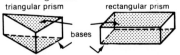

triangular prism   rectangular prism

bases

Probability A number that tells how likely it is that a certain event will happen. It is the number of favorable outcomes divided by the number of possible outcomes.

Proportion A statement that two ratios are equal.

$$\frac{2}{5} = \frac{12}{30}$$

Pyramid A polyhedron with one base. The other faces are triangular.

triangular pyramid   rectangular pyramid

Quadrant One of the four parts into which a plane is divided by two perpendicular lines.

Quadrilateral A polygon with four sides.

Radius A segment whose endpoints are the center of a circle and a point on the circle.

Ratio A pair of numbers that expresses a rate or a comparison.

Rational number Any number that can be expressed as either a terminating decimal or a repeating decimal.

$$4\frac{3}{4} = 4.75 \quad \frac{1}{3} = .33 \ldots$$

Ray Part of a line that has one endpoint and extends in one direction.

Reciprocals Two numbers whose product is 1; for example, $\frac{3}{4}$ and $\frac{4}{3}$.

Rectangle A parallelogram with four right angles.

Regular polygon A polygon that has all its sides congruent and all its angles congruent.

Repeating decimal A decimal in which one or more digits keep repeating.
.5181818 . . .

Repetend The part of a repeating decimal that keeps repeating. A bar is often shown above the repetend.
.5181818 . . . = .5$\overline{18}$

Rhombus A parallelogram whose sides are congruent.

Right angle An angle whose measure is 90°.

Scalene triangle A triangle in which no two sides are congruent.

Scientific notation A way of expressing a number by writing it as a decimal between 1 and 10 times a power of 10.
$352 = 3.52 \times 10^2$

Segment Two points in a line and all the points between them.

Semicircle An arc that is one-half of a circle.

Significant digits In a measurement, the digits needed to tell how many times the unit of measure is used. The measurement 7.60 meters has three significant digits, 7, 6, and 0.

Similar figures Figures having the same shape but not necessarily the same size.

Sine For a given acute angle in a right triangle, the ratio:

$$\frac{\text{length of opposite side}}{\text{length of hypotenuse}}$$

Square A rectangle with four congruent sides.

Square root A number a is the square root of a number b if $a \times a = b$. 3 is the square root of 9.

Surface area The total area of all the faces of a space figure.

Tangent For a given acute angle in a right triangle, the ratio:

$$\frac{\text{length of opposite side}}{\text{length of adjacent side}}$$

Terminating decimal A decimal with a limited number of nonzero digits. Examples are .5 and .0082.

Transversal A line that intersects two or more lines in the same plane.

Trapezoid A quadrilateral with one pair of parallel sides.

Triangle A polygon with three sides.

Trigonometric ratios *See* Cosine, Sine, *and* Tangent.

Variable In an expression or an equation, a letter that represents a number.

Vertex (1) The common endpoint of two rays that form an angle. (2) The point of intersection of two sides of a polygon. (3) The point of intersection of three or more edges of a space figure.

(1)   (2)   (3)

Volume A number indicating amount of space inside a space figure.

Index